ECOLOGY OF ANIMAL PARASITES

Ecology of animal parasites

BY JEAN G. BAER

Professor of Zoology, University of Neuchâtel; Lecturer

in Helminthology, Tropical Institute in Basle; formerly

Visiting Professor of Zoology, University of Illinois

THE UNIVERSITY OF ILLINOIS PRESS, URBANA, 1952

COPYRIGHT 1951 BY THE UNIVERSITY OF ILLINOIS PRESS

MANUFACTURED IN THE UNITED STATES OF AMERICA

Second Printing 1952

Third Printing 1958

Fourth Printing 1964

QL
757
B28
c. 2

TO DR. CHARLES JOYEUX, EMERITUS PROFESSOR

OF PARASITOLOGY AT THE UNIVERSITY OF AIX-

MARSEILLE, WITH WHOM MOST OF THE IDEAS EX-

PRESSED IN THIS BOOK HAVE BEEN OFTEN DIS-

CUSSED IN THE COURSE OF OUR COLLABORATION

FOR TWENTY-FIVE YEARS

CONTENTS

INTRODUCTION

Dans la nature, les non-réussites, les échecs, sont élim-inés et par conséquent nous ne voyons que les réussites.

L. CUENOT

The title of this book may seem somewhat preten-tious to students of ecology accustomed to collecting data and observations on organisms concentrated within a given area. It has been chosen intentionally to stress the fact that today our knowledge of para-sites is much more extensive than might be supposed from current textbooks, and even from those that are devoted entirely to the medical or veterinary aspects of the question.

An attempt has been made to review the field of parasitology from all possible angles and to show that parasites are subject to the same general laws that govern all free-living organisms. The latter, however, are adapted in various ways to widely different biotopes whereas parasites have adapted themselves to a very specialized, and consequently limited, en-vironment. The association of the parasite with its host is also a problem of ecology and all the more interesting in that, in many cases, it is possible to furnish indisputable evidence that such associations originated several thousands of centuries ago.

It is the writer's contention that a taxonomic background is absolutely essential to a complete understanding of the relationships between the para-sites and their hosts. This is the broad basis on which modern parasitology has been built up and to over-look it would be an unpardonable error.

The materials collected for this book represent two courses in parasitology that the writer was in-vited to give as Visiting Professor in the Graduate College of the University of Illinois. They do not pretend to furnish an exhaustive review of the sub-ject; many facts are assumed to be known and con-sequently have been omitted. Several of the ideas expressed are not new but are presented in a differ-ent manner; some may be premature and others may be proved to be erroneous. The aim of this book is to stimulate the reader's thoughts in new fields and to encourage him to consider old problems from new angles.

In the following chapters, the writer has found it necessary to define certain terms that are usually used in a somewhat loose sense but that really cor-respond to very definite types of animal associations. Adaptations to parasitism are examined from both the morphological and the biological angles, the stress being laid on the latter rather than on the former—especially in groups that are entirely parasitic, where there are no free-living species with which the para-sites can be compared. Such a general outline fur-nishes the basis for examining the ecology of host-parasite relationships and will also enable the reader to gain a more complete understanding of the physi-ological peculiarities of parasites. Using the data available, the writer has attempted to discern how parasitism in animals has arisen.

During his stay at Urbana the writer has continu-ously benefitted from the support and encourage-ment of Dr. Harley J. Van Cleave, and the ensuing friendship has led to the editing of these lectures in their present form. He has enjoyed the hospitality of Dr. Van Cleave's laboratory, the generous loan of his personal library, and the stimulating atmosphere of his research program. In the world of today, such gifts as these are landmarks in the life of a man.

The writer is also greatly indebted for their whole-hearted collaboration to the members of the staff in the department of zoology and to those in the Natural History library. Their friendly attitude to-ward a fellow scientist has done much toward a better understanding of the problems shared in com-mon.

The drawings have been prepared by Mrs. Kather-ine Hill Paul, department artist, who with her usual skill has contributed much to making the text at-tractive.

ix

LANDMARKS IN PARASITOLOGY

The following dates and facts have no pretense of being complete. They have been chosen more for the new ideas that subsequently resulted from the discovery than for the importance of the discovery itself. To stress the historical aspect of the data presented, they have been arranged in chronological order, regardless of their nature.

1603.   The first recognizable description of *Diphyllobothrium latum* is published by Felix Platter of Basle.

1666.   First mention of parasitic crustaceans, argulids, by F. Baldner of Strassburg (France).

1675.   A protozoan is described for the first time by the Flemish craftsman, Antony van Leeuwenhoeck.

1700.   Publication in Paris of the first treatise on human helminths by Nicolas Andry.

1781.   First experimental life cycle of a tapeworm is obtained by Peter Abildgaard in Copenhagen.

1835.   Richard Owen discovers *Trichinella* in London.

1837.   *Trichomonas vaginalis* is discovered by Alfred Donné in Paris.

1841.   Description of the first blood parasite, a trypanosome, by Gustav Valentin of Bern.

1845.   Felix Dujardin of Rennes shows the relationships between cysticerci and taenia.

1852.   In Dresden, Friederich Küchenmeister obtains the experimental cycle of the dog tapeworm, *Taenia pisiformis*.

1852.   The first parasitic snail is discovered and named *Entoconcha* by Johannes Müller of Berlin.

1853.   First pig is rendered measly experimentally by Edouard Van Beneden of Liège.

1854.   First experimental infestation of man by *Taenia solium* by Carl Vogt of Geneva.

1861.   Rudolf Leuckart of Leipzig infests a calf with *Taenia saginata* cysticerci.

1869.   H. Krabbe, a Danish physician, discovers that each order of birds possesses its particular tapeworms.

1870.   Discovery of human intestinal amoebae in Calcutta by T. R. Lewis.

1877.   The life cycle of *Wuchereria bancrofti* is established by Patrick Manson in China. This is the first case of an insect vector of a larval parasite.

1880.   Alphonse Laveran, a French army doctor, discovers the protozoan nature of the malarial parasite.

1880.   G. Evans, in the Punjab, discovers that the disease known in elephants as "Surra" is caused by trypanosomes, thus establishing their pathogenecity.

1881.   Simultaneously, R. Leuckart in Germany and G. Thomas in Great Britain discover the life cycle of *Fasciola hepatica* and describe for the first time the larval development of trematodes.

1882.   Max Braun of Koenigsberg furnishes experimental proof of the plerocercoid nature of the larvae of *Diphyllobothrium latum*.

1883.   Rudolf Leuckart discovers the heterogonic life cycle of *Strongyloides stercoralis*.

1884.   In Paris, Yves Delage describes the life cycle of a rhizocephalan (*Sacculina*) and establishes its affinities with cirripeds.

1886.   Alfred Giard, a French biologist, introduces the notion of parasitic castration.

1889.   The role of ticks in the transmission of Texas Fever is demonstrated by Frederick L. Kilborne in the United States.

1892.   The first direct life cycle of a tapeworm is described by B. Grassi and G. Rovelli in Italy.

1895.   Ronald Ross discovers the transmission of bird malaria through a mosquito in India.

1898.   Ross's discovery is substantiated for human malaria by Grassi and his collaborators in Italy.

1902.   The first human trypanosome is described by J. E. Dutton from Africa.

1904.   Arthur Looss, in Cairo, accidentally infests himself with larvae of *Ancylostomum duodenale* and thus discovers their penetration through the skin.

1911.   The life cycle of *Trypanosomum gambiense* is worked out for the first time by F. K. Kleine and M. Taute in Germany.

1913.   The first complete life cycle of a schistosome is worked out by K. Miyairi and M. Suzuki in Japan.

1916.   F. Stewart and B. H. Ransom, in the United States, discover the migration of ascaris larvae through the lungs.

1918.   F. Rosen and C. von Janicki in Neuchâtel discover that the life cycle of *Diphyllobothrium latum* requires two intermediate hosts.

PART ONE

Animal associations, definitions

To understand the true meaning of a parasitic adaptation, and consequently the nature of the association that has arisen between two partners, it is necessary to examine briefly the principal types of associations that have been recorded so far.

When analyzing animal associations, one must keep in mind both the morphological and the physiological aspects of the problem. It is very important to be able to form an unbiased opinion of the association and especially in regard to its necessity for either of the two partners.

Far too many anthropocentric ideas have been introduced into several of the definitions currently used, because the older authors were influenced primarily by the morphological rather than by the physiological aspect of the association. Consequently, they usually failed to discover to what extent the associations were of a permanent or of a transitory type.

All animal associations may be divided into two groups which differ fundamentally (see diagram p. 7). In the first case, all the associates belong to the same species, they tend to form colonies, and within these there appears a very definite type of specialization. This affects both the morphology and the physiology of the individuals which, in turn, influence the ecology of the specialized individuals. A colony of termites, for instance, contains a queen, workers, soldiers, males and, sporadically, young females. All work together and lead a socially organized life, yet each group possesses its own particular type of morphology and ecology. Such specialized colonies are found, of course, among other hymenopterons which lead a highly socialized existence.

It is important to emphasize that within these colonies, each individual has arisen from a distinct egg whereas a colony of hydroids is the result of the cleavage of a single egg. It is not a colony in the true sense of the word, but a primitive metazoan, low in degree of specialization.

The varied aspects of parasitism, symbiosis, commensalism, and phoresis are as truly within the scope of ecology as are the problems of predation, succession, geographical distribution, and relations with the physical environment.

PHORESIS AND COMMENSALISM

The second type of association is characterized by the fact that its members belong to different species. An analysis of such associations is much more difficult than that of the previous ones since they should be subjected, as far as possible, to experimental conditions to determine the true nature of the bond between the different partners.

There is no doubt that such associations originated from species having similar ecological needs in regard to both food and environment, these conditions being the only bond between them. This is especially true of sedentary organisms. A typical association of this kind would be an oyster bed, for the organization of which there exists no fundamental necessity. The type and number of the associates may vary a great deal and differ from one region to another, but the ultimate chances for the entire association to subsist in a more or less permanent fashion will depend on the successful adaptation of each individual species.

It is only natural that such ecological associations attract all kinds of predatory animals, since they have every chance of finding there their favorite food. The predators in turn are followed by scavengers and in this way very complex associations are formed.

Scavengers, hiding from predators, burrow in among the various members of the association. Probably in such cases protozoans and coelenterates, and other organisms also, attach themselves to the scavengers. The latter, thus camouflaged, would stand a greater chance of survival than those not so protected. The protective coating of a crab would of course vary according to the species that compose the association into which it has introduced itself as a scavenger. There is nothing teleological about such associations. Their successful survival is the outcome of natural selection, since they benefit the individuals so protected.

It is important to emphasize that camouflage is entirely accidental. An oyster covered with a growth

1

of hydroids derives no evident benefit from this covering. But it is quite possible that an organism which attaches itself indiscriminately to another of a different kind may eventually gain an advantage from this support. Attachment to an animal which moves around continually may be advantageous, as it would provide a greater and more varied food supply or raise its metabolic rate to a higher level by an increase in oxygen intake resulting from the continual movements through water. Here again there would be a selective influence that might eventually lead to some degree of specialization.

Numerous species of sedentary infusorians, vorticellids for example, are found attached to the surface of the body of water fleas and some other aquatic arthropods. They have become specialized in that movement has become indispensable for their metabolism. If fragments of chitin together with the attached protozoans are kept motionless in water, the protozoans die. They will survive, however, if the fragments are moved about continually. Although the nature of the supporting partner is indifferent, the other associate has become physiologically specialized. There is no kind of specificity in such associations, since the only condition for them to be effective is that the supporting partner be continually moving.

Such associations are usually termed *phoresis* and the supporting partner is spoken of as the host. Phoretic associations may be permanent, as above, or they may be transitory, arising at definite stages of the life cycle of free-living or parasitic organisms.

The trianguloid, the first larval instar of the so-called Spanish fly, attaches itself to the body of a bumblebee as it comes to feed on flowers. In this way, the larva is transported to the bee's nest where it leaves the host to penetrate into one of the cells. It devours both the bee larva and the honey and enters into a new larval instar. Phoresis is absolutely necessary for the larval cantharid which finally becomes a predator and should never be called a parasite, especially since it lives within the nest and not upon the host.

Phoresis does not necessarily imply that one of the two partners is attached in a more or less permanent fashion to the other. For instance, a small European fish known as the fierasfier is found inside the so-called respiratory tree and the intestine of sea cucumbers. To feed, the fish emerges only at night and then for short periods, returning immedi-

ately to its shelter (Fig. 1). If such fish are kept in an aquarium they may remain alive even when the holothurians are removed, but only if no other

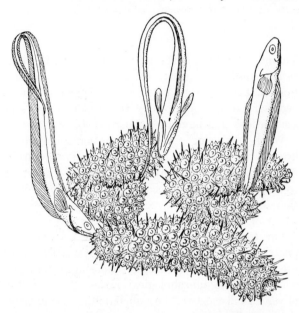

FIG. 1. A case of endophoresis. Holothurians with fierasfier leaving and entering via the cloaca (Emery).

species of fish be introduced—since these invariably eat the fierasfier. Such an association might be termed endophoresis; it is vital for the fish but indifferent for the holothurian. In several cases, it has been found that the fierasfier may become predator and feed on the organs in which it lives, but since these regenerate rapidly the host suffers no irreparable damage.

One of the most extraordinary cases of what might also be called endophoresis is that of the vorticellid ciliate, *Ellobiophrya donacis* Chat. & Lwoff, which is found in certain species of mussels. It has so far been reported from only the wedge shell, *Donax vittatus* da Costa, where it is found attached in a very peculiar manner (Fig. 2). The usual single stalk found in other vorticellids is duplicated in this species. The two stalks are locked together in such a way that they embrace the gill-grid. The protozoan is literally padlocked to the gills of its host, yet it is able to turn around its base like other sedentary vorticellids. When *Ellobiophrya* divides longitudinally, the individual that is detached remains free-swimming and is provided with a double crown of cilia. It swims around within the mantle cavity. Some individuals are probably expelled through the excurrent siphon. The two "legs" appear gradually and at the same time the posterior crown of cilia gradually degenerates and disappears completely as soon as the individual is padlocked to the gill-grid.

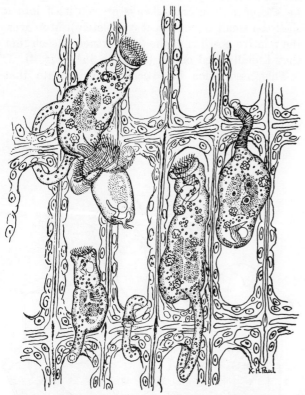

FIG. 2. *Ellobiophrya donacis* Chatt. & Lwoff attached to the gill-grid of its host. Upper left, an individual with a bud that has resulted from a longitudinal fission, showing the posterior circle of cilia (Chatton & Lwoff).

The food of *Ellobiophrya* apparently consists of small organisms and perhaps also mucus, filtered out from the sea water. This protozoan appears to be a highly specialized phoretic organism, adapted in a teleological fashion to a particular support. There is no evidence so far of the possible transfer of *Ellobiophrya* to other hosts. Such experiments would be particularly important since they might show whether this peculiar adaptation is only morphological or also physiological, and whether *Ellobiophrya* is specialized in its food habits.

Numerous cases of phoresis have been recorded and most authors usually regard this association as leading ultimately to true parasitism. One cannot deny that this might be the case, yet there is no factual evidence so far.

Turbellarian-like organisms known as temnocephalans occur within the branchial chamber or on other parts of the body of certain fresh-water crayfish. Tentacles and a sucker-like organ enable them to crawl about on their hosts and they feed on the minute organisms that occur in their environment (Fig. 3). They can also abandon their host and pass

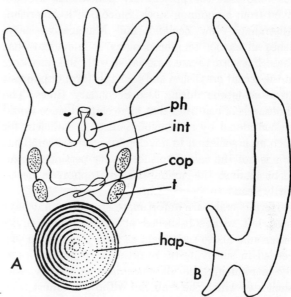

FIG. 3. Diagrammatic morphology of a temnocephalan. A. Ventral view. B. Lateral view. cop.—male copulatory organ. hap.—haptor. int.—gut. ph.—pharynx. t.—testis.

on to another one. However, since the eggs are attached to the surface of the crayfish, on hatching the young temnocephalans immediately find suitable conditions for their existence. The fact that several authors have successfully maintained these flatworms in daily renewed water, without their hosts, and have been able to observe that they live normally and produce eggs, indicates that this is again a case of phoresis comparable to those mentioned above. Here, however, it is possible to obtain some evidence as to the length of time during which these organisms have been associated with their hosts.

Temnocephalans are found principally on species of parastacids that possess a very peculiar geographical distribution. They occur in streams and rivers of Australia, New Zealand, Madagascar, and of some of the Polynesian Islands and are also found in South America. Carcinologists who have studied this particular problem come to the conclusion that the ancestors of present-day parastacids first appeared as such during early Cretaceous times. At that time Australia, New Zealand, and Madagascar, as well as South America, were united by the paleantarctic continent and became detached from one another in the middle of Tertiary times.

Since sea water presents an insurmountable barrier to most fresh-water organisms, it is possible to conclude that the present-day parastacids are derived from a common stock. Since South American, Australian, New Zealand, and Madagascar crayfishes all harbor temnocephalans, it is evident that these flatworms were associated with the ancestors of the recent crayfishes and that this form of phoresis arose sometime during late Secondary times. The thousands of centuries that have elapsed since would be considered by most evolutionists as sufficient for such an association to develop into parasitism. That this is not the case furnishes a very pertinent argument against the assumption that phoresis necessarily leads to parasitism.

Hermit crabs are unfortunate creatures that have been left with soft-shelled abdomens which invite other animals to seek them as food. They have succeeded in surviving by resorting to expedients, i.e., by introducing the abdomen into an empty snail shell into which the crab can withdraw almost completely. These crabs are true psychopaths, endowed with a flight-complex that incites them to hide themselves. This complex is satisfied whenever they discover shells already overgrown with other organisms. Their sense of camouflage is so developed that a hermit crab, grown too large for its shell and obliged to seek a larger one, may detach part of the original epizoic growth and implant it on the new abode.

The sea anemone *Sagartia parasitica* Gosse is found attached to rocks and also to empty shells where it doubtlessly finds the necessary support for its well-being. Should such a shell be chosen by a hermit crab, the sea anemone usually detaches itself and seeks a more stable support. Should the hermit crab, however, belong to the species *Pagurus arrosor* Herbst the anemone remains, and a durable partnership is formed. Whenever the crab is obliged to seek a larger shell, it first detaches the anemone and places it on the new shelter. Apparently neither of the two partners profits by the other's presence and each is quite capable of living by itself. This is consequently not even a case of phoresis.

Numerous different associations of hermit crabs and actinians have been recorded, yet their true nature has hardly ever been studied experimentally and very little is known about it. But the association of *Eupagurus prideauxi* Leach with the anemone *Adamsia palliata* Forbes is of an intimate kind, since the crab uses the pedal disc of the actinian to protect its abdomen (the crab always crowds itself into a shell too small to contain it completely). Moreover, the relative position of the two partners is such that they literally feed out of the same dish (Fig. 4).

This association has become so intimate that

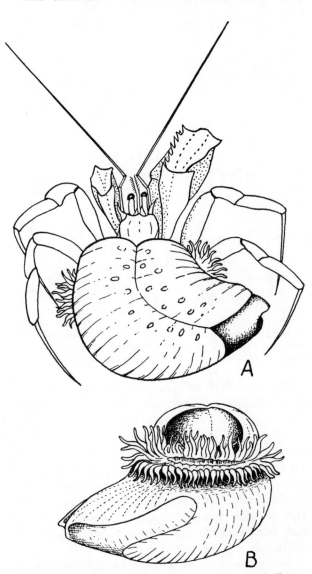

FIG. 4. *Adamsia palliata* Forbes attached to a shell containing *Eupagurus prideauxi* Leach. A. Dorsal view; the foot of the actinian protects the dorsal surface of the crab's abdomen. B. Shell from which the crab has been removed, showing the actinian's mouth opposite that of the crab (Faurot).

neither of the partners is able to survive alone. *Adamsia palliata* produces toxins that are deadly when injected into crabs, but *Eupagurus prideauxi* appears so far to be the only species that possesses natural antibodies toward these toxins. This may be interpreted in two ways. In the first case, it is possible to envisage the presence of antibodies as being the outcome of a very long association, a gradual adaptation of one of the partners to the other. In the second case, one might assume that the blood of *E. prideauxi* has always contained these antibodies and that this species was preadapted to living in close association with *Adamsia*.

From what is known of the habits of hermit crabs and their association with sea-anemones, one is inclined to adopt the second of the two ideas. This would also account for the almost permanent nature of this particular association as compared to the others. In such cases, it is usual to speak of the two partners as messmates or commensals and the association is named *commensalism*.

Commensalism implies that the association is to the mutual benefit of both partners. In the case just mentioned, for instance, the hermit crab profits by the presence of the sea-anemone which enables it to enlarge its shelter and keep off undesirable predators. The sea-anemone benefits directly, as it may digest easily the food that the crab tears up into small pieces.

It is clear that such animal associations must be carefully analyzed, using experimental methods whenever possible. One cannot classify them into distinct categories without knowing the exact nature of the association and, especially, to how great an extent it is obligatory to either of the two partners. It is more than likely that both phoresis and commensalism have arisen from ecological associations in which certain members were protected, either accidentally or intentionally, by camouflage. But in no case does one of the partners provide the other with vital foodstuffs without which it could not survive. This means that both partners have retained their entire physiological independence, although they may, for ecological reasons, be unable to survive when separated.

Commensalism never leads to parasitism and it is also fundamentally distinct from symbiosis with which it is sometimes confused.

SYMBIOSIS

The paunch of ruminants and the cecum of members of the horse tribe contain enormous numbers of ciliates belonging to many species and to several genera. The rumen of a cow may contain as many as 50,000 ciliates per cubic centimeter and this means that the average weight of infusorians contained in the entire rumen would be approximately 2.8 kilos.

The nature of this association has been the matter of much speculation, and it is in only comparatively recent years that it has been determined on an experimental basis.

Cultures *in vitro* show that probably there exist at least two distinct groups of these protozoans, one represented by the genera *Diplodinium* and *Eudiplodinium* which produces cellulase and cellobiase and the other, which includes *Entodinium*, that cannot produce these two enzymes and consequently cannot utilize cellulose directly but must rely on cellulose-splitting bacteria (Fig. 5). In cultures the

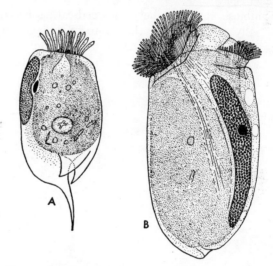

FIG. 5. Symbiotic ciliates from cattle. A. *Entodinium caudatum* Stein. B. *Diplodinium hegneri* Becker & Talbot (Becker & Talbot).

rate of fission of these ciliates is about once every twenty-four hours and approximately 69 per cent, by weight, of *Protozoa* is produced daily (Hungate). When these die and disintegrate they provide the host with about 20 per cent of its total nitrogen requirements. Consequently, these ciliates are concerned both with the carbohydrate and protein metabolisms of the host.

Defaunated ruminants, i.e., those that have been deprived of their ciliates, are able to utilize cellulose only if cellulose-splitting bacteria have developed sufficiently to replace the infusorians.

It is clear that the association of protozoans and herbivorous mammals is of a very intricate nature. Since the ciliates die in the presence of oxygen, they find in the methane gas-filled rumen almost perfect conditions, including a source of their indispensable food. Their metabolism consequently is intense and enables them to multiply very rapidly although their longevity is only about one day. Their total number therefore remains fairly constant and proportionate to the amount of food available. The host that harbors such ciliates profits by their presence. It can use larger amounts of carbohydrates than it could if the cellulose were split up by bacteria alone and it also derives a notable quantity of animal protein from the dead bodies of the ciliates.

Consequently, this type of association is of mutual benefit to both partners who have each lost their physiological independence. Such an association is termed *symbiosis*.

Symbiosis also exists between wood-eating insects, especially termites, and their intestinal flagellates (Fig. 6). In this case, evidence of their providing the host with notable amounts of nitrogen and probably

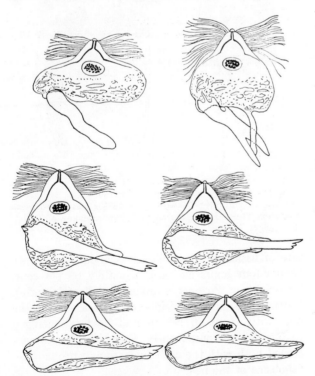

FIG. 6. *Trichonympha* sp. from the gut of a termite showing mode of ingesting fragments of wood (Swezy).

also carbohydrates is derived from the fact that defaunated termites fail to survive and also that the higher termites, those that cultivate fungi and certainly use them as a source of nitrogen, do not harbor flagellates.

There is no conclusive evidence of symbiosis having ever led to parasitism, although several authors assume this to be the case.[1] It is possible that both symbiosis and parasitism have originated in a somewhat similar way and have evolved on parallel lines. Evidence shows that flagellates evolved together with their hosts, so that it would be reasonable to assume that these symbionts were already present in termites during the Carboniferous period. The approximately three hundred million years that have elapsed since then do not appear to have been sufficient to turn the symbionts into parasites!

PARASITISM

Parasitism is an association of an entirely different kind in which the host provides the parasite with substances that it has elaborated and that are essential for the parasite's nutritional requirements. A parasite has usually lost to some degree the power to synthesize certain vital substances and must therefore rely on the host to furnish them. Consequently, such an association is even more intimate than any of those mentioned above since it implies the reliance of the parasite upon its host. The greater the loss of the power to synthesize its essential nutritional requirements, the more intricate will be the relationship between the parasite and the host. This is known as host specificity, the knowledge of which is fundamental to establishing the degree of parasitic adaptation.

Parasitism so defined implies that a state of unstable balance exists between the two partners since they necessarily react upon each other, even if, normally, neither is a menace to the other. Should, however, the parasite produce toxins prejudicial to the host, or injure it in some other way, the balance will be upset in favor of the parasite. On the other hand, if the host reacts to the presence of the para-

[1] A curious instance of parasitism being transformed into symbiosis is that recorded by Vuillemin and Legrain (*C. R. Acad. Sc. Paris*, 118:549–551). Plants from the Sahara desert that harbor the root nematode *Heterodera radicicola* Greef are able to withstand the drought much better than those not so infested, since under the attack of the parasite, the plants lignify the walls of giant cells and use these cavities as water reservoirs.

site by producing antibodies or other substances that interfere with normal development, the balance will be upset in favor of the host.

Consequently, what might be termed the ideal parasite, that is, the successfully adapted parasite, exists only in theory since both the parasite's and the host's existence may be jeopardized by extraneous factors independent of either.

No mention will be made of vertebrates as parasites, since in no single instance has the significance of such possible associations been analyzed.

The males of ceriatoid fishes are, it is true, grafted onto the bodies of the females, but so far there exists no indication of the way in which this occurs. Moreover, from preserved materials it appears that this association might be considered as secondary hermaphroditism, since the males are reduced to the state of a testis.

Social parasitism, as it is sometimes called, is found among birds, cowbirds and some cuckoos, but this bears no relationship to animals that are both physiologically and morphologically adapted to parasitism.

It has often been assumed that the embryos of mammals are parasites, parasitic within the maternal organism. But, if this were the case, it would also be necessary to consider all abnormal growths that appear either on the surface or within the body as parasites. This would apply equally well to all fertilized ova that have not yet left the maternal organism or that develop partly therein, as in certain fishes and amphibians.

The preceding diagram illustrates the different types of associations mentioned.

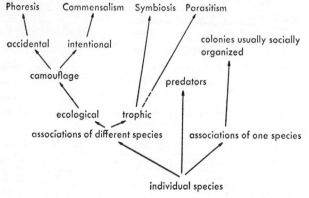

REFERENCES

BAER, J. G. 1931. Etude monographique du groupe des Temnocéphales. *Bull. Biol. France et Belgique*, 65:1–57, 5 figs., 5 pls.

———. 1946. Le Parasitisme. 232 pp., 139 figs., 4 pls. Lausanne et Paris.

BECKER, E. R., & TALBOT, M. 1927. The Protozoan fauna of the rumen and reticulum of American cattle. *Iowa State Coll. Sc. J.*, 1:345–71, 27 figs.

CANTACUZÈNE, J. 1923. Le problème de l'immunité chez les Invertébrés. *C. R. Soc. Biol. V. J.*, pp. 48–119.

CHATTON, ED., & LWOFF, A. 1929. Contribution à l'étude de l'adaptation de *Ellobiophrya donacis* (Ch. et Lw.). *Bull. Biol. France et Belgique*, 63:321–49, 4 figs., pls. 8–9.

CLEVELAND, L. R. 1925. The effects of oxygenation and starvation on the symbiosis between the termite, *Termopsis*, and its intestinal flagellates. *Biol. Bull.*, 48:309–26, 1 pl.

———. 1926. Symbiosis among animals with special reference to termites and their intestinal flagellates. *Quart. Rev. Biol.*, 1:51–60.

EMERY, C. 1880. Le specie del genere Fierasfier del golfo di Napoli. *Fauna et Flora Neap.*, vol. 2, 76 pp., 10 figs., 9 pls.

FAUROT, L. 1910. Etude sur les associations entre les Pagures et les Actinies. *Arch. Zool Exp.* (5), 5:421–86, 3 figs.

HUNGATE, R. E. 1942. The culture of Eudiplodinium neglectum, with experiments on the digestion of cellulose. *Biol. Bull.*, 83:303–19

———. 1943. Further experiments on cellulose digestion by the protozoa in the rumen of cattle. *Ibid.*, 84:157–63.

PEARSE, A. S. 1942. Introduction to parasitology. ix + 337 pp., 448 figs. Springfield.

PART TWO

Adaptations to parasitism

Parasitism is a biological phenomenon which has appeared at different times among almost all groups of living things. Parasites do not constitute a distinct morphological entity, but there are certain biological peculiarities that appear to be common to many of them. Organs and structures that are important or even essential for free-living organisms often become lost or greatly modified in parasitic forms. Structures for locomotion, special sensory organs, and, in extreme adaptations, even specialized digestive organs become modified or even disappear completely. This is sometimes misnamed parasitic degeneration. Parasites are more or less highly specialized organisms that are adapted to a particular environment and that usually show, besides their structural simplification, a distinct hyperactivity of certain organs, especially of the reproductive glands.

In phyla that contain both free-living and parasitic forms, one generally finds that the parasite has evolved new organs usually in connection with the mode of attachment to its host. Such structures are nearly always derived from pre-existing organs.

One would think that a parasitic mode of life would produce, to a certain degree, convergence of several morphological characteristics, and that these would constitute a sort of hallmark of parasitism. This is not the case nor is it possible to attribute any particular structure to a parasitic mode of life.

For instance, suckers are typical organs of attachment found in flukes and tapeworms, yet they are also common in temnocephalids and cephalopods as well as in several species of fishes.

The mouth parts of parasitic grubs are in no way different from those of grubs that live as saprozoites. The complete atrophy of the gut as found in several parasitic crustaceans is also reported for many of the free-living forms.

Such facts tend to show that at various periods different organisms have established themselves as parasites and that each one has adapted itself individually, having sometimes evolved completely modified organs. These organs may be traced back to basic morphological characters of the group from which the parasites have arisen.

If the reproductive capacity of a parasite is compared with that of the free-living species, in almost every case the parasite possesses a greatly increased reproductive capacity. It is evident that in certain cases hyperactivity of the genital glands has enabled the parasite to adapt itself successfully to new conditions. In free-living copepods, for instance, there appears to be a definite reproductive cycle that usually coincides with a particular season, whereas in parasitic copepods egg production is a continuous process without seasonal fluctuations. This is also the case for most endoparasites living either within the gut or in natural cavities of the host. The increased reproductive activity is probably due to the great amount of nourishment that most parasites derive from the continual and intimate contact with their host, since ectoparasites which are not closely attached to their host do not usually show evidence of increased reproductive powers. The segmented strobila of a tapeworm should be considered as a particular case of sexual hyperactivity, as each segment contains complete hermaphroditic reproductive systems.

Another physiological trait that might be considered as a parasitic adaptation is the ability that several species possess of increasing the number of larval forms. A single egg gives issue to a great number of larvae either by splitting the original ovum or by a more delayed process that involves intermediate larval types such as are found in trematodes. This is usually known as polyembryony and is not necessarily restricted to parasites. It is also found in free-living *Protozoa* (*Foraminifera*) and in mammals (*Armadillo*).

It is evident that polyembryony has had a great influence on the selective evolution of parasitism. Forms possessing this type of development are more often found among parasites than among free-living organisms. This is another example of the way in which a basic biological trait may influence an evolutionary process and finally appear as a particular adaptation.

Schizogony and sporogony in *Protozoa*, production of cercariae in trematodes, budding of cestode larvae, and polyembryony in chalcidid wasps are all similar biological phenomena, differing in detail but basically comparable.

There is hardly a single phylum that does not contain some species which is adapted in a more or less successful manner to parasitism. Such parasites may sometimes furnish important information as to how a free-living organism has become adapted to a parasitic mode of life.

Parasitic adaptations are not necessarily morphological only, they are sometimes physiological without any sign of a structural change. In such cases, experimental methods alone make it possible to discover the nature of the adaptation in the same manner as they reveal physiologically adapted species or subspecies among free-living animals.

In phyla that consist of parasites exclusively, their origin remains a matter of speculation since free-living ancestors, if they ever existed, are unknown. Information may be gained, however, from a study of the intimacy of the host-parasite relationship and also from the various ways in which parasites may infest new hosts. Even among parasites it is possible to discover different degrees of adaptation to a common mode of life.

When the life cycle of a parasite requires only a single host within or upon which the parasite spends either its entire existence or one phase of it, the host represents the biotope, i.e., the ecological environment of the parasite and, consequently, its presence is absolutely indispensable to the latter.

In many instances the life history requires that the parasite pass through successive hosts, the precise definition of which is not always clear. Such hosts are usually referred to as intermediate hosts and since their presence may be either essential or optional, both for ontogenetical and ecological reasons, it is important to provide some criterion for designating them.

When a larval parasite develops in an intermediate host to a point beyond which no further morphological differentiation occurs, it is obvious that such a host will be ontogenetically indispensable. Life histories of parasites, sometimes require one, two, or very rarely, three successive intermediate hosts. In each host, larval development proceeds to a stage beyond that attained in the preceding one. These intermediate hosts will be called the first, second,

and third intermediate hosts and the host in which the larvae finally become adult will be called the final or definitive host.

An optional intermediate host is one which the larvae usually enters passively, along with ingested food. The larvae are able to survive for considerable time without the new environment affecting in any way their ontogeny. Such larvae will invariably remain at the same stage of development as when first swallowed by this host. Such an intercalary host is not at all necessary for the successful completion of the life cycle and may even, in certain cases (see page 147), prevent this from occurring. At other times, however, such an intercalary host becomes indispensable for ecological reasons, as for example when the intermediate host containing infestive larvae is not eaten normally by the final host, the intercalary host feeds on the intermediate host and is in turn eaten by the final host.

The presence of such potential intermediate hosts was first recognized by Joyeux & Baer[1] who named them "hôtes d'attente" implying that their presence within the cycle is not essential and could neither favor nor hinder its completion. Unfortunately, this expression cannot be translated into English and retain the meaning it has in French. The terms vicarious host and transport host are frequently used although they express inadequately the idea contained in "hôte d'attente." For this reason the designation paratenic host is proposed since being derived from the Greek $\pi\alpha\rho\alpha\tau\epsilon\acute{\iota}\nu\omega$ = to prolong, to draw out, i.e., to complicate the life cycle, it has the same meaning in all languages. The basis for this concept is one of ontogeny, as no larval form undergoes any development in a paratenic host.

Consequently, life histories of parasites that require more than one host will contain one or more intermediate hosts and a final or definitive host. Into this circuit may be inserted a paratenic host, invariably appearing between the final intermediate host and the definitive host, which may either divert the cycle tangentially or lead to its normal conclusion.

Several instances occur in which the paratenic host has become ecologically indispensable and introduces into the life history a potential intermediate host of a particular type.

[1] *Biologie Medicale*, Paris, 1934, 24:1–25.

Protozoa

Protozoa as a whole show a wide variety of types and structures that one hardly associates with unicellular organisms. Most modern authors no longer consider the protozoan organism as homologous to a single metazoan cell. Although it possesses only a single nucleus, a protozoan shows evidence of distinct differentiations into organelles functioning like digestive, locomotor, and nervous systems.

All the major groups of protozoans, except the sporozoans and the suctorians, contain both free-living and parasitic forms. Sporozoans are entirely parasitic and suctorians are sedentary, although they are often found attached to the surface of fresh-water organisms.

It is found that protozoans have become adapted to every known type of biotope so that there is nothing very remarkable in their having successfully adapted themselves to parasitism. By comparing the free-living forms with the related parasitic forms, it is possible to determine the parasitic adaptations.

The high degree of plasticity of the protozoan organism makes it difficult to distinguish, from a morphological standpoint, between parasitic adaptations and responses of the organism to its environment. For instance, trypanosomes, both from the blood stream of vertebrates and from the latex of certain plants, possess an undulating membrane that is usually considered an adaptation to parasitism. However, when these parasites enter the insect host, the undulating membrane disappears and the organism adopts the so-called *crithidia* type of morphology. The undulating membrane reappears when the trypanosomes have multiplied within the insect host and have entered into its salivary glands. This tends to show that this undulating membrane is not a parasitic adaptation, but only the response of an organism to the viscosity of its environment.

The absence of a mouth in astomous ciliates is usually regarded as an adaptation to parasitism since these organisms live in the gut or in the coelomic cavity of invertebrates and occasionally in vertebrates. No evidence exists, however, that these ciliates possess a monophyletic origin and it is quite possible that the absence of a mouth might reflect convergence. Many other ciliates which have also adapted themselves to the parasitic mode of life possess a distinct cytopharynx. Several species of astomous ciliates have a rudimentary, cup-shaped anterior depression that looks like a sucker and functions as an organ of attachment (*Haptophrya*) (Fig. 7). Such rudimentary organs of attachment are

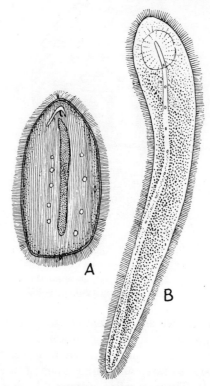

Fig. 7. Astomous ciliates. A. *Hoplitophrya hamata* Cép. bearing a small harpoon-like hook. B. *Haptophrya gigantea* Maupas with a sucker-like organ (Cépède).

also found in certain flagellates of the genus *Giardia* which live in the gut of various mammals, including man. Hooks and harpoons, seen in certain species of astomous ciliates, are found in several species of gregarines among the sporozoans (Figs. 8 and 9).

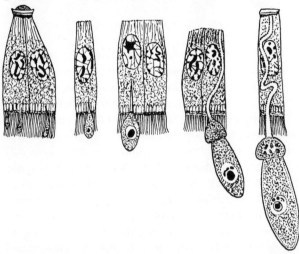

FIG. 8. *Pyxinia moebiusi* L. & D., showing different stages of development of the epimerite in the gut epithelium of an insect (Léger).

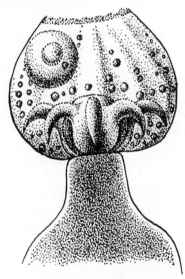

FIG. 9. *Corycella armata* Lég., showing the complicated structure of the epimerite within a gut epithelial cell (Léger).

Whenever their environment becomes unfavorable, many species of free-living protozoans surround themselves with a membrane from a secretion of their body surface, and enter upon a period of quiescence. These so-called cysts enable *Protozoa* to survive until conditions become favorable for their

free-living existence. Such cysts are very resistant to drying and can remain viable for a great length of time, sometimes for several years. It is more than probable that parasitic forms living in the intestine have arisen from such cyst-producing species since this property would enable them to pass through the gut unharmed, if conditions were unfavorable. Encystment has become the normal mode of dispersion for intestinal parasites and enables them to pass from one host to another. In several cases, it has become cyclic, occurring at regular intervals; in others it is found only when the normal conditions within the gut are modified. It is observed that species of *Giardia*, for instance, survive and multiply without ever forming cysts and that these appear suddenly when conditions are altered, as for example when diarrhea sets in.

These properties should not be considered as parasitic adaptations since they exist also among the free-living forms from which the parasites derived. Such parasites are preadapted and have been able to implant themselves in a new biotope.

Many parasitic protozoans, especially sporozoans, undergo extremely complicated life cycles, comprising not only several successive hosts but also distinct evolutionary stages that are morphologically different. Moreover, the outcome of such a cycle is a great increase in the number of parasitic individuals. Such complicated life histories are usually cited as examples of parasitic adaptations, yet they are also found, although not so frequently, among certain free-living forms. The complex life cycle of *Foraminifera*, which involves two distinct generations that can be distinguished on a morphological basis, is an example. The megalospheric forms give issue through sexual reproduction to the microspheric forms that multiply asexually and give rise to another megalospheric generation. Consequently, each phase corresponds to both a morphological and a physiological stage in the life cycle of the same organism.

In apostomean ciliates, a truly remarkable life cycle is observed that has, so far, never been found in any other free-living protozoans. Different phases appear in a cyclic fashion, each phase being associated with a distinct supporting organism (Fig. 10). In *Spirophrya* a cystlike organism known as the *tomont* is attached to the surface of a hydroid. The contents of the cyst divide into a large number of *tomites* (four to eighty-two). The latter escape by rupturing the cyst wall and are considered the propagative forms. They attach themselves to the surface of copepods, *S. subparasitica* Chatt. & Lwoff, occur-

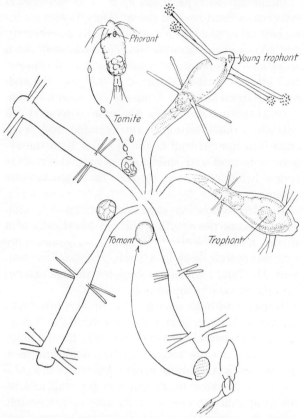

FIG. 10. Diagram of the life cycle of *Spirophyra subparasitica* Chatt. & Lwoff on a fragment of hydroids (Chatton & Lwoff).

ring on the surface of *Idyaea furcata* (Baird). This stage is known as the *phoront*. When a copepodbearing phoront is swallowed by a hydroid, it is digested by a gastrozoite within two hours. During this short interval the *phoront* has penetrated into the body of the copepod, through the chitinous body wall which has been softened by the digestive juices of the hydroid, and becomes a trophont or vegetative form that increases rapidly in size and contains numerous food bodies. The ciliated trophont is expelled from the hydroid together with the undigested remains of the copepod. After swimming around for some time, the trophont attaches itself to the surface of a hydroid and becomes a tomont.

In other words, this is a free-living ciliate whose life cycle involves three distinct phases, two of which are phoretic on a hydroid and a copepod respectively

and the third endophoretic within a hydroid. The so-called phoront stage constitutes the propagative phase, the trophont, the vegetative phase; and the tomont, the reproductive phase.

In *Phoreotrophrya* all three phases are found on the same supporting host, a crustacean, *Nebalia geoffroyi* M. Edw., the phoronts and tomonts being attached to the appendages, and the trophonts, to the cast-off molt. In *Calospira*, the phoronts are attached to an harpacticid and the trophonts are found within its fresh remains. The tomonts, on the other hand, are free in the sea. *Hyalospira* is the only apostomean, so far discovered which is associated with fresh-water organisms. The phoronts are attached to the body hairs of a species of freshwater shrimp, *Xiphocaris elongata* G.-M. Trophonts have been recovered from molts of this host and tomonts from crevices in the stream bed. Unfortunately, nothing is known of any form of sexual reproduction in this group of ciliates but it is an extremely interesting instance of a free-living protozoan that has become specialized in regard to its habitat. The presence of *Hyalospira* on fresh-water shrimps is of particular interest since these hosts probably entered fresh water with their commensals from the sea, as far back as Cretaceous times. This is another example of the adaptive powers of protozoans.

Alternating generations in the course of the life cycle are also found in sporozoans. We do not wish to imply that sporozoans are therefore related to ciliates but only to stress that certain biological analogies may be found in their respective life cycles.

In sporozoan life cycles there are usually three and more rarely two distinct phases that differ from one another in their morphology, their physiology, and their habitat. Male and female gametes fuse to form a zygote. The zygote passes into sporogony, a phase in which the fertilized ovum divides into one or several haploid spores, each spore containing a distinctive number of sporozoites. They represent the infestive stage which can continue the life cycle only if the sporozoites be introduced into the host either passively, when the first host or the spores are eaten by another host, or actively, when the sporozoites are inoculated together with the saliva of an arthropod. In both cases the sporozoites undergo asexual multiplication, through multiple fission, within the cells of the host. The sporozoites finally burst and liberate the so-called schizozoites. Since each schizozoite is able to repeat this mode of reproduction a great number of times, schizogony must be considered the invasion phase, a stage in the life cycle during which the parasites spread throughout the host's body. Male and female gamonts also arise through schizogony. They give issue to the gametes which will fuse together to form the zygote. The appearance of the zygote marks the end of the reproductive stage and the beginning of the phase during which, as we have seen, the ovum divides into spores that will be expelled from the host's body. Sporogony should therefore be considered as the propagative phase since both the spores and the sporozoites enable the parasite to reach new hosts which will be invaded by the reappearance of the schizogonic phase (Fig. 11).

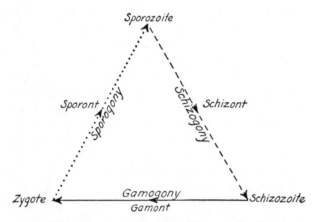

Fig. 11. Diagram of the three phases of the sporozoan life cycle.

When we examine the different types of life cycles in sporozoans, we find that, in every case, these phases correspond to definite stages in the life history of the parasites.

Gregarines are exclusively parasites of the gut and natural cavities of arthropods, annelids, and, very rarely, tunicates. Except for a small minority of species, schizogony does not occur and consequently, the host is never invaded by parasitic germs. Compared with other sporozoans, gregarines are large organisms and often have organelles of attachment with which they fix themselves either to the surface or inside of the host's cells. Infection of new hosts takes place whenever they ingest the spores eliminated by another host.

In *Coccidia*, two types of life cycles are apparent. *Eimeria* Schn. is found almost exclusively in the gut epithelium of many vertebrates, but occasionally also in insects. The parasites pass through the three phases and consequently an intense invasion of the gut wall results.

In the second type of life cycle, a second host is involved, as in *Aggregata eberthi* (Dobell) where schizogony takes place in a crab and both gametogony and sporogony in a cuttlefish. The crab swallows a spore and the sporozoite penetrates through the gut wall into the peritoneal tissue. In this way, the crab accumulates enormous numbers of schizozoites in its coelomic cavity. When the crab is eaten by a cuttlefish, the sporozoites are liberated and penetrate into the gut wall of the mollusc. Here the zygote is formed and sporogony occurs, the mature spores being evacuated through the intestine into the sea.

In *Haemogregarina stepanowi* Danilewsky, schizogony takes place within the red blood cells of a turtle, *Emys orbicularis* L., and both gametogony and sporogony occur in a leech, *Placobdella catenigera* M. Tand., which reinoculates the sporozoites into the blood of another host.

Haemosporidians also have a similar life cycle. In *Plasmodium*, a genus that contains the human malarial parasites, schizogony occurs in the red blood cells. Gamonts are sucked up by anopheline mosquitoes and the resulting zygote, known as the ookinete, penetrates through the mid-gut wall and remains attached to the outer surface of the stomach. After sporogony the individual sporozoites penetrate into the salivary glands of the mosquito and, consequently, they are inoculated into another host when the mosquito feeds.

It is possible to find three successive hosts in several species of piroplasms. In *Babesia*, schizogony occurs in the red blood cells of cattle. This genus is peculiar, however, because each sporozoite divides only once and consequently but two schizozoites are found in the erythrocytes. When infested blood is drawn up by ticks, ookinetes are formed within their stomach wall. They, however, pass through the wall and penetrate into the uterine eggs in female ticks. It is here that sporogony occurs. Being capable of ameboid movements, the spores are called sporokinetes. Consequently, when the young ticks hatch, their salivary glands are already packed with sporozoites. It is obvious that the life cycle of *Babesia* can be completed in female ticks only and that the infested offspring constitute a third host in the life history. On the other hand, since oviposition in ticks can occur only when the female is gorged with blood, transmission of the parasites from the mother to the offspring is assured (Fig. 12).[1] Host and para-

host. Such an attempt implies the discovery of the original mode of ingress of the parasite into the host.

We have already seen that cyst-forming, free-

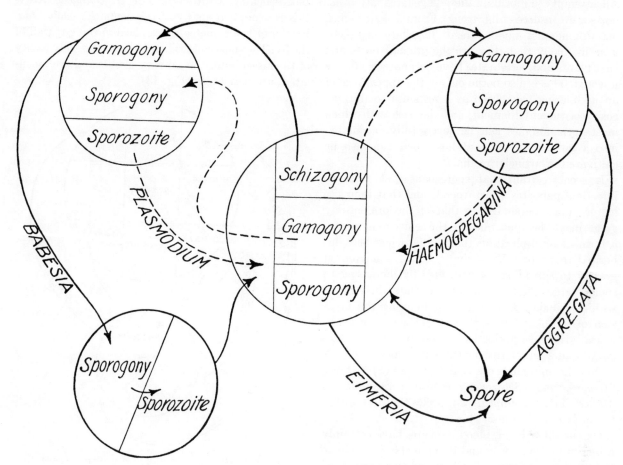

Fig. 12. Diagram of the different types of sporozoan life histories. Each circle represents a different host.

sites have become so intimately adapted to one another that the hazard of a possible loss of germs has disappeared. It is very likely that the peculiar biological nature of this life cycle has made survival possible for this sporozoan parasite which produces only two schizozoites. There is nothing teleological about this at all.

The above examples of sporozoan life cycles make it clear that these progressively complicated life histories are parasitic adaptations. It might be of interest to try to discover which host is the primary

[1] It should be remembered that many ticks only gorge themselves once before each molt, and that a fully gorged female is therefore unable to transmit the parasites to another host since it always dies after oviposition.

living protozoans are without doubt preadapted to an accidental ingestion by a vertebrate and are thus capable of gaining access to a new biotope. For instance, a ciliate, *Colpoda steini* Maupas, found in fresh water, has been observed to adapt itself to the gut of the land slug, *Agriolimax agrestis* L. The "parasitic" forms are somewhat larger than the free-living individuals but this may be due to modified physical conditions that arise within the gut of a slug. Curiously enough, in cultures the free-living forms divide by binary fission within a cyst but this phase is lacking in the "parasites" (Reynolds, 1936).

Certain species of flagellates may also be physiologically preadapted as observed in a species that usually lives in the latex of euphorbias but which has also been found in the gut of lizards. Normally, latex-inhabiting forms are transmitted from one plant to another by coreidae bugs of the species

Chariesterus cuspidatus (Distant). The lizard *Cnemidophorus lemniscatus* (L.) is an insect feeder and infests itself with the flagellates by feeding on the bugs. All attempts to inoculate these flagellates into other hosts were unsuccessful (Strong). From what is known of the numerous forms of parasitic flagellates in insects, it seems likely that they are the original hosts and that plants and vertebrates have become secondarily infected. This is also borne out by the appearance of an undulating membrane as a response to the viscosity of the environment, and the ease with which most trypanosomes can be successfully inoculated into a number of different hosts and can also be cultivated in artificial media.

It seems certain that sporozoans first arose as intestinal parasites of arthropods and that their life history must be similar to that of the present-day gregarines. The appearance of the schizogonic phase, a form of multiplication that perhaps has been inherited from some free-living ancestor, contributed greatly to spreading the parasites by increasing to such a large extent the number of individual germs within a single host and also by favoring the invasion of the neighboring tissues. Schizogregarines illustrate this assumption as in these parasites schizogony occurs either free in the gut (*Caulleryella*) or within the epithelial cells of the gut wall (*Spirocystis*, *Merogregarina*). Schizogony is also intracellular in *Mattesia* and *Lipotropha*, two species that live within the body cavity of insect hosts.

On the other hand, blood parasites have certainly arisen in the same way and it is possible to envisage the intermediate steps that have led to a specialized form of parasitism. The genus *Schellackia* has been recorded from lizards in which both schizogony and gametogony occur within the cells of the gut wall. The spores pass into the blood capillaries and enter the red blood cells, thus being distributed throughout the blood stream. Mites feeding on lizards swallow blood containing infested corpuscles. Since the lizards eat the mites, they become infested with sporozoites.

Lankesterella is found in frogs. Schizogony occurs in the reticulo-endothelial cells where the gametes are formed also. The spores accumulate in the liver and the spleen of the frog and penetrate into the red blood cells, thus entering the blood stream. Leeches feeding on the frogs draw up infested blood and inoculate the parasites into another host when they feed again.

The genus *Haemoproteus* is parasitic in birds and reptiles. Schizogony occurs within the reticulo-endothelial cells but gametogony is found only within the erythrocytes. The gamonts pass into the gut of blood-sucking arthropods. For *H. columbae* Kruse this is a pupiparous fly of the genus *Pseudolynchia*. Fusion of the gametes takes place in the gut wall of the fly. The sporozoites liberated into the body cavity of the insect enter the salivary glands and are inoculated into new hosts (Fig. 13).

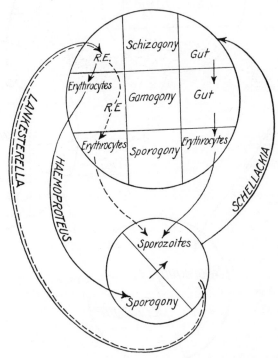

Fig. 13. Diagram of the way in which sporozoans originally passed from the gut into the blood. Large circle represents vertebrate host and small circle, invertebrate host.

When we compare these three types of life histories, we find that in both *Schellackia* and *Lankesterella* infestation of a subsequent host is brought about through mechanical transport. In the first case, the arthropod host is eaten; in the second case, the leech injects the sporozoites directly into the host. Yet in neither case is the passage through an indispensable intermediate host necessary, since the parasites do not undergo any change during their sojourn. In *Haemoproteus* both the zygote and the ensuing sporogony take place in the body cavity of the fly, an indispensable link in the life cycle of the parasite.

There seems to be no doubt whatever that the blood-inhabiting flagellates have originated from species living in invertebrates and that they are therefore the primary hosts. The blood-inhabiting sporozoans have originated from intestinal forms, and all three phases of their life history occur primarily in the same host. The occurrence of sporogony in another host, an invertebrate, is a secondary modification of the life cycle. Consequently, we may conclude that the two types of blood-inhabiting

FIG. 14. Young trout parasitized by *Myxosoma cerebralis* (Hofer). Both the nerve centers and hypophysis have been injured, as is indicated by the curvature of the tail and by the extension of the melanophores (Scheuring).

protozoans have arisen in different ways and that for the flagellates the primary host is an invertebrate and the secondary host a vertebrate. In sporozoans, the primary host is a vertebrate and the secondary host an invertebrate.

Cnidosporidians have a different type of life cycle. The spores are formed in complex plurinuclear organisms, the so-called pansporoblasts, which are always intracellular. The spores are liberated usually after the death of the host. Infection takes place after penetration of the sporozoites into the gut and from there, via the blood stream, into the elected organs. Microsporidians can harm their host greatly by destroying the cells in which they develop. The numerous spores that are found in vertebrates and invertebrates show a distinct tendency to develop only in a specific environment such as a particular region of the host's body. *Myxosoma cerebralis* (Hofer) attacks the cartilage and perichondrum of the skull in trout fry (Fig. 14). *M. catostomi* Kudo destroys the muscles and connective tissue of suckers. *Henneguyia psorospermica* Thel. forms cysts on the gills of pike and perch, *H. oviperda* (Cohn) within the ovary of female pike, causing sterility in advanced cases, and *H. mictospora* Kudo in the urinary bladder of sunfishes (*Lepomis* spp.).

REFERENCES

CHATTON, ED., & LWOFF, A. 1935. Les Ciliés apostomes. *Arch. Zool. Exp.*, vol. 77, 453 pp., 211 figs., 21 pls.

DOFLEIN, F., & REICHENOW, E. 1929. Lehrbuch der Protozoenkunde. 5te Aufl., 1262 pp., 1201 figs., Jena.

KUDO, R. 1946. Protozoology. 3rd edition, 778 pp., 336 figs., Springfield.

REYNOLDS, B. D. 1936. *Colpoda steini* a facultative parasite of the land-slug, *Agriolimax agrestis*. *J. Parasit.*, 22:48–53.

STRONG, R. P. 1924. Investigations upon flagellate infections. *Am. J. Trop. Med.*, 4:345–85.

WENYON, C. M. 1926. Protozoology. 1563 pp., 565 figs., 20 pls. London and New York.

Mollusca

It seems unusual that a phylum so highly organized as that of mollusks should contain several parasitic species and that morphologically specialized forms should be able to adapt themselves to parasitism.

We find evidence that different groups of mollusks have become parasitic and that distinct types of adaptation to parasitism have arisen. Ectoparasitic forms have evolved in a way different from endoparasites. In all of these, it is possible to observe regression of certain organs and the appearance and growth of new structures that have not existed previously.

Mollusks present two distinct types of parasitic adaptations. In the first, parasitism is resorted to by larval forms only, the corresponding adults being free-living whereas in the second, the adults only are parasitic and the larval forms free-living.

To illustrate the diversification of host relations and morphological adaptations of mollusks to parasitism, conditions in the *Unionidae* and in a series of peculiarly modified gastropods will be discussed. A series of genera will be compared, some of which are only commensals or predators while others show varied morphological and biological adaptations to specialized forms of parasitism.

Parasitism among larvae, sometimes called protelian parasitism, is found only in bivalve mollusks and constitutes a normal stage in the life cycle of fresh-water unionids. Consequently, parasitism in larval unionids is neither accidental nor occasional but represents an important stage in the life history of the species.

Female unionids incubate their eggs in brood pouches that are formed in the gills. On hatching the larvae are expelled through the excurrent siphon. The number of eggs produced by a single fresh-water clam is something remarkable; several hundred thousand to over a million larvae may be thrown out by a single mussel.

The larval unionids, known as *glochidia*, possess a characteristic morphology. A single glochidium has two small, hornlike shells or valves that protect the so-called embryonic mantle. The valves are mobile around their base and can be applied against one another by the contraction of a small transverse muscle that unites them. A gland located between the two valves, near their base in the region of the hinge, secretes a viscous fluid that hardens on contact with the water and emerges as a long thread from between the valves. The embryonic mantle bears sensory organs along its free edge. The shape of the valves is usually more or less triangular or heart-shaped, although in some species the valves are shaped somewhat like the head of an axe (*Proptera*). In several species, the apex of each valve bears on its inner margin an articulated hook or spine that folds back when the two valves are apposed. Smaller fixed spines are also found on either side of the hinged spine (*Anodonta, Unio, Strophitus*). In other species the valves are spineless (*Margaritana, Lampretes, Proptera*).

The glochidia are expelled in large masses from the clam and in some species remain attached to one another by their threads, forming small bunches that fall to the bottom. Their specific weight is so close to that of water that the slightest disturbance of the water throws up clouds of glochidia. The turmoil caused by the fins of passing fishes is sufficient to create a veritable tempest of glochidia that brings them into contact with their host. Most of the larvae are drawn in by respiratory movements of the fish and distributed over the gills or other parts of the body. Glochidia with articulated spines usually attach themselves to the fins and sometimes to the epidermis, whereas unarmed larvae (Fig. 15A) fix themselves onto gill filaments.[1]

In both cases the tissues of the host are imprisoned between the valves. When articulated spines are

[1] Hookless glochidia of *Quadrula heros* have been found on the fins of the sheepshead *Aplodinotus grunniens* Rafin. (Surber).

present, these first pierce the tissues and then fold back, so that the larval bivalves are literally clipped onto their host. The host's epidermis reacts strongly

that the glochidium derives its necessary metabolites from disintegration products of its own body. The adductor muscle is the first organ to be digested

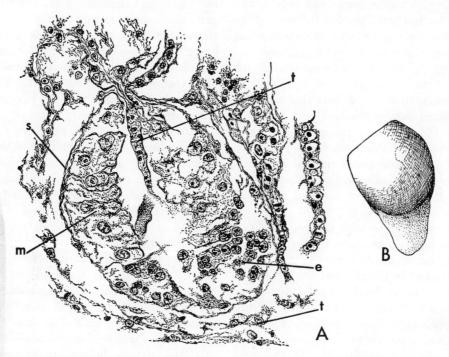

FIG. 15. A. Section through a gill to which a glochidium of *Elliptio complanatus* (Dillwyn) is attached. B. Young clam freshly detached from the fish. e.—embryonic cells. m.—larval mantle. s.—larval shell. t.—gill tissue from the host (from an original slide presented by Dr. M. Matteson).

to the presence of the parasites and in a short time covers them completely. This host reaction is not accompanied by any local multiplication of the cells. The epidermis grows over the parasite much in the same way that it would cover a small wound (Arey). Neighboring cells migrate to the site of the lesion at a much faster rate than they would if it were an ordinary wound. When it is entirely enclosed within the epidermis of its host, the glochidium undergoes complete metamorphosis which is seldom accompanied by an increase in size except perhaps in the case of *Proptera laevissima* Lea. The colder the water, the longer the duration of metamorphosis and the easier it is to follow all the successive steps. The host tissues, enclosed within the valves, are gradually liquefied by a secretion arising from cells located in the embryonic mantle. The liquefied tissues are absorbed by the mantle and serve as nourishment. When all the host tissues are digested, it is found

and it is followed soon after by the larval mantle. During this time new structures are being formed. Definite organs, such as an intestine, heart, liver, gills, foot, and mantle, replace the embryonic organs. Metamorphosis is now terminated and the tiny mussel is seen to move around within its cyst, the walls of which become gradually thinner. Finally, thrusting out its foot, the young mussel breaks through the epidermis and falls to the bottom where it burrows in the mud and grows into an adult clam (Fig. 15B). All the energy necessary to accomplish larval metamorphosis is not derived entirely from the tissues of the host. The glochidium does not need to be in contact with the host's blood, for its cyst wall is not abnormally vascular. It is, however, probable that the glochidium benefits from its respiratory exchanges from the immediate vicinity of capillary vessels. Part of the materials used for building up the young mussel are derived from the disintegrated tissues of the glochidium. This metamorphosis is comparable to the nymphal stage in insects.

Protelian parasitism (Tucker) appears to be a necessary stage in the life history of all unionids even in *Anodonta imbecilis* Say where it had been considered optional (Lefevre & Curtis). These authors also assume that metamorphosis of *Strophitus edentulus* Say occurs within mucus threads containing the glochidia which are formed in the body of the female, and later are expelled into the surrounding water. This observation is questioned by Arey.

Experimentally, glochidia may be made to attach themselves to many kinds of fishes and even to tadpoles and axolotls, yet it appears that complete larval development can be obtained only when the glochidia affix themselves to particular species of fish which seem to be fairly specific for a given mussel. In fish other than these, natural resistance to the glochidia seems to exist, although these attach themselves to the fish they are sloughed off before metamorphosis is completed.

The European species of mussels, *Anodonta cygnaea* (L.), *Unio batavus* Lam., and *Margaritana margaritifera* (L.), are always found on cyprinids, the first species attached to the gills and the last two to the fins. Complete larval development of *A. cygnaea* has been obtained on axolotls (Fausseck). In this country, the glochidia of *Lampsilis anodontoides* Lea attach themselves to the gar pike, *Lepisosteus osseus* L.; those of *Lampsilis luteola* Lam. to the large mouth bass *Huro salmoides* (Lacep.), and those of *Hemistema ambigua* Say to the gills of mud puppies, *Necturus maculatus* Rafin. Even normal hosts acquire some kind of immunity that appears after the third consecutive infestation. The skin of the fish becomes unsuitable for further glochidial development in exactly the same way as that of an unfavorable host (Arey). An antagonism between glochidia and parasitic copepods also seems to exist. Twenty specimens of the latter on a short-nosed gar, *Lepisosteus platostomus* Rafin., are sufficient to cause a skin reaction that will prevent the glochidia from attaching themselves (Wilson).

The enormous number of glochidia produced by a single female mussel might appear as a physiological adaptation, somewhat teleological in nature, to a parasitic mode of life. Yet other bivalves, oysters for example, produce enormous numbers of young. These, however, do not have a parasitic existence but become sedentary as soon as they are expelled into the sea. Incubation in the gill pouches is found only in fresh-water bivalves. In all cases where the number of eggs is small, as in *Sphaerium*, incubation proceeds until metamorphosis is terminated. In *Mus-*

culium partumeium (Say) eighteen to twenty-four eggs may be incubated simultaneously. But there is evidence that these small fresh-water bivalves do not live longer than one year. The length of life of unionids is much greater than this and during this time growth continues. This might account for the larval mussels being expelled before attaining their complete development, since the female utilizes part of its food requirements for growth. Yet no explanation can be found as to why the incompletely formed clams attach themselves to fishes.

Parasitic adult snails do not form a homogeneous group although there is evidence of their possessing converging anatomical characters. Curiously enough, all the known parasitic snails belong to the prosobranchiate gastropods and are usually placed with the *Aglossa*, i.e., they are deprived of a radula.[2]

Snails are recognized as predators or commensals of other snails, tunicates, and echinoderms, but all the parasitic species are associated with echinoderms only. This is all the more interesting since both prosobranch mollusks and echinoderms are among the most ancient invertebrates and their fossils are found together in early Paleozoic beds. A fossil commensal, *Platyceras spiralis* Hall, has been found at Crawfordsville, Indiana, on the arm of an early Triassic crinoid and another species has been reported from a crinoid recovered from Devonian beds in the Eifel (Germany).

Although our knowledge of parasitic gastropods has increased greatly in recent years, the nature of their association with the hosts is not always clear and it is probable that further research will reveal that a number of species recorded as parasitic are sedentary predators.

Species of the pyramellid genus *Odostomia* are found free in the sea, under stones, and associated with bivalve mollusks. *O. scalaris* Macg. introduces its proboscis in between the two valves of a mussel, feeding on the organisms in the branchial chamber (Fig. 16). This species is apparently a very specialized feeder and may also thrust its proboscis into the mouth of tubicolous annelids. A false foot that surrounds the proboscis appears to exist. The eggs are deposited upon the host and the snails are found to be protandrous hermaphrodites (Fretter & Graham). *O. tellinae* Pelseneer lives within the mantle cavity of

---

[2] *Entovalva mirabilis* (Voeltzkow) is a lamellibranch mollusk that has been recovered from the intestine of a *Synapta*. It does not appear to be a true parasite.

a species of clam from the China seas. It pierces the mantle and feeds on the blood of its host. Both species are, however, anatomically identical and give no evidence whatever of having adopted a parasitic mode of life. *O. tellinae* should be considered as being a predator just as *Dolium*, a species of gastropod that pierces the corona of sea urchins. *Dolium* is almost as large an animal as its victim and is therefore always considered a predator, whereas *Odostomia*, which is much smaller but feeds in the same manner, is usually considered a parasite.

Mucronalia variabilis Schep. & Nierstr. is found crawling over the body surface of a holothurian, *Synapta ooplax* Marenzeller, but it may also occur within the intestine. When located in this organ, the snail pierces the wall and becomes a predator. This is

FIG. 16.   FIG. 17.

FIG. 16. *Odostomia scalaris* Macq. with proboscides inserted between the valves of a clam (Pelseneer).

FIG. 17. Male and female specimens of *Thyca stellasteris* Koeh. & Vaney on the arm of a crinoid (Koehler & Vaney).

borne out by the absence of the morphological traits so frequently observed among parasitic snails. Capulids belonging to the genus *Thyca* are related to the fossil forms mentioned above. These species are always found on starfishes from tropical waters. Although their morphology differs little from that of the free-living species, they show a distinct adaptation to a new mode of life. Sexual dimorphism is marked (Fig. 17), the males being much smaller than the females and, like *T. crystallina* (Gould), the males possess a shell of an entirely different shape from that of the females (Adam). The principal adaptive character is a so-called false foot, a muscular disc that surrounds the mouth opening whereas the true foot, recognizable by the presence of the pedal glands, is smaller. An operculum is present in all of the species, but it is much reduced in *T. crystallina*. These species are always found in the ambulacral grooves of the starfish. They appear to feed on

blood and disintegrated muscle fibers that are probably predigested outside the body of the snail by secretions from its salivary glands. Reduction of the foot and appearance of a false foot are parasitic adaptations (Fig. 18).

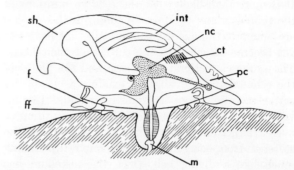

FIG. 18. Diagrammatical section of *Thyca entoconcha* Sarasin upon its host. ct.—ctenidium. f.—foot. ff.—false foot. int.—gut. m.—mouth. nc.—brain. pc.—pallial cavity. sh.—shell (P. & F. Sarasin).

Several species of the genus *Melanella* have been reported from crinoids and starfishes. *M. equestris* (Koeh. & Van.) is one of the few that has been carefully studied. Here also the foot is reduced, although the operculum persists. There is no false foot, but around the base of the proboscis there appears a small funnel-shaped organ, the so-called pseudopallium, the function of which is not clear (Fig. 19).

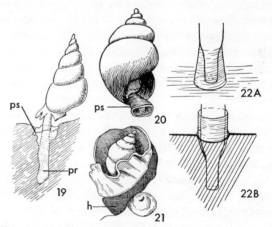

FIG. 19. *Mucronalia palmipedis* Koeh. & Vaney on its host. pr.—proboscis. ps.—pseudopallium (Koehler & Vaney).

FIG. 20. *Mucronalia mittrei* Petit with retracted proboscis, showing the inverted pseudopallium, ps. (Nierstrasz).

FIG. 21. *Megadena holothuricola* Rosén *in situ*. h.—host tissue (Rosén).

FIG. 22. Diagram of the possible function of the pseudopallium. A. Before penetration of the proboscis. B. After penetration.

Yet if we compare *M. equestris* with species of the related genus *Mucronalia*, it is found that here also a pseudopallium exists although apparently it is inverted. In *M. mittrei* Petit this is particularly visible when the proboscis is retracted (Fig. 20). It is more than likely that the relative positions of the proboscis and the pseudopallium in this species are similar to those of the young snails that have not yet become attached to the surface of their hosts. The proboscis perforates the skin and the plates of the echinoderm, probably by exuding a chemically active secretion from its digestive glands. The inverted pseudopallium enables the proboscis to move over a larger surface of skin, while preventing the secretion from being diluted in sea water, functioning much like a diving bell. Once the rostellum has pierced the plates and is extended to its full length, the pseudopallium necessarily becomes everted (Fig. 22).

Megadenus holothuricola Rosén is attached to its host in much the same way, although the snail is found within the respiratory tree of a sea cucumber, the proboscis piercing the wall of the organ and lying free in the body cavity of the host. *M. voeltzkowi* Schep. & Nierstr. has been recovered from the body cavity of another species of holothurian with its proboscis implanted in the ring canal. In both of these species the foot has ceased to be a locomotory organ, an opercule is not found, but the pedal glands persist. The eyes are buried beneath the skin and are probably nonfunctional as such. The intestine is short and the stomach and liver tend to form a single organ. The pseudopallium is considerably developed and folds back around the base of the shell (Fig. 21).

Stilifer contains species that are closely associated with their hosts. Curiously enough, *S. sibogae* Schep. & Nierstr. lives partially embedded in the epidermis at the base of a spine of a sea urchin. This species is a hermaphrodite whereas both *S. linkiae* Sarasin and *S. celebensis* Kukenthal are deeply embedded in the tissues of starfishes and are apparently bisexual. The only visible evidence of their presence is a very small opening through which the tip of the shell projects (Fig. 23). In both of these two species, the pseudopallium is considerably developed, almost completely enclosing the entire snail (Fig. 24). Blood sinuses are found in the proboscis and around the mouth. When they become stended the proboscis itself becomes turgescent

(Fig. 25). A small foot still exists although the pedal glands have disappeared. The eyes are rudimentary, yet two otocysts are preserved and the nervous system is condensed into a large ganglionic mass at the base of the proboscis.

In both *S. linkiae* and *S. celebensis* water is drawn into the pseudopallial cavity by the proboscis acting like a piston in a pump (Hirase), or simply by the

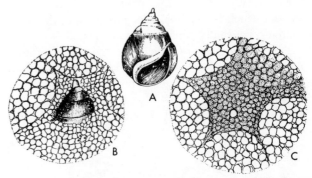

Fig. 23. *Stilifer celebensis* Kükenth. A. Shell. B. Snail burrowing into an asterid. C. Host tissues almost completely covering the shell (Hirase).

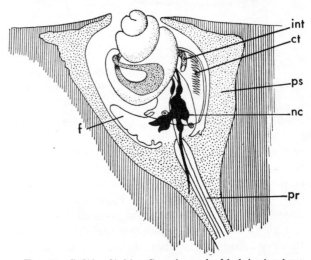

Fig. 24. *Stilifer linkiae* Sarasin embedded in its host. ct.—ctenidium. f.—foot. int.—gut. nc.—brain. pr.—proboscis. ps.—pseudopallium (partly from Nierstrasz).

walls contracting. The current is necessary to renew the supply of water to the ctenidium and also for evacuating the sexual products and the feces. The males of these two species are unknown and they are supposed to be free-living (Hirase). But it might be possible that these are protandrous hermaphrodites. The only species that has been thoroughly investigated, *S. sibogae*, is an hermaphrodite with a well developed male copulatory organ.

Gasterosiphon deimatis Koeh. & Van. (Fig. 27) represents what might be considered the ultimate stage of development for an ectoparasite, since it

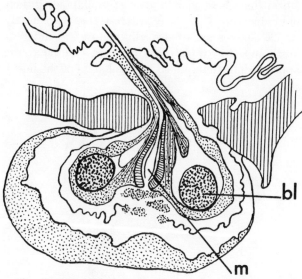

FIG. 25. Diagrammatical section through the mouth bulb of *Stilifer* sp. bl.—blood sinus. m.—mouth (Nierstrasz).

has become almost entirely endoparasitic. This parasitic snail is also much larger than the preceding ones and attains a length of nearly 120 mm. Only two specimens have been recovered so far from the body cavity of a holothurian, *Deima blakei* Theel (Fig. 26). The parasites were found attached to the body wall by a hollow stem with a round opening on the surface of the host. The stem is about 9 mm. long and swells out abruptly to a pear shape. A long, thin tube grows from this swelling, the distal end of which probably lies free within the body cavity of the host but was found attached to a marginal vessel of the intestine. The true nature of this problematic parasite is found on opening the pear-shaped portion. Within this lies the visceral mass of the snail with its characteristically twisted structure, yet all trace of a shell has disappeared. There are no eyes, no tentacles, nor any evidence of a heart although blood sinuses appear to exist at the base of the proboscis. The proboscis is extremely long and the mouth is at its distal end. The esophagus opens into a stomach with numerous diverticula surrounded by hepatic cells. There is neither a gut nor an anus. This snail is hermaphroditic. Although the detailed anatomy of the species is not well known,

it is usually assumed that the pear-shaped swelling is a pseudopallial cavity that has completely surrounded the body of the snail. In this cavity the eggs are laid and undergo a period of incubation, until they are sufficiently developed to be expelled into the sea through the hollow stem of the pseudopallial cavity. The walls of this stem are heavily incrusted with lime salts, and its lumen bears cilia. It is not possible to state whether this interpretation is correct, because recent work on other species has shown a different type of formation of this so-called brood pouch.

Entocolax is also a parasite of holothurians and is located within the body cavity of its host in a manner very similar to that of *Gasterosiphon*, yet the two genera are fundamentally different.

A short, hollow stem attaches the larger end of this pear-shaped organism to the body wall of the host. The other end tapers to a tubular organ about 35 mm. in length. The pear-shaped portion is a brood pouch, containing cocoons with several eggs each. The mouth is located at the free extremity and opens directly into a spacious hepatogastric pouch. There is no stomach, intestine, or anus. *E. ludwigi* Voigt appears to possess a short, ciliated esophagus, connecting the mouth with the digestive organs. All traces of a foot, heart, or gill have disappeared. The specimens found attached in this manner are all females. A single large ovary occupies the base of the brood pouch into which a short uterus opens. There is no evidence that a spiral structure has been retained. In young specimens, the siphonal cavity contains a relatively large number of dwarf males (fifteen to twenty-five) (Fig. 28). These are minute, almost spherical organisms the greater part of which is a testis that opens into a short vas deferens. As soon as the testis has discharged its function, the dwarf male disintegrates.

The histological structure of the brood pouch, as compared to the pseudopallial cavity in other species, shows that the two organs are not homologous in spite of their assumed identical functions for the brood. In *Entocolax* the brood pouch is formed by the terminal portion of the female genital duct which becomes enormously dilated and, consequently, the opening of the so-called siphonal cavity on the surface of the host is the primitive vaginal orifice (Heding & Mandahl-Barth) (Fig. 29).

Although the mode of entrance of the young parasites into the host has not been discovered for all of the species, it is of interest to note the relationship between the site on the host where the snail is attached and its habits. *E. ludwigi* has been recovered from *Myriotrochus rinkii* Steenstr. and is found attached to the wall of the body cavity of the holothurian, close behind the dorsal tentacles. That this position is not accidental is shown by the fact that this host lies buried in mud leaving only the dorsal tentacles and a small portion of the dorsal inter-

very small shell. They measure hardly more than 0.5 mm. in length (Fig. 30).

More evidence and especially experimental results will have to be obtained before it will be possible to affirm that these snails are strictly adapted to their individual hosts. It is of interest that two nearly similar species are ecologically adapted to different hosts and that their mode of ingress in each case appears to be determined by the habits of the hosts.

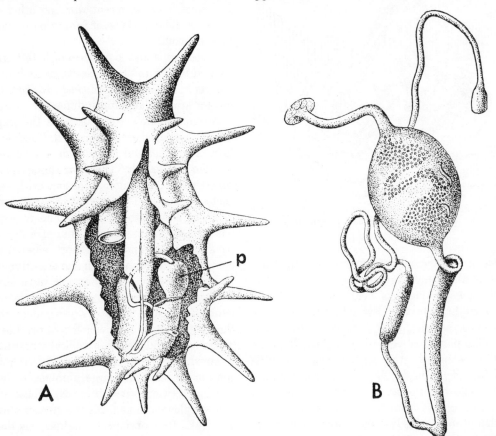

FIG. 26. A. *Deima blakei* Theel containing a specimen of *Gasterosiphon deimatis* Koeh. & Vaney. p.—parasite. B. Parasitic snail (Koehler & Vaney).

radius exposed. *E. schwanwitschi* Heding occurs on the peritoneal surface of the host's intestine, the brood pouch opening into the gut. The host in this case belongs to the species *M. eurycyclus* Hdg. that buries itself in mud leaving only the mouth opening protruding. Consequently, infestation takes place through the intestine. Young snails have been observed entering the host's mouth (Schwanwitsch).

In both species, the young snails that emerge from the cocoons are free-swimming and possess a

Entoconcha appears like a whitish worm about 8 cm. long, attached to the marginal blood vessel of the gut of an holothurian. *E. mirabilis* Müll. was the first parasitic snail described, although it was not recognized as such at the time.[3]

The mouth of *E. mirabilis* pierces the host's blood

[3] Müller thought that he had discovered holothurian organs that produced small snails, hence the name *Entoconcha* and "snail tubes" given by him to these hypothetical organs. His scientific authority was so great that in spite of severe criticisms it was ten years later before his interpretation was shown to be wrong and that these "snail tubes" were nothing else than greatly modified parasitic prosobranchs.

vessel and lies within the host's body drawing up the blood into the hepatic gut of the parasite. The internal anatomy is incompletely understood but seems to be closely related to that of *Entocolax*, although nothing is known of the way in which the brood pouch is formed. This, incidentally, opens into the body cavity of the host. At its distal extremity, the brood pouch is slightly swollen and here are found dwarf males (Schwanwitsch) (Fig. 31). The larvae are of the veliger-type with a minute shell. Nothing

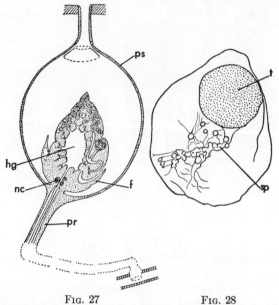

FIG. 27   FIG. 28

FIG. 27. Diagrammatical section of *Gasterosiphon deimatis* Koeh. & Vaney. f.—foot. hg.—hepatic diverticula. nc.—brain. pr.—proboscis. p.—pseudopallium (Vaney).

FIG. 28. Dwarf male of *Entocolax ludwigi* Voigt. sp.—spermduct. t.—testis (Heding & Mandahl-Barth).

is known of the way the larvae enter the host nor of the ensuing larval metamorphosis.

In both *Enteroxenos* and *Thyonicola*[4] we encounter modified snails in which the mouth and all trace of digestive organs have disappeared (Figs. 32, 33). These parasites are usually 6 to 8 cm. in length and as many as thirty or forty have been recovered from a single host, *Thyone serrata* Britt., that was itself only 3.5 cm. long (Mandahl-Barth).

Experimental infestation of *Cucumaria japonica* Semper with larval forms of *Parenteroxenos dogieli* (*Thyonicola mortenseni*) first of all shows that the larva of this species is very similar to that of *Enter-*

[4] *Parenteroxenos* Iwanow is a synonym of *Thyonicola*, the latter name having priority.

oxenos oestergreni. According to Iwanow, the cocoons, expelled with the feces of the holothurian, burst on coming into contact with sea water and liberate the young snails. The snails are only 0.1 mm. in length and seem to be unable to survive for any length of time. They are ingested by the holothurian together with its food and thus enter the gut. The larva undergoes regressive metamorphosis in which it sheds its shell together with the mantle and a mass of cells that corresponds to the vitelline cells of Bonnevie but that Iwanow interprets as representing the entoderm. The primitive stomodaeum closes and appears as a very small vesicle (Fig. 34B). The larva now migrates into the host's gut wall, no doubt with the aid of the pedal glands, since these disappear soon after. At this stage, the epidermis sheds its cilia and a cellular mass, interpreted as the genital anlage, appears in the mesoderm. As development proceeds, the stomodaeal cavity increases in size and tends to grow at one end toward the epidermis which it finally reaches. The cavity opens on the surface directly into the lumen of the host's gut through a ciliated canal. Meanwhile, the ovary has increased in size and the oviduct has become apparent; it finally opens into the stomodaeal cavity. The larval snail grows out into the body cavity of the host, pushing the peritoneum with it just as in *Enteroxenos*. Finally, near the base of the ciliated canal in the mesoderm a cellular mass appears that differentiates into a testis. Nothing is known of how this mass of cells migrates from the common genital anlage to its present location. Consequently, in *Thyonicola* and probably also in *Enteroxenos*, the brood pouch is formed from the primitive stomodaeum and has therefore nothing in common with a pseudopallial cavity, as has been assumed by Iwanow (Figs. 35 and 36).

In *Enteroxenos*, all communication with the host's gut appears to have disappeared. As this parasite is found with irregular swellings located in different parts of its body, and these are filled with masses of eggs, it is probable that the eggs are liberated by the bursting of the swellings in the body cavity of the host. They would thus be expelled together with the viscera of the holothurian, as this is the only way they could reach the outside.

The veliger larva of *Enteroxenos* appears to be somewhat more widely differentiated than that of *Thyonicola*, since the latter lacks a heart, statocysts, and kidney, and possesses only rudimentary nerve ganglia. The dedifferentiation process, described as necrobiotic by Iwanow, is probably the same in both cases.

Paedophoropus dicoelobius Iwanow represents a

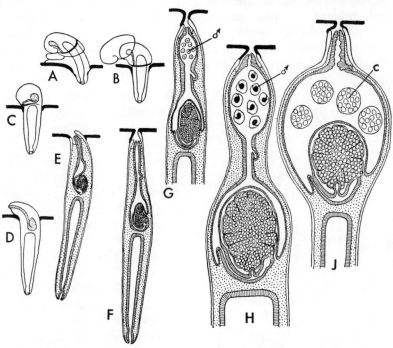

FIG. 29. Diagram of the supposed mode of entrance of *Entocolax* into its host, and the formation of the brood pouch. Dwarf males located in G and H at the distal end of brood pouch. c.—cocoons filled with ova (partly from Heding & Mandahl-Barth).

FIG. 30. Larval shell of *Entocolax*, showing no tendency to a spiral structure. Compare with Figure 39 (Heding & Mandahl-Barth).

different type of parasitic snail that appears to possess converging characters. On closer examination this is found to be in no way related to the other parasitic mollusks. It has also been recovered from an holothurian, *Eupyrgus pacificus* Oestergr., where one specimen was observed in the Polian vesicle and two others in the respiratory tree. In all cases,

however, the proboscis had penetrated into the body cavity and was attached to the peritoneal surface of the host's gut. The sexes are separate and there exists a marked sexual dimorphism, the males being less than half as large as the females. The largest female measured 5.5 mm. (Fig. 37).

The distal portion of the esophagus immediately following the mouth opening is surrounded by glands that probably secrete a proteolytic enzyme which enables the parasite to predigest its food. This seems likely since the esophagus opens directly into an hepatic gut and that there is no stomach, terminal gut, or anus. There is a reduced renal organ but all traces of respiratory organs have disappeared. The visceral mass furnishes no evidence of a spiral structure, although a rudimentary columnellar muscle is retained; and there is no shell. The foot has two lateral expansions that are relatively well developed in the male (Fig. 38). They attain enormous proportions in the female and assume the role of a brood pouch into which the uterus opens. The pedal gland is more developed in the female than in the male and its secretion is discharged into the brood pouch where it swells up, filling the pouch and enclosing the cocoons. The larvae have a very thin shell but no velum. Their visceral sack is spirally wound and they creep along the bottom on emerging

(Fig. 39). Nothing is known of the way in which they gain access to their host.

Ctenosculum hawaiiense Heath and *Asterophila japonica* Randall & Heath have been recovered from the skin of starfishes, where their presence caused swellings on the arms. In *Ctenosculum* the swelling opens on the surface in a longitudinal slit with teeth. It is recorded that this parasite can move around within its cyst and protrude its snout

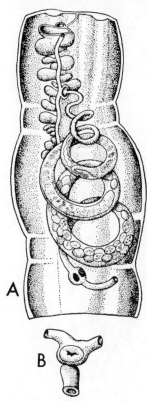

FIG. 31. *Entoconcha mirabilis* Müll. A. Snail attached to the dorsal vessel of host; complementary males are seen in the subterminal swelling. B. Anterior end implanted in the dorsal vessel (Baur).

from the opening to feed on any organisms living in the mud. If this is true, it would not be a parasite at all but rather a curious type of commensal.

In *Asterophila* the parasite is completely covered by the epidermis of the host and it appears to be a true parasite. Neither of the above genera is sufficiently known to be placed correctly among any of the truly parasitic mollusks.

The seventeen genera of parasitic snails do not form a continuous series of forms adapted to different types of parasitism. Several species previously reported as parasites must be considered today either as commensals—*Pseudosacculus okai* Hirase, *Melanella distorta* (Philippi)—or as predators—*Odostomia*

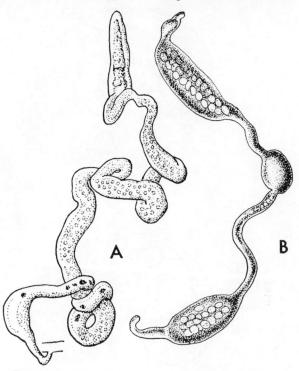

FIG. 32. A. *Thyonicola mortenseni* M.-Barth (Mandahl-Barth). B. *Enteroxenos oestergreni* Bonnev. gravid specimen (Bonnevie).

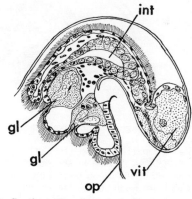

FIG. 33. Section of a larva of *Enteroxenos oestergreni* Bonnev. gl.—pedal gland. int.—gut. op.—opercule. vit.—remains of yolk cells (Bonnevie).

scalaris Macg., *O. tellinae* Pels., *Mucronalia variabilis* Schep. & Nierstr., *Angustispira spengeli* Pels. It is also possible that among the lesser known ectoparasitic species some will be revealed as not true parasites.

So far, three distinct types of parasitic adaptations have been disclosed and they appear to correspond to three separate lines of evolution from a polyphyletic stock.

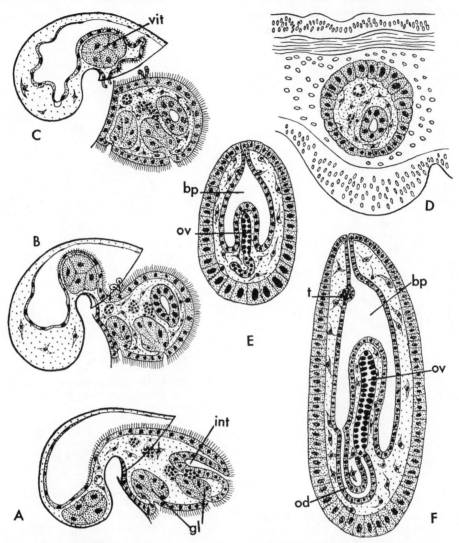

FIG. 34. Various stages of the development of *Thyonicola* (*Parenteroxenos*) in the gut wall of its host. A–C. The larva loses its shell and is swallowed by the host. D. Section of gut wall with larva. E–F. Two successive larval stages showing formation of the brood pouch. bp.—brood pouch. gl.—pedal gland. int.—gut. od.—oviduct. ov.—ovary. t.—testis. vit.—remains of yolk cells (redrawn from Iwanow).

respond to three separate lines of evolution from a polyphyletic stock.

The first of these groups shows evidence of common ancestors, the genera are evidently related to one another; and they all possess to some degree a pseudopallium. We have furnished an explanation of the possible function of this organ when the para-

site first attempts to penetrate into the epidermis of its host. It is also probable that as the snails pene-

trate deeper into the tissues of the host, the pseudopallium becomes a sort of protective covering from the surrounding tissues. At least this is what most authors believe to be the correct interpretation of this organ, but we consider this evolution as being secondary. It is more than likely that the presence of a pseudopallial cavity has enabled the parasite to maintain a constant flow of water around its ctenidium, when deeply embedded in the tissues of its host. This would not be the case if a pseudopallium were absent and, consequently, the presence of this organ has enabled the parasite to survive new conditions that have arisen from its constant urge to seek more nourishment.

There is not enough evidence to warrant the statement that *Gasterosiphon* also belongs to this group and that in this genus the pseudopallial cavity has become a brood pouch. It is likely that further research may disclose that the brood pouch develops as in *Entocolax* and related genera.

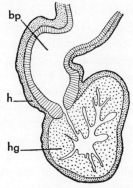

FIG. 35. Section of *Thyonicola* in the host's gut. bp.—brood pouch. h.—peritoneum of the host. hg.—gut of the host (Mandahl-Barth).

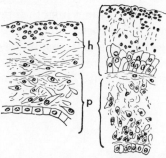

FIG. 36. Section through both the gut wall of the host and the body wall of *Thyonicola* showing how intimately the two tissues are united. h.—peritoneum of the host. p.—body wall of the parasite (Mandahl-Barth).

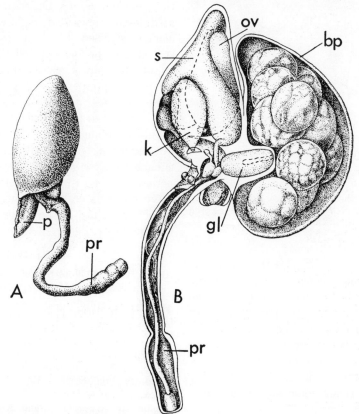

FIG. 37. *Paedophoropus dicoelobius* Iwanow. A. Male. B. Section of a female. bp.—brood pouch derived from an expansion of the foot. gl.—pedal gland. k.—kidney. ov.—ovary. p.—penis. pr.—proboscis. s.—diverticulum of stomach (Iwanow).

These are true endoparasites, although they penetrate through the skin or the gut of their hosts. As all endoparasites, they are bathed in the fluids of the host. Their reproductive power is increased and a much greater egg production has become possible by a modification of existing organs. The vagina and oviduct become enormously dilated and function both as a receptacle for the eggs and as a brood pouch.

In *Paedophoropus*, the foot is transformed and is adapted as a brood pouch but this genus shows evolutionary trends distinct from the previous types.

The intimacy of parasitic adaptation in mollusks may be judged by the gradual regression of the digestive organs. These adapt themselves to liquid food of high nutrient content. The disappearance of the

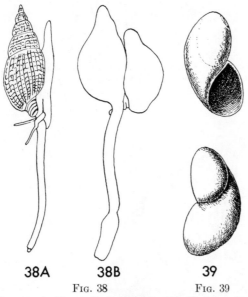

38A   38B   39
Fig. 38   Fig. 39

Fig. 38. A. *Nassa*. B. *Paedophoropus*. Showing the comparative development of the foot (Iwanow).

Fig. 39. Larval shells of *Paedophoropus* showing the tendency to wind spirally. Compare with Figure 30 (Iwanow).

stomach, intestine, and anus implies that all of the food is resorbed and consequently that it is entirely liquid and predigested before being taken in by the parasite. Finally all traces of digestive organs have disappeared and the parasites assimilate their food directly from the surrounding tissues of the host with which they are practically incorporated.

The distribution of sexes in mollusks is highly variable; in a given genus some species are hermaphroditic and others bisexual. This condition is so labile that in many instances there may be seasonal alternation of sex in the same individual and in extreme instances, males have entirely disappeared leaving only parthenogenetic females. It is, there-

fore, not surprising to find the same conditions among the parasitic species. Sexual dimorphism cannot be attributed to parasitism, since it is constantly found in the free-living species. However, dwarf males, probably neotenic larvae, have never to our knowledge been reported from free-living snails. Their appearance in *Entoconcha* and *Entocolax* has no doubt enabled these parasites to become highly specialized, since the hazards for successful fertilization would otherwise be far too great for their survival.

Finally, the foot that represents such an important organ in free-living forms has evolved, in parasitic species, along different lines. It is enormous in the females of *Paedophoropus* and has entirely disappeared in *Entoconcha*, *Entocolax*, *Enteroxenos*, and *Thyonicola*, while in the other genera its reduction is variable. The false foot is an entirely new adaptation.

It is clear that mollusks have been able to adapt themselves to parasitism with the remarkable plasticity of their organs. Different organs independently at different times and in different groups have become specialized. The trend toward specialization is still visible and has enabled the parasitic species to adapt themselves successfully to their hosts. Although our present knowledge is too scanty to determine the host-parasite relationship, it is probable that we are dealing with very old associations. It should be remembered, however, that echinoderms are about the only potential hosts that are sluggish enough to allow snails to climb over them and that perhaps the host-parasite relationship that we observe today is only the result of natural selection, involving failure of the snails to attach themselves to other hosts.

REFERENCES

ADAM, W. 1933. Note préliminaire sur le male de Thyca crystallina. *Bull. Mus. Roy. Hist. Nat.*, vol. 9, no. 39, 4 pp.

AREY, L. B. 1932. The formation and structure of the glochidian cyst. *Biol. Bull.*, 62:212–21, 1 pl.

———. 1932. The nutrition of glochidia during metamorphosis. *J. Morph.*, 53:201–21, 11 figs.

———. 1932. A microscopical study of glochidian immunity. *Ibid.*, 53:261–319.

BAUR, A. 1864. Die Eingeweideschnecke in der Leibeshöhle der *Synapta digitata*. *Nov. Acta Leop. Carol.*, 31:1–60, 8 pls.

BONNEVIE, K. 1902. *Enteroxenos oestergreni*, ein neuer in Holothurien schmarotzender Gastropode. *Zool. Jahrb. Anat.*, 15:731–92, 6 figs., pls. 37–41.

BRUUN, A. F. 1938. A new entocommensalistic bivalve,

Entovalva major n. sp., from the Red Sea. *Vidensk. Medd. Dansk. Naturh. For.*, 102:163–67, 1 fig.

FAUSSECK, V. 1901. Ueber den Parasitismus der *Anodonta*-Larven. *Verh. Int. Zool. Congr. Berlin*, 761–66.

FRETTER, V., & GRAHAM, A. 1949. Feeding and reproduction in the Pyramellids. *Nature*, 163:361–62.

HEATH, H. 1910. A new genus of parasitic gastropods (*Ctenosculum*). *Biol. Bull.*, 18:99–108, 1 pl.

HEDING, S. C., & MANDAHL-BARTH, G. 1938. Investigations on the anatomy and systematic position of the parasitic snail *Entocolax* Voigt. *Medd. om Groenl.*, vol. 108, 40 pp., 38 figs.

HIRASE, S. 1927. *Sacculus okai*, a new parasitic gastropod. *Annot. Zool. Jap.*, 11:115–28, 2 pls.

———. 1932. The adaptive modifications of the gastropod *Stilifer celebensis* Kuk., a parasite on the starfish *Certonardoa semiregularis* (Müll. & Trosch.). *Proc. Malac. Soc. Lond.* 20:73–76, pls. 7–8.

IWANOW, A. W. 1937. Die Organisation und die Lebensweise der parasitischen Molluske *Paedophoropus dicoelobius* Iwanow. *Acta Zool.* 18:111–208, 24 figs., 2 pls.

———. 1948. Metamorphosis of the parasitic snail *Parenteroxenos dogieli* Iwanow. *Rep. Acad. Sc. USSR*, 61:765–68, 8 figs. (Russian).

JONKER, A. 1916. Ueber den Bau und die Verwandschaft der parasitischen Gastropoden. *Tijd. Need. Doerk. Vereen.*, 5:19–93, pls. 2–4.

KOEHLER, R., & VANEY, C. 1903. *Entosiphon deimatis*, nouveau mollusque parasite d'une holothurie abyssale. *Rev. suisse Zool.*, 11:23–41, pl. 2.

LEFEVRE, G., & CURTIS, W. C. 1910. Studies on the reproduction and artificial propagation of fresh-water mussels. *Bull. U. S. Bur. Fish.*, 30:105–202, 4 figs., pls. 4–17.

MANDAHL-BARTH, G. 1941. *Thyonicola mortensi* n. gen. n. sp., eine neue parasitische Schnecke. *Vidensk. Medd. Dansk. Naturh. For.*, 104:341–51, 11 figs.

NIERSTRASZ, H. F. 1913. Die parasitische Gastropoden. *Erg. Fortschr. Zool.*, 3:532–93, 32 figs.

RANDALL, J., & HEATH, H. 1912. *Asterophila*, a new genus of parasitic gastropods. *Biol. Bull.*, 22:98–106, 2 pls.

ROSÉN, N. 1910. Zur Kenntnis der parasitischen Schnecken. *Acta Univ. Lund, N. F. Afd.*, vol. 2, p. 6.

SURBER, TH. 1913. Notes on the natural hosts of fresh-water mussels. *Bull. U. S. Bur. Fish.*, 32:101–16, pls. 29–31.

SCHWANWITSCH, B. N. 1917. Observations sur la femelle et le mâle rudimentaire d'*Entocolax ludwigi* Voigt. *J. russe Zool.*, 2:1–147, 10 figs., 4 pls.

TUCKER, M. E. 1928. Studies on the life cycles of two species of fresh-water mussels belonging to the genus *Anodonta*. *Biol. Bull.*, 54:117–26.

VANEY, C. 1913. L'adaptation des Gastropodes au parasitisme. *Bull. Sc. France et Belgique*, 47:1–87, 65 figs.

VOELTZKOW, A. 1891. *Entovalva mirabilis*, eine schmarotzende Muschel aus dem Darm einer Holothurie. *Zool. Jahrb. Syst.*, 5:619–28, pl. 42.

WILSON, CH. B. 1917. The economic relations, anatomy and life history of the genus Lernaea. *Bull. U. S. Bur. Fish.*, 35:165–98, pls. 6–15.

CHAPTER THREE

Turbellaria

Free-living flatworms show a variety of forms that are adapted to a great number of different biotopes. Most of the species are carnivorous, feeding on flesh as well as on decomposed organic matter. In an aquarium they are useful as scavengers.

It is usually assumed that the present-day turbellarians represent the outcome of more ancient types from which the trematodes and the cestodes have arisen also. There is no doubt whatever that such a relationship exists between the free-living and the parasitic flatworms yet we cannot, at present, find evidence as to the probable structure of the hypothetical common ancestors.

We know far too little about the physiology and reproduction of most marine species. Neoteny, a frequent occurrence among parasites, has been reported once from a free-living species, *Graffizoon lobatum* Heath, a marine polyclad (Heath), although it may exist in other forms.

It is not surprising that such plastic and ubiquitous organisms as turbellarians have evolved along many different lines and consequently that several distinct morphological and physiological directions are apparent.

Many turbellarians are associated with other organisms in a more or less permanent fashion, yet the nature of such associations has hardly ever been studied in detail. Polyclads are frequently found in marine shells where apparently they feed on mucus and small organisms or detritus which are always found in such habitats. Since the same species are said to occur also free in the sea, their presence in the shell is probably accidental. It is true that *Euprosthiostomum viscosum* Palombi seems to possess a particular, glandular field that secretes a viscous fluid with which the worm attaches itself to the inner side of the shell inhabited by a hermit crab.

Since this species of turbellarian has never yet been reported as free-living, it might be considered a commensal (Palombi).

Notoplana ovalis Bock is frequently found between the foot and the mantle of a limpet, *Patella oculus* Born, but it also occurs free beneath stones. *Hoploplana inquilina* (Wheeler) inhabits the branchial chamber of the snail, *Sycotypus canaliculatus* Gill., and apparently feeds only on mucus. It is usually assumed to be a commensal (Wheeler). Such turbellarians may easily become predators. The species *Stylochus inimicus* Palombi, the so-called oyster "leech," penetrates into the shells of living oysters and feeds on their contents. These polyclads may even become a menace in the oyster industry. The oysters attempt to defend themselves against the attacks of the worm by walling it off with a barrier of conchiolin secreted by the mantle (Pearse & Wharton).

In none of these examples do the turbellarians show any evidence of a morphological adaptation.

Among triclads, two species of the genus *Micropharynx* are found attached to the surface of the body of rays occurring in northern waters. These species are true parasites, since the gut is filled with epithelial cells from the host's skin. The pharynx is much smaller than in related free-living species and a distinct, subventral organ of attachment enables the parasite to cling to its host (Awerinzew). The small pharynx may be correlative with the mode of nutrition and also with the fact that the parasite is attached to its host and has become partly sedentary.

The alleocelids *Hypotrichina tergestina* Calandr. and *H. marsilensis* Calandr. are also attached to the surface of shrimp-like leptostraceans (*Nebalia* spp.) by their anterior extremity which is distinctly flattened. The dorsal surface of these worms is not ciliated.

Endoparasitic turbellarians are all rhabdocoelids and can be grouped together in the Dalyelloids (Bresslau). Although a ciliated epidermis occurs in all these forms, rhabdites have almost completely disappeared or, when present, are found only in certain definite parts of the body. Free-living tur-

34

bellarians expel their rhabdites either in defense or to capture their prey by surrounding it with a cloud of mucous matter which entangles the victim. Endoparasitic turbellarians, being in constant and close contact with a source of nourishment, no longer need to capture their prey; consequently, their rhabdites are less abundant.

Dalyelloids are found both in the gut and in the body cavity of echinoderms and more rarely also of sipunculids. Their anatomy possesses certain structural peculiarities that occur also in temnocephalans and in monogenetic trematodes which show a phylogenetic relationship that is lost, however, in a very dim past!

Little is known about the biology of parasitic rhabdocoelids, particularly how they enter their hosts. Their association with echinoderms seems to indicate that they became adapted to parasitism a long time ago. Yet none of these endoparasitic forms gives any evidence of increased fertility or of greater egg production than in free-living species. Consequently, one might question their being true endoparasites and therefore consider them as endocommensals. It is impossible to answer this question as no experimental investigation has been undertaken on this association. A worm even if only a few millimeters in length will find proportionately less nourishment in the gut of an invertebrate than in the gut of a vertebrate. This shortage of food could not permit greatly increased reproductive powers such as are found when there is an excess of food.

The only known species in which an endoparasitic mode of life has influenced the internal anatomy of a rhabdocoelid is *Fecampia*. This, incidentally, is the only known parasitic turbellarian that possesses a life cycle comprising a larval stage that is distinct, morphologically, from the adult and of which one phase only is parasitic.

The larvae of *Fecampia xanthocephala* C. & M. are free-living. They possess a mouth and a gut and in the hind end of the larva appear the so-called embryonic germinal cells. The larva penetrates into the body cavity of an isopod, *Idotea neglecta* Sars, and becomes adult. The way in which the young worm enters its host has not been determined. Once inside the body cavity, the larva grows and increases in length. It loses its mouth and pharynx, the gut remaining as a longitudinal slit closed at each end. The eyes and the rhabdites disappear completely and as soon as this regressive metamorphosis is terminated, the genital organs appear and the worm gradually becomes opaque. This is due to the presence of a large number of glands located beneath the skin that increase considerably in size. When the parasite is fully adult, it escapes from its host, probably by breaking through the skin where the chitinous layer is thinnest, and drops to the sea bottom. With the secretion from its cutaneous glands, the worm forms a pear-shaped cocoon in which it remains, laying its eggs. When all the eggs have been produced, the worm disintegrates. The eggs are retained in capsules each containing two eggs. In *Fecampia spiralis* Baylis parasitic in an Antarctic isopod, the cocoon is coiled into a flat spiral that is attached onto the ventral surface of the host.

A closely related species, *F. erythrocephala* Giard, occurs in hermit crabs only. Unfortunately nothing is known of its life history.

The examples cited above show clearly the distinct evolutionary trends that have appeared among turbellarians and indicate that few of them have become successful, well adapted parasites.

REFERENCES

AWERINZEW, S. 1925. Ueber eine neue Art von parasitären Tricladen. *Zool. Anz.*, 64:81–84, 4 figs.

BAER, J. G. 1938. On the anatomy and systematic status of *Cleistogamia holothuriana* Faust, 1924. *Rec. Ind. Mus. Calcutta*, 40:159–68, 5 figs.

BAYLIS, H. A. 1949. Fecampia spiralis, a cocoon-forming parasite of the Antarctic isopod Serolis schythei. *Proc. Linn. Soc. Lond.*, 161:65–71, 8 figs., pls. 3–4.

BRESSLAU, E. 1928. Turbellaria. *Handb. Zool.*, 2:52–320, 308 figs.

CAULLERY, M., & MESNIL, F. 1903. Recherches sur *Fecampia* Giard, Turbellariés, rhabdocoeles parasites internes des crustacés. *Ann. Fac. Sc. Marseille*, 13:131–67, 3 figs.

HEATH, H. 1928. A sexually mature turbellarian resembling Müller's larva. *J. Morph.*, 45:187–207, 15 figs.

PALOMBI, A. 1936. Policladi liberi e commensali raccolti sulle coste del Sud Africa, della Florida e del Golfo di Napoli. *Arch. Zool.*, 23:1–45, 27 figs., 1 pl.

PEARSE, A. S., & WHARTON, G. W. 1938. The oyster "leech," *Stylochus inimicus* Palombi, associated with oysters on the coasts of Florida. *Ecol. Monogr.*, 8:605–55, 37 figs.

WHEELER, M. 1894. Planocera inquilina, a polyclad inhabiting the branchial chamber of Sycotypus canaliculatus Gill. *J. Morph.*, 9:195–201, 2 figs.

CHAPTER FOUR

Annelida

Though segmented roundworms live in many diverse ways, their anatomical structure remains fairly constant. Their locomotory organs appear to be closely adapted to their mode of life and, therefore, are used as a basis for determining the principal groups.

Polychaetes possess parapods and setae that have developed into swimming appendages; they are essentially marine forms. Oligochaetes (earthworms) have no parapods and their setae are commonly limited to the ventrolateral surface of the worm. In all terrestrial forms the setae are short and sometimes hardly perceptible while in aquatic species they are often long and slender and aid in swimming. Finally all trace of setae have disappeared in leeches and a sucker enables them to attach themselves to a support when feeding.

Curiously enough, each of these three fundamental groups of annelids has also given rise to parasitic species that show, in almost every case, definitely specialized adaptations to parasitism.

Among polychaetes, predators are frequently found; they constitute the flesh-eaters of the group and even commit cannibalism.

Several species, described as parasites, have been reported from the body cavity of other annelids. *Oligognathus parasiticus* Cerrutti has been found only three times in the coelomic cavity of *Microspio mecznikowianus* (Clap.). Except that the pharyngeal teeth are smaller, this worm resembles the free-living forms. It should be noted, however, that in no case were the so-called parasites sexually mature, nor was there any trace of genital organs. This is also true for *O. bonelliae* Spengel from the body cavity of an echurid, *Bonellia*. As to *Haematocleptes terebelloides* Wirén, reported from the blood sinuses of *Terebelloides stroemi* Sars, it is not known whether

this annelid is a true parasite or not. It has lost its spinning glands and the setae are completely buried within the parapods. Further research will be necessary to determine if these modifications should be considered parasitic adaptations. In the cases cited, the absence of sexually mature forms may indicate that these worms are not true parasites.

Among syllids especially, predators commonly possess a protractile pharynx which contains "chitinous" stylets that pierce the victim's skin and lacerate the tissues. The only known parasitic polychaete also possesses such stylets but these are curiously modified to enable the parasite to attach itself to its host. The entire body of the annelid has undergone a profound change as a consequence of this new mode of life and this gives evidence of definite adaptations to parasitism.

Ichthyotomus sanguinarius Eysig is found affixed to the fins of an eel, *Myrus vulgaris* L., from the Gulf of Naples. The organs of attachment are two protrusible stylets located on the dorsal and the ventral surfaces of the proboscis. Each has an individual set of muscles (Figs. 40–43). The free extremity of the stylet is somewhat spoon-shaped and bears a row of small barbs along the outer edge. The posterior extremity of the stylet is bifid and several muscles are attached to each branch. Between the free extremity and the bifid branches of the stylet a peculiar articulation is found which coincides with a similar structure of the other stylet to form a so-called cup and ball articulation (Fig. 43). When the stylets are exserted, they articulate with one another and their posterior extremities are pulled in opposite directions. Their free extremities possess a scissors-like movement. Since the scissors only open when the stylets have pierced the host's skin, the parasite is securely anchored to the host. The anterior segment of the annelid, including the so-called prostomium, is also modified and resembles a larval worm more than an adult. The tentacles are reduced and the entire extremity forms a deep, cup-shaped organ around the proboscis. Consequently, when the latter is inserted into the host tissues, the cup-shaped anterior extremity is closely applied to the

36

skin. Blood from the lacerated capillaries is drawn into the gut of the worm and completely fills it. The gut walls in this species of annelid are evaginated laterally and penetrate far into the parapods, thus increasing to a very great extent the total capacity of the organ. Since all trace of respiratory organs and of blood vessels have disappeared, it is assumed that the parasite utilizes the host's blood for its own metabolic exchanges. On either side of

is observed. Although both male and female worms are present, side by side, the females appear to be protandrous hermaphrodites, both eggs and sperms being found before the separate males are mature. Unfortunately, nothing is known of the ultimate development of the eggs and larvae. The eggs are freed by autotomy of the posterior segments.

The peculiar mixture of larval and adult characters in this parasitic annelid indicates that *Ich-*

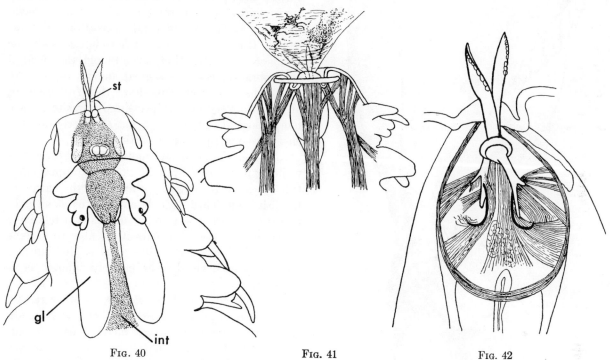

FIG. 40   FIG. 41   FIG. 42

FIG. 40. *Ichthyotomus sanguinarius* Eysig, anterior extremity. gl.—glands. int.—gut. st.—stylets (Eysig).

FIG. 41. *Ichthyotomus sanguinarius* Eysig attached to a fin, showing how the contraction of the muscles forms a sucker-like organ around the stylets (Eysig).

FIG. 42. Dissection of the pharyngeal bulb of *Ichthyotomus*, showing attachment of the muscles to the stylets (Eysig).

the proboscis and opening near the base of the latter are four glands, two of which are extremely large. The secretion of these glands, it is believed prevents the host's blood from coagulating. The entire body of *Ichthyotomus* is flattened dorsoventrally and, curiously enough, the worms are found to be sexually mature when only 2 mm. in length and have only thirty segments. The worm grows to a total length of 8 to 10 mm. and contains as many as seventy to one hundred segments, yet no morphological change

thyotomus sanguinarius is a neotenic larva that has become precociously mature, no doubt by feeding on the blood of the host. All of its parasitic adaptations, such as haemolytic glands, stylets, anterior sucker, etc., can be traced to similar organs in free-living species. Haemolytic glands have arisen from the so-called "poison" glands of predators. The flattening of the body and also the appearance of lateral gut outpocketings are secondary adaptations. Neoteny, always favorable to parasites since it enables them to produce eggs or larvae within a shorter time, is a consequence of the constant supply of rich food in a parasitic mode of life. A somewhat similar type of neoteny has been described in free-living annelids for *Nereis dumerilii* Aud. & Edw. (Hemplemann). This species of worm possesses three distinct types of adults, one of which is a neotenic larva. The latter, after producing eggs, undergoes metamorphosis and becomes a mature adult worm. It has been observed that these neotenic larvae make their appearance only in well fed cultures.

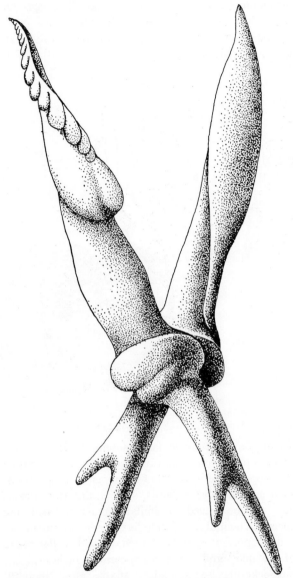

FIG. 43. Stylets of *Ichthyotomus* freed from the muscles to show mode of articulation with one another (Eysig).

The nature of the host-parasitic relationship of *Ichthyotomus* appears, at first sight, to be very intimate, since the parasite has only been recorded from eels, mostly *Myrus vulgaris* L. and much less frequently from *Conger vulgaris* L. and *Sphagebranchus imberbis* de la R. Experimental evidence shows that specificity is due to extraneous factors and not at all to any direct influence of the host on the parasite. Many species of fishes may be infested solely because they remain motionless. It has been possible to obtain successful results with other species of eels, *Ophichthys serpens* L. and *Muraena helena* Bonap.; with blennies, *Blennius ocellaris* L., *Gobiocapito* C.V., and *Motella maculata* Riss.; with stargazer, *Uranoscopus scaber* L.; as well as with *Julis vulgaris* Flem.; and species of fishes that live in the same environment as the normal hosts but that are never found to harbor the natural infestations of these worms. It has even been possible to infest an electric ray, *Torpedo ocellata* Rud., even though the blood of elasmobranchs contains a great amount of urea (20 to 23 gms. per liter). This shows that *Ichthyotomus*, although a very highly specialized parasite from a morphological standpoint, is not absolutely dependent, physiologically, on a particular host.

Any fish that remains motionless is susceptible to being parasitized by these worms. It appears that this condition is more important than the nature of the fish itself. This might be interpreted as an indication that this type of parasitism is of a relatively recent origin, since the parasite is able to survive not only on hosts that are distantly related but also on species with blood of an entirely different composition.

It is evident that *Ichthyotomus*, as other related syllids, are preadapted organisms and that conditions for a successful attack on the host are particularly well realized in the mud bottom of the Gulf of Naples. This parasite has never been found again since it was first studied by Eysig, nor does it appear to have been reported from other parts of the world. But this may be due solely to the fact that nobody has really looked for it.

The true nature of the neotenic polychaetes known as histriobdellids is not known. These appear to be commensals that are associated with decapod crustaceans. *Histriobdella* occurs in the branchial chamber of the common European lobster and the Norwegian lobster, and appears to have been reported only from the North Sea and the English Channel. *Stratiodrilus*, on the other hand, is found only on fresh-water crayfishes and of the three known species, one is found in Australia, one on Madagascar, and one in South America. This geographical distribution is exactly the same as that of temnocephalans and indicates the very great age of these species.

Among polychaetes, myzostomids occupy a particular place. They are greatly modified annelids,

intimacy with their hosts. A few species occur as messmates, moving freely about the surface of their

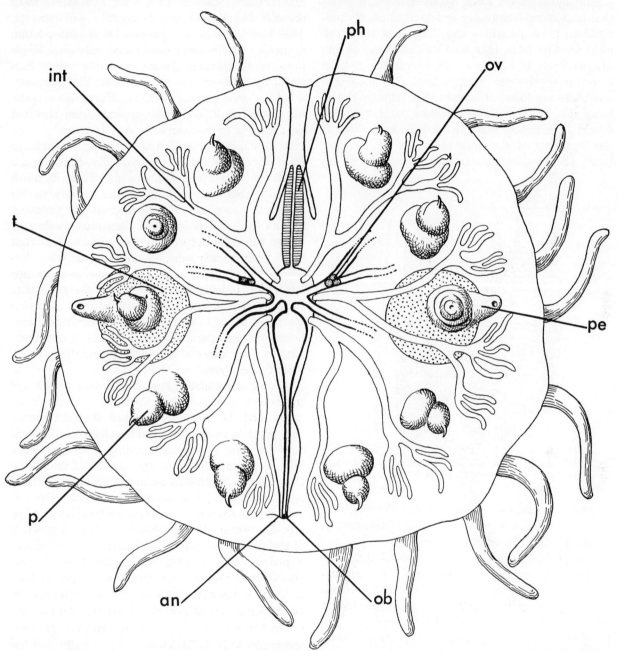

FIG. 44. Diagrammatical organization of a myzostomid. an.—anus. int.—gut. ob.—opening of the body cavity through which the ova are expelled. ov.—ovarian follicles. p.—parapod. pe.—penis. ph.—pharynx. t.—testis.

flattened dorsoventrally with bilateral symmetry (Fig. 44). Myzostomids are almost exclusively associated with crinoids and show various degrees of

hosts and feeding on any detritus that they find. Other species have become sedentary and their presence on the host is marked by epidermal lesions. In *Myzostomum glabrum* F. S. Leuck., the body is concave and the short though very muscular parapods firmly grip the host's arms leaving a scar when forcibly detached. Many other species burrow into the skin of their host and cause the formation of cysts within which are often found two individuals, a male and a female. From recent research, it seems that myzostomids are more or less distinctively protandrous hermaphrodites and that all of the specimens are first male, then female. This is the case in *M. cirriferum* F. S. Leuck., whereas in *M. glabrum* F. S. Leuck. the male stage is somewhat prolonged and males are found attached to the females. Sometimes also, dwarf or accessory males occur, yet these should be interpreted as young hermaphrodites at the beginning of the male stage. In *M. pulvinar* Graff, the two sexual stages are separated by an

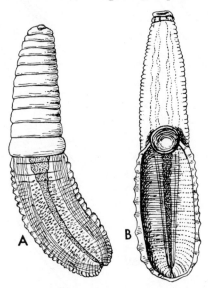

FIG. 45. *Aspidodrilus kelsalli* Baylis. A. Dorsal view. B. Ventral view showing the flattened hinder body and the sucker (Baylis).

intermediate, asexual phase in which the species is no longer a male and not yet a female. Consequently, sexual dimorphism may be observed here.

The species *Myzostomum pulvinar* Graff and *Mezomyzostomum reichenspergeri* Remsch are endoparasites and occur in the intestine and in the coelomic cavity of the arms, respectively. *Protomyzostomum polynephris* Fedotov occurs within the coelomic cavity of an ophiurid, *Gorgonocephalus*, where it is found attached in the immediate vicinity of the genital glands on which it feeds, thus producing a partial castration of the host. As compared to the other known species of myzostomids, this particular form appears to possess a much simplified and more distinctive larval structure. This is probably not due to its being more archaic than the others, but to the nature of its food. Here again, excessive nourishment has engendered neoteny.

Several distinct species of myzostomids may be found on the same host. *Endoxocrinus alternicirrus* (P. H. Carp.) harbors six species; *Comactinia meridionalis* (A. Agass.) and *Comanthus parvicirra* (J. Müll.) each harbor nine species. On the other hand, numerous species have been found only on a single host and an identical species may quite well be harbored by different, yet related, hosts that are separated by geographical barriers. *Myzostomum costatus* F. S. Leuck. occurs on crinoids from the Red Sea, the Philippines, and the Aru Islands.

Scars have been known to occur on the arms of fossil crinoids and these are markedly similar to the lesions produced by myzostomids. There is much evidence that myzostomids existed already during Paleozoic times and that their great age furnishes also an explanation for widely separated hosts harboring the same parasites. Fossil crinoids show that these echinoderms were much more numerous formerly than they are today. Many species have died out and it is logical to assume that their parasites either died out also or became adapted to other species of hosts. Consequently, a recent crinoid harboring several species of myzostomids would represent for the latter a physiological synthesis of all their former hosts!

Among oligochaetes, parasitic forms are rare and their exact relationships to their hosts are not firmly established. It is usually assumed that the species that occur on earthworms and that feed on epidermal secretions are commensals rather than parasites. Such is the case for *Friderica parasitica* Cernosvitov that occurs on earthworms in the Balkans. Peculiar adaptations are found however in *Aspidodrilus kelsalli* Baylis from earthworms of Sierra Leone (Fig. 45). The whole ventral surface of the posterior half of this small worm, 5 mm. in length, is flattened and slightly concave forming an elongated adhesive disc. Its surface is covered with minute setae. Immediately in front of this adhesive disc there is a true sucker. In *Pelmatodrilus planariformis* Moore, a species recovered from an unidentified earthworm in Jamaica, the entire body is flattened dorsoventrally and has become transparent (Fig. 46). The parasite adheres closely to the host's skin and is able to move about with its ventral setae. The dorsal setae have almost completely disappeared. There is no doubt that these two species parasitic on earthworms are extremely specialized and consequently highly adapted to a peculiar mode of life. Further research may possibly bring other such species to light and enable us to

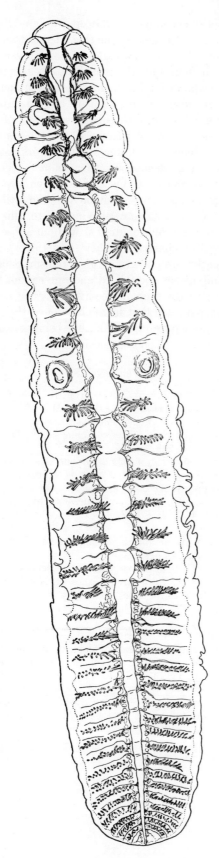

obtain a better understanding of this type of adaptation.

Schmardaella lutzi Mich. occurs in the ureters of several species of South American tree frogs and in all likelihood represents the juvenile forms of an as yet unrecognized species of the genus *Dero* Owen. The discovery of more than fifteen worms together in a single ureter seems to imply that these parasites can multiply by transverse fission. Unfortunately nothing else is known about their life history (Michaelsen).

Hirudinea, or leeches, are mostly predators, either carnivorous or saprophagous, and not more than about 25 per cent of the species could be considered as parasites. In most cases, such parasitism is usually temporary, the leech abandoning its host when it is gorged with blood and other secretions. In a few cases, these parasites may become sedentary and never leave their hosts and even appear to be associated with them in some specific way. This is especially evident among piscicolids of which numerous species have been recorded each from but a single host. *Calobdella lophii* Van Ben. & Hesse occurs only on the angler fish, *Hemibdella soleae* Van Ben. & Hesse on soles, *Cystobranchus mamillatus* Malm on burbots, *Acanthobdella peledina* Grube on salmonids, *Pontobdella muricata* L. on elasmobranchs. On the other hand, *Scorpaenobdella lubrica* (Grube) occurs on numerous species of marine teleosts and *Branchellion torpedinis* Sav. occurs on both elasmobranchs and teleosts. Only eight genera have been reported from the United States of which only two occur on fresh-water fishes (Meyer).

Piscicola geometra (L.) is found on many species of fresh-water teleosts and even on tadpoles. It has also been reported on trout in this country. *Ozobranchus margoi* Apathy has been recorded from marine turtles and also from dolphins. *Theromyzon* Philippi, however, is found only on aquatic birds and *Ostreobdella* Oka on oysters.

A curious adaptation is found in *Ozobranchus jantseanus* Oka occurring on the surface of an aquatic turtle, *Clemmys japonica* Schleg. (Fig. 47). The latter is in the habit of climbing out of the water to sun itself several times a day. The leeches are rapidly dried and shrivel up into small blackish discs without any apparent sign of life. When the turtle returns to the water, the discs swell up and the leeches resume their normal activities. It is found that this

FIG. 46. *Pelmatodrilus planariformis* Moore (cotype specimen) showing the flattened body and the peculiar arrangement of the ventral setae.

leech loses four-fifths of its weight and can remain in a state of anabiosis for several days. When dried experimentally in the sun and kept in this state for eight days, the leech became active when placed in water for one hour and a half. *O. jantseanus* consequently appears to be closely adapted to its host and it might be possible to interpret this as the effect of a selective action due to parasitism. Subsequent research work has, however, brought to light the fact that *O. jantseanus* is frequently found free-living and that this species is in no way dependent on

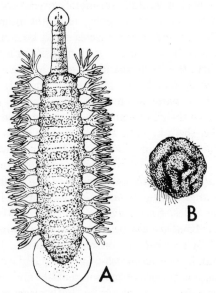

FIG. 47. *Ozobranchus jantseanus* Oka. A. Normal specimen. B. Dried specimen (Oka).

turtles. The association is purely accidental as is also the possibility for the leech to survive in anabiosis, a property that exists, although to a much less extent, in other species too.

There is no anatomical structure that would make it possible to distinguish between a sedentary parasite or a free-living species of leeches. The posterior sucker functions as an adhesive disc and resembles much more the foot of a snail than it does the sucker of a parasite. It is not more developed in sedentary forms than in predators. The only known parasitic adaptation, an evident one, is found to occur in *Hemibdella soleae* Van Ben. & Hesse, the mouth of

which, both very narrow and deep, is adapted to the spines that are located on the free edge of the scales of the sole. As only the scales of soles possess the right size of spines for the parasite to fix themselves onto, this adaptation has had a selective influence in creating an intimate host-parasite relationship.

Nothing is known of the biological aspect of these associations or their permanence. On the contrary, there is evidence that numerous predators have recently adapted themselves to a more specialized type of food and that this explains their becoming sedentary. Temporary parasitism has been facilitated since these leeches were preadapted to this kind of life and were able to adopt it without subsequent morphological changes in their structure. Leeches consequently form a group of organisms that appeared initially as specialized and one cannot therefore interpret the present free-living species as being sedentary parasites that have abandoned their host. There is no such example of nature being so careless as to the conservation of a species.

REFERENCES

AUTRUM, H., SCHLEIP, W., & HERTER, K. 1936. Hirudineen. *Bronn's Kl. Ord. Tier.*, Bd. 4, III.

CERRUTTI, A. 1910. *Oligognathus parasiticus* n. sp. endoparassita dello *Spio mecznikowianus* Clpd. *Arch. Zool. Napoli*, 4:197–209, pl. 3.

EYSIG, H. 1906. *Ichthyotomus sanguinarius* eine auf Aalen schmarotzende Annelide. *Fauna et Flora Neap.*, vol. 28, 300 pp., 34 figs., 10 pls.

HEMPLEMANN, F. 1911. Zur Naturgeschichte von *Nereis dumerilii* Aud. & Ed. *Zoologica*, vol. 25, 135 pp., 14 figs., 4 pls.

———. 1928. Archiannelida et Oligochaeta. *Handb. Zool.*, 2(7):33–212, 243 figs.

MEYER, M. C. 1940. A revision of the leeches (Piscicolidae) living on fresh water fishes of North America. *Trans. Am. Micros. Soc.*, 59:354–76.

MICHAELSEN, W. 1928. Clitellata. *Handb. Zool.*, 2(8):1–118, 103 figs.

MOORE, J. P. 1943. *Pelmatodrilus planariformis*, a new oligochaete (Enchytraeida) modified for epizootic life on Jamaican earthworms. *Notulae Naturae Acad. Nat. Sc. Philad.*, vol. 128, 7 pp.

OKA, A. 1922. Vertrocknung und Wiederlebung bei einer Susswasserhirudinee. *Zool. Anz.*, 54:91–93, 1 fig.

STUMMER-TRAUNFELS, R. VON. 1926. Myzostomida. *Handb. Zool.*, 3:132–210, 181 figs.

CHAPTER FIVE

Gordiacea

Horsehair worms, although at first sight resembling nematodes, possess an anatomical structure that is totally different and in no way even related to conditions found in members of that phylum. This is also true as to possible affinities with annelids. The modern trend is to consider these worms as forming a separate phylum that does not appear to have any direct affinities with any of the other so-called roundworms.

Several stages of the life history of horsehair worms were discovered many years ago, yet the exact life cycle has been obtained only recently by Dorier. Adult horsehair worms are free-living, in streams, ponds, and sometimes drinking troughs where their presence has given rise to the belief that they are horse hairs come to life. The most frequent species in the United States are *Paragordius varius* (Leidy) and *Gordius robustus* Leidy. In Europe the common species is *Gordius aquaticus* Duj.

After copulation, the female worms lay their eggs in strings that sometimes break up into smaller pieces. When whole, the strings measure from 15 to 22 cm. in length and contain an enormous number of eggs. *G. aquaticus* lays more than half a million eggs and *P. varius* at least six million. Toward the end of the fall the adult worms die after the eggs have been laid, the males usually dying earlier than the females. The time required for the eggs to incubate varies, of course, with the temperature of the water. For *G. aquaticus*, when the temperature is 13°C. incubation lasts thirty-five days and when it is only 10°C., seventy-four days. The larva hatches by pressing its body against the eggshell at a point where it has been softened through secretions from the larva. When liberated from its membranes, the larva appears as a tiny organism only one quarter of a millimeter in length and consists of two distinct

portions that are separated by a transverse septum (Fig. 48). The anterior portion forms a perforating apparatus, provided with spines and an armed, retractile proboscis; a septum separates it from the posterior part of the larva (Fig. 49). This posterior part shows a superficial segmentation and contains a brown, cellular mass. Part of the secretion accumulates in the hind portion of the larva where it appears as a peculiarly refrigent substance, and the remainder of the secretion may be expelled through the anterior end.

It was formerly thought that these larvae pierced the teguments of insects and penetrated into their body cavities to continue their development. May succeeded in infesting grasshoppers by inoculating larvae either via the skin or by mouth. He observed that when the larvae of *Gordius robustus* Leidy have lived free in water for some time they become incapable of further development. Evidence has been furnished that the larvae normally enter the insect via the mouth.

Within twenty-four hours after hatching, the larva encysts in the water, the cyst wall being formed by the secretion contained in the posterior part of the larva which solidifies on coming into contact with the water (Figs. 50 and 51). Dorier has discovered that the power to encyst is lost after twenty-four hours and this accounts also for the failure to infect insects by inoculation, using larvae that have remained too long in the water. Most larvae that are unable to encyst die. The colder the water the more readily do the larvae encyst; larval mortality increases with the temperature. The cysts remain viable for at least two months in water and for one month in a moist atmosphere. When cysts are swallowed by insects, the cyst wall dissolves and the larva thus liberated penetrates through the gut wall into the body cavity especially into the fat bodies. Within the body cavity of the insect, the larva undergoes complete metamorphosis. The entire anterior part with the penetrating apparatus is detached and all traces of segmentation disappear. The larva thus grows into a young gordiid with soft, white tegument. The body covering hardens and becomes brown only on contact with water, after the worm has pierced the teguments of the host and has escaped into the water. Should the host be a land insect, then the larvae can

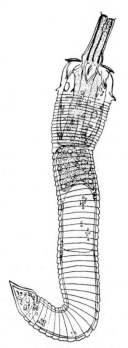

FIG. 48. Larva of *Gordius aquaticus* Duj. with its anterior perforating apparatus and the accumulation of mucoid in the posterior part of the body (Dorier).

make their escape only when the insect goes to the water. Consequently, when a larva penetrates into a suitable insect and there is no specificity in this choice, it is able to complete its development.

However, in certain hosts, insects, snails, and even fishes, the cyst wall is digested but the larva encysts anew instead of growing normally. In this way, an unsuitable host becomes a vicarious or a paratenic host that can transport the encysted larvae and thus spread the species over a wider area. When the paratenic host is eaten by a suitable host, the larva is able to renew its growth and undergo metamorphosis. Consequently, in a life cycle such as this, where there are two intermediate hosts, the first one is optional and therefore not indispensable for the life cycle. It facilitates the dispersion of the parasites and at the same time explains how purely land insects may become infested by ingesting encysted larvae washed out after a heavy rain, for instance.

Within a suitable host, development and growth proceed rapidly since within twenty-five days after an experimental infestation the young gordiids have already reached a length of 35 mm. The adult worms in this case attain more than one meter in length (Dorier).

The life history of gordiids illustrates another interesting point, namely that in no stage is there a gut

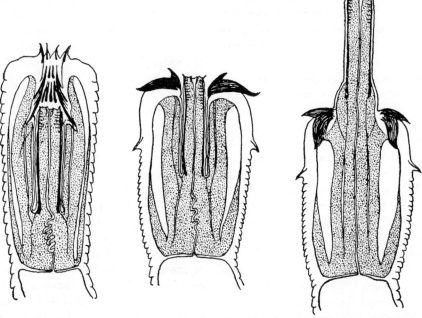

FIG. 49. Anterior extremity of Gordius larvae to show the perforating apparatus (Dorier).

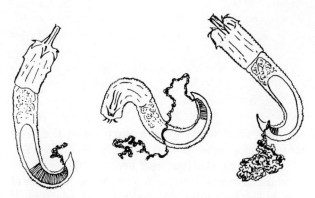

FIG. 50. Larva of *Gordius aquaticus* Duj. expelling the mucoid secretion from the hinder end of its body (Dorier).

or any other form of digestive apparatus, all nourishment being absorbed through the teguments. The larval parasitic stage, living in the fat body of insects, accumulates sufficient nourishment not only to complete its own metamorphosis, but also to enable the adult female to produce an enormous number of eggs. A closely similar type of protelian parasitism is also found in monstrillids (see page 49).

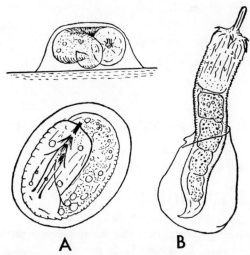

A   **B**

FIG. 51. A. Cysts of *Gordius aquaticus* larvae on the surface of the water. B. Larva hatching from a cyst.

REFERENCES

DORIER, A. 1930. Recherches biologiques et systématiques sur les Gordiacés. *Trav. Lab. Hydrobiol. Piscicult. Grenoble*, vol. 22, 180 pp., 4 pls.

————. 1935. Sur le passage à la vie latente des larves de Gordiacés. *C. R. Acad. Sc. Paris*, 200:492–94.

————. 1935. Etudes biologiques et morphologiques de la larve de *Parachorodes gemmatus* (Villot). *Trav. Lab. Hydrobiol. Piscicult. Grenoble*, 25:147–61, 2 pls.

MAY, H. G. 1919. Contributions to the life histories of *Gordius robustus* Leidy and *Paragordius varius* (Leidy). *Illinois Biological Monographs*, vol. 5, 118 pp., 21 pls.

Arthropoda

The arthropods constitute by far the largest phylum of the animal kingdom. Their peculiar anatomy together with their chitinous body covering have enabled them to become adapted to almost every type of biotope. Consequently there is nothing astonishing in finding parasitic species in almost every class of the phylum.

No matter what class of arthropods from which forms adapted to parasitism have arisen, in each case when the parasite becomes sedentary or fixed in a more or less permanent fashion to its host, it is found that appendages are reduced or lost and that considerable morphological transformations occur, especially in the mode of attachment and of feeding.

It is not possible to study arthropods as a whole when examining their adaptations to parasitism. Consequently we will refer to each class separately.

CRUSTACEA

Among entomostraceous crustaceans the greater number of the parasitic forms have apparently arisen from copepods and from cirripeds, whereas isopods and amphipods are the only groups of malacostracans that have succeeded in adopting parasitism.

It is usual to associate a crustacean with a free-living existence chiefly in an aquatic habitat and yet this class certainly includes the most deeply modified parasites actually known.

COPEPODA

In copepods, all stages of commensals, predators, and parasites occur. The parasites show all the intermediate phases between temporary and permanent parasites. It is therefore natural that these different stages of parasitism should be marked by distinct changes in certain appendages of the parasitic species and that in wholly sedentary forms the locomotor appendages have completely disappeared.

In all copepods, the head bears six pairs of appendages, namely: two pairs of antennae, one pair of mandibles, two pairs of maxillae, and one pair of maxillipeds. The thorax usually bears six pairs of swimming legs, although in females of free-living species, the sixth and sometimes the fifth pair may be lacking. The abdomen is terminated in two caudal rami.

In all free-living copepods, as also in the majority of parasitic species, the female carries the fertilized ova in ovisacs, where they are incubated.

It is possible to divide the entire life cycle into four stages, each of which in parasitic species especially, may be divided into a number of distinct phases. Each instar is separated from the preceding one by a molt. The larva that hatches from the egg is known as a *nauplius* and bears three pairs of appendages, representing the first and second antennae and the mandibles of the adult. Generally after the third molt the nauplius becomes a *metanauplius* in which additional mouth parts are formed and also the first indication of an abdominal segment appears. The metanauplius becomes a *copepodid* in which the abdomen increases in length and in which the thoracic locomotory appendages also appear. Finally, the copepodid becomes fully adult when the genital glands have developed and become functional.

The adaptation of copepods to parasitism has also influenced their life cycle in that the duration of the free-living larval stages is shortened. Reduction of the free-living stages may occur in two different ways, either the larvae remain within the egg for a longer time and, consequently, have reached an advanced stage of development on hatching, or the larval forms are also parasitic and molt while attached to their hosts.

The mouth parts of parasitic copepods are adapted for piercing the skin of the host and for sucking blood or predigested tissues. Since the cephalic appendages are also used as organs of attachment, it is not surprising that the head may be greatly modified in certain species. In most cases, grappling organs are derived from either the first or the second pair of antennae, the ends of which bear a well defined claw. In lernaeopodids, the grappling organs are formed by the second pair of maxillae, whereas in lernaeids, all the cephalic appendages have disappeared or are very much reduced as a consequence of the female being deeply embedded in the tissues of the host and being anchored by a complicated system of out-

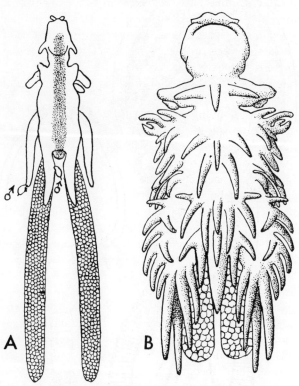

Fig. 52. A. *Chondracanthus merluccii* (Holt), showing extreme sexual dimorphism. B. *Chondracanthus zei* De la Roche female (Scott).

growths formed subsequently from the cephalothorax. In *Lernaeascus* Claus, occurring beneath the scales of fishes, the entire body is elongated and provided with two longitudinal rows of spines that retain this species in its slippery surroundings.

The ovary and the testis are always simple in free-living copepods whereas in the parasitic forms these gonads are always double. The sexes are nearly always separate and in numerous cases there is a very marked sexual dimorphism that is apparently due to the fact that the males are sometimes neotenic

larvae, neoteny having appeared at different stages of larval development. This accounts also for the truly extraordinary disproportion in size between the male and female in such cases as *Chondracanthus merluccii* (Holt) (Fig. 52) where the ratio of male to female is as 1:12,000. Hermaphroditism in parasitic copepods has apparently been recorded so far from only two genera, *Xenocoeloma* and *Flabellicola*.

Most parasitic copepods appear to have several breeding seasons in the year, some even breed continuously. It has been estimated that *Ergasilus minor* Halisch and *E. sieboldi* Nordm. from fresh-water fishes produce approximately 177,260 and 102,030,300

TABLE 1. Correlation of hatching and habits with developmental stages in families of parasitic copepods

Group	Nauplius			Metanauplius			Copepodid			Adult		
	1	2	3	1	2	3	1	2	3	1	2	3
I Ergasilids	··········			··········			··········			*********		
II Caligids	··········			··········			·····*****			*****·····		
III Pandarids	··········			··········			*********			*********		
IV Monstrillids	··*******			*********			*********			····		
V Lernaeids	†††††††††			††††††···			******···			*********		
VI Lernaeopodids	†††††††††			††††††††††			···******			*********		

···· free-swimming; **** parasitic; †††† in the egg.

eggs respectively in four breeding periods every year.

Predatory and commensalistic copepods also give evidence of morphological changes as compared to the free-living species. These will be dealt with later.

According to the way in which the life cycle of the parasitic copepods has been shortened as stated above, it is possible to form six groups of typical life histories but they do not necessarily correspond to distinct taxonomic subdivisions.

I. *All larval stages are free-swimming, only the adult parasitic.*

The species of this group are morphologically closest to the free-living copepods and have in common with these the arrangement of the eggs in ovisacs instead in strings like beads. This group contains the ergasilids, nearly all of which are found on the gills or within the branchial cavity of fishes. The bomolonchines and taeniacanthines occur on marine fishes and the ergasilinines on fresh-water species. The females only lead a parasitic life although they move about on their host, having retained certain of their locomotor appendages. They attach themselves by the second pair of antennae each of which is terminated in a powerful claw and is also provided with a series of minute spines that enable the female to adhere to the surface of its host. Males of these

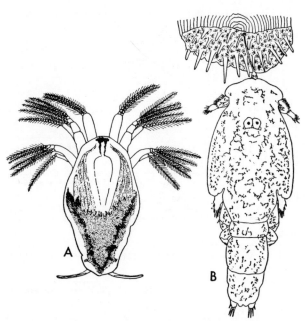

FIG. 53. *Caligus rapax* M. Edw. A. Nauplius. B. Chali mus larva attached to scale of host (Wilson).

species are free-swimming and can be found in plankton. It is probable that mating takes place before the female copepod attaches herself to the host.

II. *The first larval stages and the final adult stage only are free-swimming.*

This type of life cycle is that most usually found in caligids where the adults occur free in plankton. In this case, also, the second pair of antennae are provided with claws and sometimes as in *Caligus* have two sucker-like organs located close to the anterior end of the cephalothorax. The latter is flattened and when closely applied to the surface of a fish acts somewhat like a large adhesive disc. The nauplii are

positively phototropic and swim up close to the surface of the water (Fig. 53A). The final metanauplius stage, however, becomes negatively phototropic and approaches the bottom where the host is found. These usually belong to species of the cod and flounder families. The copepodid stage in caligids is extremely characteristic and is generally known as

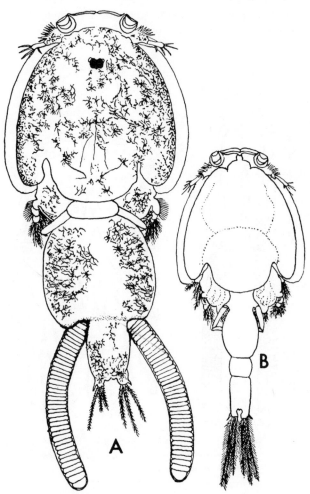

FIG. 54. *Caligus rapax* M. Edw. A. Adult female. B. Adult male (Wilson).

the *chalimus* stage. It is found attached to the host, usually to a fin or scale, by a long filament that is formed by the hardening of the secretion derived from a gland located in front of the eyes (Fig. 53B). The larvae undergo several molts while remaining attached in this way, each molt bringing it a stage nearer to the adult. When the adult male emerges from its final molt, it breaks off the thread and immediately searches for a female. The latter remains attached until fertilized and only then breaks away to lead a planktonic existence. It is found, however, that caligids never stray very far from their hosts and are found wandering over their body, sucking their food with the aid of tubular mouth parts (Fig. 54).

In chondracanthids, the life cycle is shortened since the adults appear after the first copepodid stage. Both sexes are parasitic and morphologically similar in the cecropids (Fig. 55). In pandarids, the females only are parasitic and consequently there is marked sexual dimorphism. This is even more accentuated in

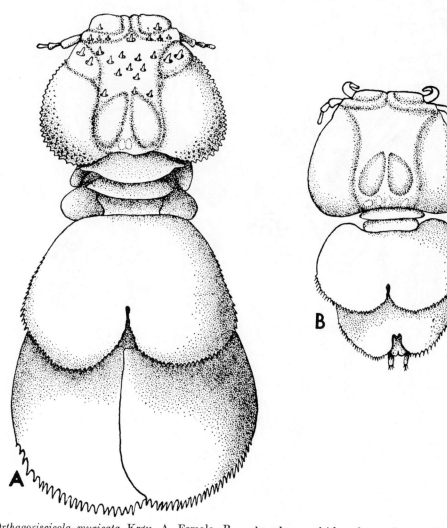

Fig. 55. *Orthagoriscicola muricata* Krøy. A. Female. B. Male (Wilson).

III. *Only one half of the life cycle is free-swimming.*

This type of life cycle is that of the pandarids and cecropids. It is also met with in other groups, especially in chondracanthids.

This life cycle recalls that of type II. However the females do not abandon their hosts but remain permanently attached to them. The males are either free-swimming (pandarids) or parasitic (cecropids).

chondracanthids where the males lead a parasitic life on the females. Pandarids appear to occur only on elasmobranchs whereas cecropids and chondracanthids are found on various species of marine teleosts.

IV. *Nauplius and mature adults only free-swimming, all the other stages parasitic.*

This very curious type of life cycle is found so far only in monstrillids, the larval stages of which are

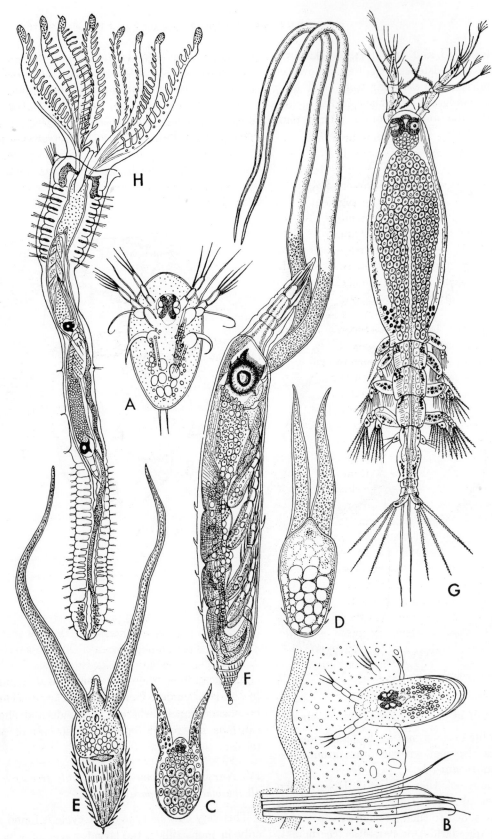

FIG. 56 (*see legend on opposite page*).

parasitic in the blood vessels of polychaetes or in the body cavity of prosobranch snails.

At no stage in the life history of these copepods is there any trace of digestive organs, neither mouth, gut, nor anus.

With its appendages the nauplius breaks its way into the skin of a polychaete. Thrusting itself through the body cavity, it finally penetrates into the dorsal blood ·vessel where it undergoes complete dedifferentiation, in the course of which the pigmented eye spots disappear and the larval appendages are resorbed (Fig. 56). A cuticular envelope appears around the parasite that bears two anterior appendages at first. Later on, probably after one or several molts, there appears a second pair of appendages and also several rows of minute spines on the end opposite to the first appendages. The entire larva, and of course the appendages, bathe in the host's blood and absorb the necessary nourishment not only to complete larval development, but also sufficient to enable the adults to mature and reproduce. Although these larval appendages cannot be derived from known structures previously described in free-living forms, they must be considered as adaptations to parasitism. These larval stages should be considered as highly modified forms of metanauplii and copepodids. The adult copepod emerges from the final molt by breaking through the blood vessel and the skin of its host. It is found that only a few hours after the parasite has emerged, there is not the slightest trace of a skin lesion.

Parasitism of monstrillid larvae in annelids does not occur frequently and has been observed only a few times. On the other hand, not all monstrillids necessarily develop within annelids since the species *M. helgolandica* Claus goes through its larval stages in the body cavity of a predatory gastropod, *Odostomia scalaris* Macg. This species of monstrillids possesses three pairs of appendages, one of which is bifid. It is interesting to compare the structure of larval monstrillids with that of the parasitic species that belong to the genus *Briarella* that live within the body cavity of nudibranchs. These possess several lateral thoracic appendages that might perhaps

be homologous with those occurring in monstrillid larvae. It is probable that these appendages are correlative with a habitat within the body cavity of mollusks, and that in both cases they should be regarded as adaptations to a particular mode of life. The probable function of such appendages is both nutritional and respiratory, since in the species *Staurosoma caulleryi* Okada the gut shows small lateral diverticula, each corresponding to a thoracic evagination (Fig. 57).

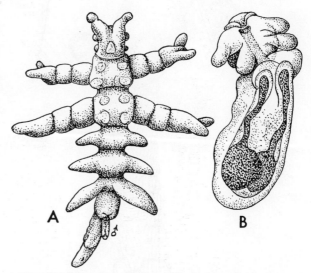

FIG. 57. *Staurosoma caulleryi* Okada from the body cavity of an actinian. A. Female with dwarf male attached to its body. B. Male greatly enlarged (Okada).

V. *Part of the larval development takes place within the egg; the third metanauplius and third copepodid stages only are free-swimming.*

In this interesting type of life cycle, the third metanauplius stage emerges from the egg and leads a brief free-swimming existence. The copepods then become parasitic on a definitive host. While the males spend their lives on this host, after fertilization the females become free-swimming before attaching themselves to another host of a different species than the first. Here they grow into enormously disproportioned organisms, so transformed that their copepod nature was recognized only several years after their discovery.

Lernaeids are deeply buried in the tissues of fishes and whales and some of the species attain as much as 15 to 25 cm. in length. Both Aristotle and Pliny described these parasites from bonitos and swordfish

FIG. 56. *Haemocera danae* (Clap.). A. Nauplius. B. Nauplius in the act of penetrating into the body of its host. C–E. Successive larval stages showing development of the appendages and also of the spinous sheath enclosing the larva. F. Fully formed copepodid. G. Adult female copepod devoid of a mouth. H. Annelid with two copepodid larvae in its coelomic cavity (Malaquin).

and supposed that the "sufferings" they caused were the reason why their hosts jump out of the water!

The fertilized females burrow with their antennae through the tissues of the host until they penetrate a blood vessel or the heart. Each genus appears to have its own particular site. *Collipravus* (Fig. 58),

comprises two separate parasitic stages between which occurs a free-swimming stage. Both parasitic stages may be found on separate hosts (*Lernaeinae*) or on different hosts but which belong to the same genus (*Lernaeenicinae*). There are consequently two successive hosts, one temporary and the other definitive.

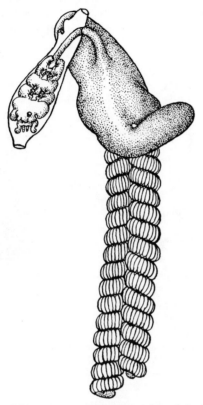

FIG. 58. *Collipravus parvus* Wils. with cephalothorax embedded in the aortic bulb of its host (Wilson).

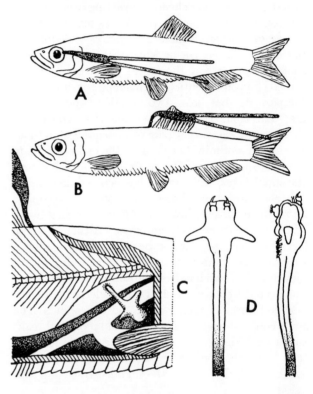

FIG. 59. A. *Lernaeenicus sprattae* (Sowerby) embedded behind the eye of a sprat. B. *Lernaeenicus encrassicola* (Turton) piercing the musculature of an anchovy. C–D. Enlarged views of the cephalothorax (Scott).

Cardiodectes, and *Haemobaphes* penetrate through the tissues of the throat to the aortic bulb. *Lernaeocera* embeds itself either within the auricle or the ventricle. *Lernaeenicus sprattae* (Sowerb.) penetrates behind the eye of the sprat to the retinal artery. Other species of the same genus burrow into the flesh and fix themselves to a bone of the skull or to the vertebral column (Fig. 59). *Pennella*, the largest of all the species, buries itself in the skin of whales and causes the formation of enormous cysts of a cartilaginous nature. The parasites attached in blood vessels or in the heart cause marked tissue reactions. These are usually of a fibromatous nature and consequently impair the normal function of the organ.

We have seen that the life history of these species

The copepodid larva usually attaches itself by its clawed antennae to the first host, a fish in *Lernaea* and *Lernaeocera*, and a cephalopod in *Pennella*. No matter how the copepod attaches itself, it undergoes a phase of development that may be compared to the nymphal stage in insects since all the locomotory appendages are lost but are reconstructed before the final adult molt. The males usually die after copulating. The female seeks its definitive host and when attached to the latter, the female undergoes a marked transformation sometimes called a regressive metamorphosis, although wrongly since all the appendages are retained. They appear to be much reduced because the female's body increases greatly in size although the appendages do not become any bigger.

The head and thorax are transformed into a complicated grappling organ that branches out into the tissues of the host and that cannot be easily removed without breaking the parasite. Unfortunately, the complete life history of most of the species is as yet unknown. The adults are so greatly modified that unless the relationship between the first larval stages and the adult parasites is established experimentally no morphological correlation is possible (Figs. 60 and 61).

VI. *The first stage copepodid larva emerges from the egg and after a brief free-swimming existence becomes parasitic.*

This type of life history is found in lernaeopodids both from marine (*Lernaeopoda, Charopinus, Clavella*) and fresh-water (*Salmincola, Achtheres, Basanistes*) fishes.

The copepodid bears two pairs of swimming appendages and both the second pair of maxillae and the maxillipeds bear a strongly developed terminal claw. While still in the egg, there appears in the anterior part of the larval head, a long, narrow tube that is rolled up. It is formed by a cephalic gland similar to that found in caligids. In this case, however, the gland functions before the egg hatches. As soon as the larva emerges, the tube is unrolled. At its end is a small button-like swelling. The copepodid now seeks its host and, slitting the skin with its powerful claws, pushes the button-shaped terminal thread under the epidermis. As soon as the larva is thus attached, it molts and on emerging from its ecdysis, is found to have lost all of its locomotor appendages. After the second molt, the copepodid detaches the anchoring thread with the second pair of maxillae which remain as the only point of attachment for the larva. After the fifth molt, the male breaks away and after having undergone another ecdysis becomes adult (Fig. 62). With its cephalic appendages, the male crawls over the surface of the fish feeding on mucus and perhaps also on blood. After copulation the male dies and the fertilized female remains definitely attached to the host and increases considerably in size. Since the cephalic gland continues to secrete, the terminal button grows larger and is firmly gripped by the host tissues. In *Lernaeopoda scyllicola* (Leigh-Sharpe), the male does not die but remains permanently attached to the female near the base of its cephalothorax at a point where peculiar glands, known as bromatophores, are

located. It appears that the secretion of the latter is used as nourishment by the male (Gray) (Fig. 63).

The life history of a great many parasitic copepods is as yet unknown either because the males, being free-swimming, have not been found, or because the

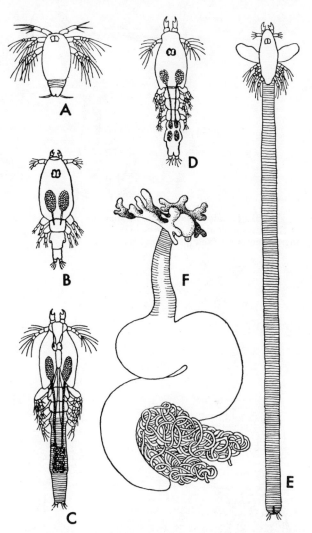

FIG. 60. *Lernaea branchialis* L. A. Nauplius. B. Young female. C. Fertilized female at stage when it abandons its first host. D. Mature male. E. Fertilized female when attached to second host. F. Mature female (Scott).

difference in size and structure of the sexes is so great that they cannot be correlated without resorting to experimental demonstration of life cycles.

One of the most peculiar parasitic copepods known is *Xenocoeloma brumpti*, a species related to the lernaeopodids, that is parasitic on marine annelids. This is one of the most deeply modified species of copepods since all appendages have been lost and the parasite relies on the host's skin for its protection,

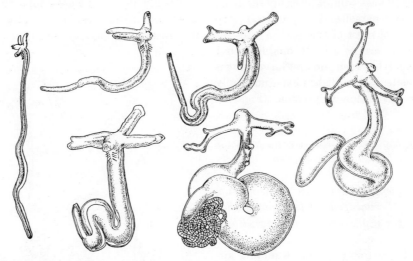

FIG. 61. *Lernaea branchialis* L. showing various stages in the development of the thoracic anchors and in the twisting of the body (Schuurmanns-Stekhoven).

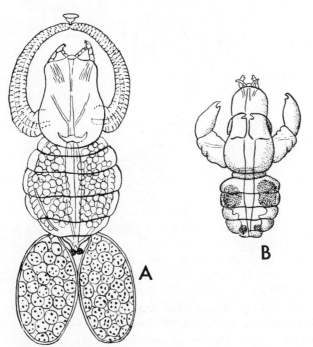

FIG. 62. *Achtheres percarum* Nordm. A. Female. B. Male greatly enlarged (Scott).

ordinary copepod is also hermaphroditic and were it not for the egg strings that appear on the surface of the host, it would never have been recognized as a copepod (Fig. 64).

The life history of *Xenocoeloma brumpti* C. & M. is only partly known. The way in which the larval stages gain access to the host unfortunately has

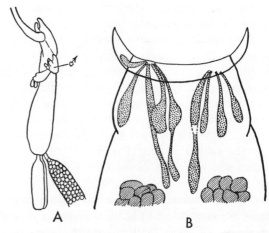

FIG. 63. *Lernaeopoda scyllicola* L.-Sharpe. A. Male attached to the female. B. Enlarged portion of a female showing the bromatophores opening on the left side only of the dorsum (Gray).

never been observed. The nauplius that emerges from the egg resembles that of the monstrillids in the complete absence of digestive organs; it appears to be free-swimming. The earliest parasitic stage so far discovered is enclosed within the host's skin where it causes a tissue reaction. As the parasite grows out,

and on the host's food for its nourishment. It is literally within the skin of its host and derives its nourishment from an outgrowth of the host's body cavity that penetrates into the parasite. This extra-

pushing the host's skin before it (Fig. 65), the coelomic lining penetrates the body of the copepod so that finally, the parasite is reduced to a mass of reproductive glands between two layers of host tissues, an outer layer, the skin, and an inner layer, the coelomic epithelium (Fig. 65). This is the most highly specialized type of parasite that can be conceived since it is reduced to a set of hermaphroditic reproductive organs literally grafted into the host.

Argulids or carp lice, although not true copepods in the taxonomic sense, are closely related (Fig. 67). Moreover, their adaptation to temporary parasitism

rately on stones or other inanimate objects. There are neither ovisacs nor egg strings.

Argulids move about on their hosts either on the surface or within the branchial cavity. Since they have lost none of their swimming appendages, they are able to swim freely, abandon their host, or pass onto another one. Each species of parasite apparently possesses its favorite host, but in absence of the latter it can feed on any available host. The genus *Argulus* Müll. contains species that occur simultaneously on both fresh-water and salt-water fishes, especially on migratory fishes. *A. megalops* Smith,

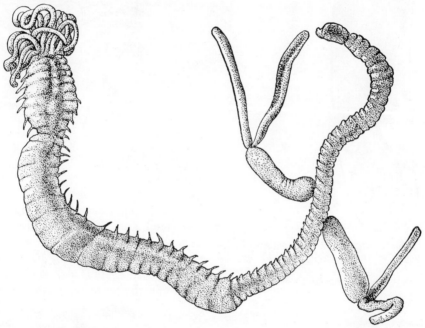

FIG. 64. *Polycirrus arenivorus* Caull. parasitized by two specimens of *Xenocoeloma brumpti* C. & M. (Caullery & Mesnil).

has proceeded along lines similar to those of the caligids. Each of the first pair of antennae is provided with a powerful claw with which the parasite attaches itself to the surface of the fish. The second pair of maxillae is, curiously enough, modified so as to form two sucker-like organs (Fig. 68). The cephalothorax is flattened and a series of small spines on its ventral surface enable the carp louse to move about on its host without slipping off. The mouth parts are adapted for piercing and sucking. Consequently, the parasites feed on blood and mucus.

Female argulids differ from all other copepods, except notodelphids, because the eggs are laid sepa-

taken from a marine fish and placed directly in fresh water with minnows, attached itself immediately and fed on them as if no change of environment had occurred (Wilson, 1902).

A great many genera and species of parasitic copepods, including *Xenocoeloma* described above, have been described from marine invertebrates. Twenty genera at least are known from echinoderms, fifteen from annelids, more than sixty from ascidians, and a large number from mollusks. Unfortunately, these have in most cases been mentioned only once, often badly described, and nothing is known about the nature of their association with the host. Nearly all of the species described from mollusks appear to be commensals except *Briarella*, already mentioned above. In most of the numerous species from ascidians there appears to exist a distinct sexual dimorphism due to the fact that the gravid females no longer leave

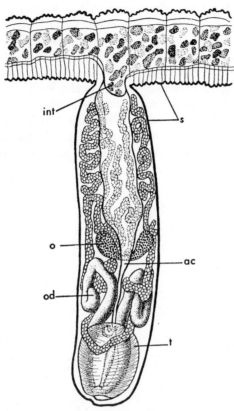

FIG. 65. *Xenocoeloma brumpti* C. & M., section of the parasite and the host. ac.—axial cavity formed by the host's coelom. int.—host's gut. od.—oviduct. ov.—ovary. s.—skin of both the host and the parasite. t.—testis (Caullery & Mesnil).

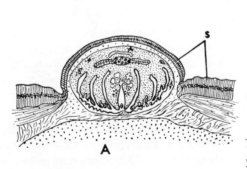

FIG. 66. *Xenocoeloma brumpti* C. & M. A-B. Sections through the body wall of the host with young stages of the parasite. ac.—axial cavity in formation. s.—skin of host and parasite (Caullery & Mesnil).

their host. Several of the species found on echinoderms are said to cause the formation of nodules

especially visible on starfish and brittle stars. Yet the way in which these nodules arise does not appear to have been studied.

An interesting association of copepods with an invertebrate is that of an harpacticid that lives, per-

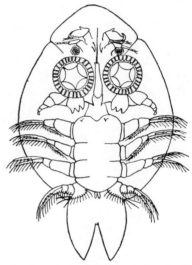

FIG. 67. *Argulus pugettensis* Dana female. Ventral view showing the two suckers and the flattening of the cephalothorax (Wilson).

haps as a commensal, in the branchial chamber of both land and shore crabs. In the West Indies, *Cancricola jamaicensis* Wils. occurs on the gills of the land crabs *Cardiosoma guanhumi* Latr. and *Microphrys bicoronata* (Latr.), and *Cancricola plumipes* Humes in the branchial chamber of *Sesarma reticu-*

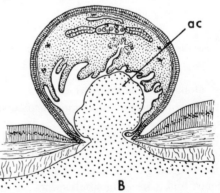

latum (Say). The species *Cancricola wilsoni* Pearse occurs in Japan on the gills of both *Sesarma haematocheir* (de Haan), a land crab, and *S. pictum* (de Haan), a shore crab.

Cancricola has lost none of its swimming appendages but its mandibles are modified to a tubelike organ and both the maxillae and maxillipeds bear claws. Nothing very definite is known about the biological relationships existing between the "parasite" and its host. The tiny harpacticid, less than one millimeter in length, feeds on mucus and blood from the host's gills. On the other hand, the life cycle of both associates must be similar, since the crab remains on land for at least eleven months at a time and returns to the water for a period of only ten days to lay its eggs. Since the copepod's eggs are unable to develop without water, they must be held within the oviducts of the female until the crab returns to the sea. That this is probably true is borne out by the observation that females of *Cancricola* on crabs returning from the sea never have eggs within their oviducts but females on crabs going down to the sea do.

Some evidence has been given as to the possible existence of a parallel evolution of the host and the parasitic copepods showing that the lower the position occupied in the scale of *Metazoa* by the host, the more primitive the structure of the parasite (Leigh-Sharpe). This may appear to be the case at first sight although it must not be forgotten that absolutely nothing is known of the life histories of the species parasitic on invertebrates. Even the adults have rarely been observed alive; most of them have been described from preserved materials.

Moreover, entomostraceous crustaceans apparently possess extraordinary powers of adapting themselves to changes in their environment. This is of course well known for planktonic species such as *Bosmina* and *Daphnia*, the shape of which is dependent on the temperature and hence the density of the water. Similar changes have not been observed in free-swimming copepods, but they appear almost immediately after the copepods change their mode of life.

There is no doubt whatever that all these changes observed in the morphology of parasitic copepods are adaptive although they do not affect, simultaneously, all the parts of the body. As long as the parasitic females are able to move about on their host, there is no sign of any sexual dimorphism other than the presence or absence of egg strings and a slight difference in size.

The increasing length of the egg strings in caligids causes a mechanical hindrance to the females and consequently reduces their ability to swim freely. With the appearance of dorsal plates on the thorax,

movement is still more inhibited. This is especially evident in pandarines that are obliged to crawl over the body of their host although they have retained their swimming legs. Since the dorsal plates are not so greatly developed in the males, they remain free-swimming. In cecropines, however, both the males and the females have become sedentary and consequently both show a reduction in size of their swimming legs.

In lernaeids, we have seen that copulation takes place while on the first host and that the males die soon after, whereas the females seek a second host to which they become permanently attached although they retain small swimming legs. Consequently one

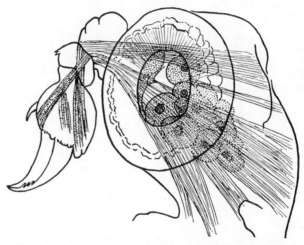

FIG. 68. Second maxilla of *Argulus foliaceus* L. showing the claw being dropped at a molt and replaced by a sucker (Claus).

cannot speak of sexual dimorphism in this case. This does occur, however, and in marked fashion when the males also become permanently attached. In lernaeopodids, both the female and the male lose their swimming legs at the copepodid stage after becoming attached to their host. The female remains attached once and for all the rest of its life, whereas the male chalimus, on becoming mature, breaks its thread and fixes itself to the body of the female by its cephalic appendages. Since the female increases rapidly in size and the male does not grow, a marked sexual dimorphism sets in and the males appear as tiny organisms on the female's body. As soon as they have deposited their spermatophores, they abandon the female and die.

In most free-living and also in a great many parasitic copepods the respiratory mechanism is controlled by peristaltic movements of the gut that introduce water which acts as an oxygen vector. The movements of the gut thus keep in constant motion the liquid contained within the haemocoel. In dichelestiids, this type of respiration is supplanted by a network of vessels that branch out into a series of appendages of the cephalothorax and that remain bathed by water (Fig. 69). In *Lernaeenicus*, the body of the adult female is extremely long and thin and it is probable that gaseous exchanges take place through the skin. In *Pennella*, cuticular respiration is concentrated in fine, filiform, caudal appendages on the body of the female and this is probably also the function of similar appendages found in sphy-

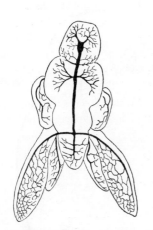
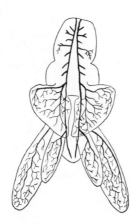

FIG. 69. *Lernanthropus breviotiae* Rathb. females showing the vascular network visible through the integument (Wilson).

riids (Fig. 70). The cuticle of *Lernaeocera* is heavily chitinized, thus reducing cuticular respiration to a minimum. Moreover, the cephalothoracic outgrowths act as purely mechanical anchors. Consequently, both oxygen and food enter by the mouth in the form of blood from the host and a vigorous two-way peristalsis keeps it in constant motion within the gut of the parasite. It is found that the body fluid of this parasite is hypotonic to sea water as long as it remains attached to its host. The blood of the latter is also hypotonic but more so than that of the parasite. Consequently, there exists a complex osmotic system that no doubt plays a part in the gaseous exchanges of this parasite (Sproston & Hartley).

In view of their extraordinary power to adapt themselves to every form of parasitism, parasitic copepods give one the impression of being of poly-

phyletic origin. From what we can gather from their life histories, however, we would be inclined to conclude to the contrary, yet no satisfactory explanation can be forthcoming until a great deal more research work has been done on this interesting group of parasites.

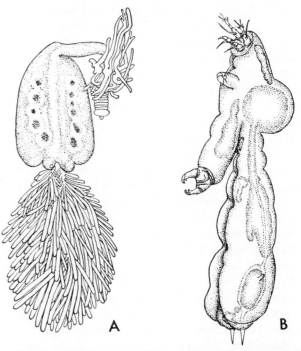

FIG. 70. *Rebebula cornuta* Wilson. A. Female with caudal appendages. B. Male greatly enlarged (does not burrow into the tissues of the host) (Wilson).

REFERENCES

CAULLERY, M., & MESNIL, F. 1919. *Xenocoeloma brumpti* C. & M. Copépode parasite de *Polycirrus arenivorus* C. *Bull. Biol. France et Belgique*, 53:161–233, 20 figs., pls. 1–4.

GRAY, P. 1926. On the nutrition of the male of *Lernaeopoda scyllicola*. *Parasitology*, 18:299–301, 4 figs.

HALISCH, W. 1940. Anatomie und Biologie von *Ergasilus minor* Halisch. *Zeitsch. Parasitenk.*, 11:284–330, 27 figs.

HUMES, A. G. 1941. A new Harpacticoid copepod from the gill chambers of a marsh crab. *Proc. U. S. Nat. Mus.*, 90:379–86, fig. 18.

LEIGH-SHARPE, W. H. 1928. Degeneracy in parasitic Copepoda in relation to the distribution of their hosts in time. *Parasitology*, 20:421–26.

MALAQUIN, A. 1901. Le parasitisme évolutif des Monstrillides. *Arch. Zool. Exp.* ser. 3, 9:81–232, pls. 2–8.

MONOD, TH., & DOLLFUS, R. PH. 1932. Les copépodes parasites de mollusques. *Ann. Parasit.*, 10:129–204, 30 figs.

SPROSTON, N. G., & HARTLEY, P. H. T. 1941. The ecology

of some parasitic copepods of gadoids and other fishes. *J. Mar. Biol. Assn.*, 25: 361-93, 2 figs.

———. 1941. Observations on the bionomics and physiology of *Trebius caudatus* and *Lernaeocera branchialis* (Copepoda). *Ibid.*, 25:393–417, 5 figs.

WILSON, CH. B. 1902. North American parasitic copepods of the family Argulidae, with a bibliography of the group and a systematic review of all known species. *Proc. U. S. Nat. Mus.*, 25:635–742, 23 figs., pls. 8–27.

———. 1904. A new species of Argulus, with a more complete account of two species already described. *Ibid.*, 27:627–55, 38 figs.

———. 1905. North American parasitic copepods belonging to the family Caligidae. Part 1.—The Caliginae. *Ibid.*, 28:479–672, 50 figs., pls. 5–29.

———. 1907. North American parasitic copepods belonging to the family Caligidae. Part 2.—The Trebinae and Euryphorinae. *Ibid.*, 31:669–720, 18 figs., pls. 15–20.

———. 1907. Additional notes on the development of the Argulidae, with description of a new species. *Ibid.*, 32:411–24, pls. 29–32.

———. 1907. North American parasitic copepods belonging to the family Caligidae. Parts 3 and 4.—A revision of the Pandarinae and the Cecropinae. *Ibid.*, 33:323–490, 18 figs., pls. 17–43.

———. 1908. North American parasitic copepods: new genera and species of Caliginae. *Ibid.*, 33:593–627, pls. 49–56.

———. 1908. North American parasitic copepods: a list of those found upon the fishes of the Pacific coast, with descriptions of new genera and species. *Ibid.*, 35:431–81, pls. 46–83.

———. 1911. North American parasitic copepods. Part 9.—The Lernaeopodidae. *Ibid.*, 39:189–226, pls. 29–36.

———. 1911. North American parasitic copepods belonging to the family Ergasilidae. *Ibid.*, 39:263–400, 38 figs., pls. 41–60.

———. 1911. North American parasitic copepods. Descriptions of new genera and species. *Ibid.*, 39:625–34, pls. 65–68.

———. 1912. Descriptions of new species of parasitic copepods in the collections of the United States National Museum. *Ibid.*, 42:233–43, pls. 30–34.

———. 1915. North American parasitic copepods belonging to the Lernaeopodidae, with a revision of the entire family. *Ibid.*, 47:565–729, 15 figs., pls. 25–56.

———. 1917. North American parasitic copepods belonging to the Lernaeidae with a revision of the entire family. *Ibid.*, 53:1–150, pls. 1–21.

———. 1919. North American parasitic copepods belonging to the new family Sphyriidae. *Ibid.*, 55:549 604, pls. 50–59.

———. 1922. North American parasitic copepods belonging to the family Dichelesthiidae. *Ibid.*, 60:1–100, pls. 1–13.

———. 1924. New North American parasitic copepods, new hosts and notes on copepode nomenclature. *Ibid.*, 64:1–22, pls. 1–3.

———. 1932. The copepods of the Woods Hole region, Massachusetts. *U. S. Nat. Mus. Bull.*, vol. 158, 635 pp., 316 figs., 41 pls.

CIRRIPEDIA

Adult barnacles are sedentary organisms that are found attached to either inanimate objects or living organisms. Their larvae, however, are free-swimming and bear a distinct resemblance to those of copepods. Sometimes, species are found attached to living supports with which they are incorporated in a very peculiar fashion. For instance, *Chelonibia* Leach occurs on the shell of marine turtles. It is in no way a parasite, but possesses a many-branched system of roots that penetrate into the bone of the plastron. Likewise, *Tubincella* Lam. occurs in the epidermis of whales. It possesses calcareous plates with transverse ridges that grow into the epidermis as if the barnacle were screwed into the skin. Both these instances are examples of phoresis.

The development of cirripeds comprises a certain number of successive larval stages that are separated by molts. A nauplius larva which hatches from the egg closely resembles that of copepods except that it bears two hornlike appendages on either side. After five molts, the antennae become prehensile organs and at the next stage the larva appears to be enclosed within two thin-shelled valves that resemble an ostracod, hence the name cypris stage given to this larva. The valves are not only united along the dorsal surface but also on the ventral surface, close to the middle of the larva; this latter character distinguishes a cypris larva from a true ostracod. On the other hand, a cypris larva may be compared to the pupal stage in insects. It undergoes complete metamorphosis as soon as it has become attached by its antennae to its future support and then grows into an adult barnacle.

It is difficult to perceive in which way cirripeds have become parasitic, since no stages that might be considered as intermediate are found although some authors have claimed that they do exist. *Anelasma*, for instance, occurs partly buried in the skin of sharks. The part that emerges on the surface is devoid of calcareous plates and possesses somewhat reduced mouth parts as well as shorter cirri than are usually found in other species. The part that is buried in the skin, on the other hand, is pear-shaped and bears very numerous short, branched, rootlike appendages that penetrate into the tissues of the host and pass through the dermis into the underlying muscle layer. It seems that these roots secrete some enzymatic substance that dissolves the surrounding tissues, since they appear to be liquefied and even necrotic where they are in contact with the roots (Fig. 71). The slight reduction of the mouth parts

anus. Finally, the sexual glands are hermaphroditic whereas all other species of barnacles have separate sexes. *Rhizolepas*, as its name implies, was considered by Day as constituting a link between true barnacles (*Lepas*) and *Rhizocephala*, the wholly parasitic forms.

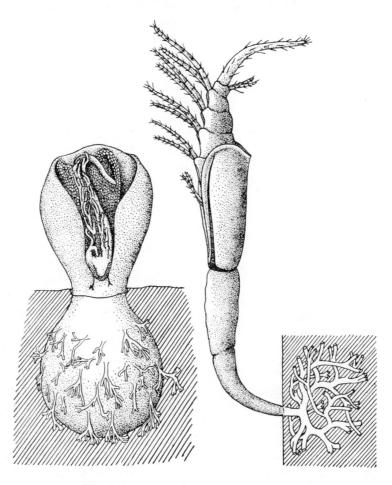

FIG. 71

FIG. 72

FIG. 71. *Anelasma squalicola* Lovén embedded in its host (Johnston & Frost).

FIG. 72. *Rhizolepas annellidicola* Day attached to its host by a root system (Day).

and the cirri, on the one hand, and the presence of a root system buried in the host's tissues on the other, seem to indicate that *Anelasma* is on the way to becoming a true parasite. This is also the case for *Rhizolepas* that occurs on an annelid, *Laetmonica producta* Grube. This species is attached to its host by a system of deeply embedded roots (Fig. 72). The "free" extremity shows definitely that the mouth parts and cirri are much reduced and that the intestine no longer opens on the surface, nor is there an

There certainly appears to be a slight superficial resemblance between the root system of this parasite and that of the *Rhizocephala*, but all the rest of the anatomical details are distinctly of the free-living barnacle type that never occur to the slightest degree in *Rhizocephala*. Unfortunately nothing is known of the life history of this species, so that any further comparison is impossible. However, from what we know about the life history of rhizocephalans, it seems very likely that these have arisen from some group that has since disappeared, or that has never had any free-living ancestors.

Rhizocephala are extremely modified cirripeds that

are always found upon other crustaceans, mostly on decapods and occasionally on isopods also. The principal stages of the cirripedian life cycle are retained, and both the nauplius and the first cypris stages are identical with those of barnacles, except that there is no trace of a mouth or gut (Fig. 73).

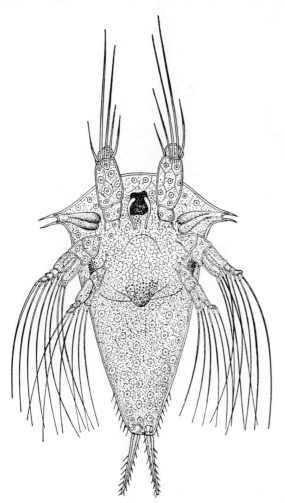

FIG. 73. *Sacculina carcini* Thomps. nauplius (Delage).

Incidentally, it is these larval stages that have made it possible to connect *Rhizocephala* with cirripeds. It should be remembered that only a few life histories have been investigated in detail, namely those of *Sacculina carcini* Thomps. and *Triangulus munidae* Smith, and that it is quite possible that further research may reveal other types.

In *Sacculina*, the cypris larva manifests a marked negative phototropism and, consequently, becomes active only after dark. It attaches itself to the surface of a crab and invariably seeks a place at the base

of a hair where it remains fixed by its antennae. Here it undergoes complete metamorphosis that resembles somewhat that occurring in lernaeopodids. All locomotor appendages, the swimming legs together with their muscles, are shed, leaving an undifferentiated, cellular mass enclosed within the two valves of the cypris. These cells give rise to a very peculiar organism known as the *kentrogon* larva within which appears a short tube or dart (Fig. 74). After the kentrogon larva is completely formed, it is seen that the dart pierces the crab's teguments, making an opening into its body cavity. The entire cellular mass then flows from the kentrogon, through the dart into the crab's body cavity and is thus inoculated into the blood sinuses. In this way, the mass of embryonic cells is carried by the blood stream to the ventral surface of the gut to a position immediately behind the paired intestinal diverticula. Here the embryonic cells begin to multiply and a system of roots branches out in all directions (Fig. 75). These are the future elements which will later spread throughout the entire body cavity and through which the adult parasite will receive its nourishment. This part of the body is known as the *sacculina interna*. At the base of the root system, there appears a rounded cellular mass, the future *sacculina externa* that will contain the reproductive organs. At this stage, the parasite migrates along the surface of the gut to a place situated near the single diverticulum. The future *sacculina externa* now grows and begins to press on the tissues of the ventral surface of the host. The effect of this increasing pressure is to destroy the muscles and then the hypodermis immediately above the parasite. The chitinous tegument becomes thinner and finally is dissolved and the external form of the parasite is thrust through the opening where it is now free to grow into an hermaphroditic adult. The internal anatomy of the latter is very complicated; the sexual glands are enclosed in a so-called mantle cavity that opens on the surface through a small orifice. It is within this mantle cavity that the eggs are first laid and then incubated, so that larvae in the nauplius stage emerge from the mantle cavity. It had been formerly supposed that the *sacculina externa* could emerge from the body cavity only after the host had molted and when the teguments were still soft and yielding (Delage) yet more recent research has shown that this is not the case and that the parasite emerges as stated above (Foxon). It has not yet been ascertained how the

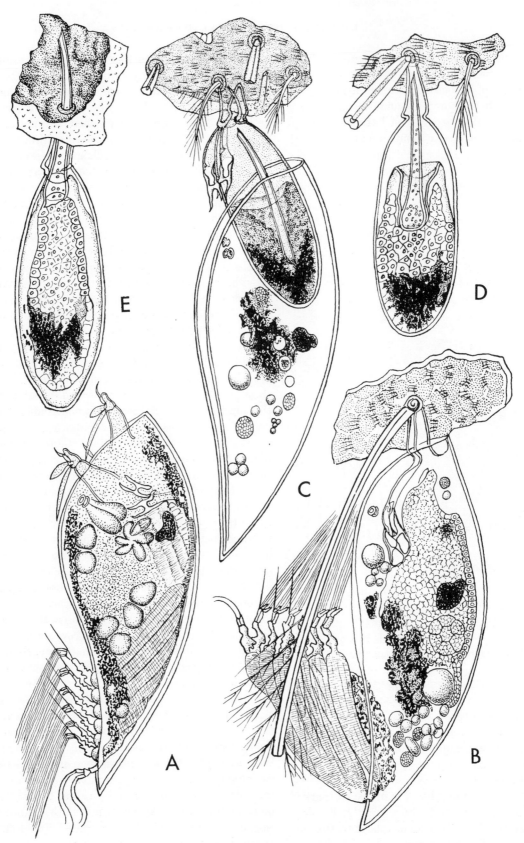

Fig. 74 (*see legend on opposite page*).

parasite dissolves the chitinous teguments, whether this is a purely mechanical process or whether there exists some larval secretion that acts chemically on chitin. Formation of the root system and of the external form proceeds very slowly. In the case of *S. carcini* nine months elapse between the penetration of the kentrogon and the appearance of the external form on the surface of the crab's abdomen.

Sacculina carcini on *Carcinus moenas* L. appears to breed the whole year round with a maximum production of nauplii from August to December and a minimum from January to March (Plymouth). When the parasite occurs on *Portunus holsatus* Leach it apparently breeds once, between March and May, and then it is shed. The difference in behavior of the same parasite on two different hosts would seem to

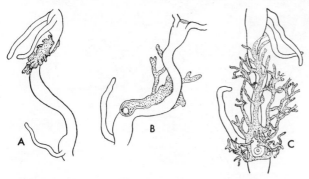

FIG. 75. *Sacculina neglecta* (Fraisse). A–C. Successive stages of the formation of the internal form and the root system (Smith).

indicate that *C. maenas* is the normal host whereas *P. holsatus* is only an occasional host.

A sacculinized crab ceases to molt, although it can certainly live for at least two years with its parasite. The latter affects the host's entire metabolism and induces, in many cases, profound morphological changes which will be dealt with later (see page 174). Moreover, an infested crab is not protected from subsequent infestations. Cases are known in which two, and more rarely three or even four *Sacculinae* have occurred simultaneously on a single host. A specimen of the crab genus *Munida* has been recorded as bearing *Triangulus munidae* Smith and *Lernaeodiscus ingolfi* Brink.

FIG. 74. *Sacculina carcini* Thomps. A. Cypris larva. B. Cypris attached to its host by its antennae and shedding its locomotory appendages. C. Kentrogon larva. D–E. Stages of penetration of the kentrogon into the crab (Delage).

The parasitic genera *Thompsonia* and *Gemmosaccus*, that occur on *Pagurus* spp., periodically shed their external form and a new one regenerates on the root system to replace it.

In *Peltogaster paguri* Rathke from *Pagurus pubescens* Krøyer the internal root system develops only after the formation of the external form. The genital glands develop as protandrous hermaphrodites. Hermit crabs that are free of parasites apparently do not seem to attract cypris larvae, although these are strongly attracted to crabs bearing *Peltogaster* and more especially to the parasite itself. Several of these larvae may be found within the mantle cavity where they had been interpreted formerly as complemental males. This hypothesis has again been advanced recently by Reinhard in this country. Although there is not the slightest trace of a testis in these larvae, they are seen to expel their cellular content into the mantle cavity where these cells appear to grow into spermatogonids and also nurse cells. These cells are stored in the spermiducts of the adult parasite. As these cypris larvae are found only in young females, Reinhard supposes that the first batch of eggs are fertilized by heterogonic sperm while all the other batches are fertilized by homogonic sperm. Further research work will no doubt be necessary before this interpretation can be accepted as the usual procedure.

The presence of complemental males is all the more interesting since apparently the genera *Thompsonia*, *Sylon*, *Sesarmaxenos*, and *Mycetomorpha* (Fig. 76) do not possess any testes and the eggs are said to develop parthenogenetically.

Several species of *Rhizocephala* have been reported from fresh water and it seems that in this case, development within the egg reaches a more advanced stage than in salt water. In both *Sesarmaxenos* and *Ptychascus*, the larva hatches at the cypris stage. Curiously enough, this is also found to be the case in *Clistosaccus paguri* Lillj. and *Sylon hippolytes* M. Sars that live on crabs from the Polar seas. This would appear to indicate that the lower temperature of the water causes the egg to hatch only when the cypris larva is formed and seems all the more probable, since both of the fresh-water genera mentioned above occur on crabs from mountain streams, and that these, even in the tropics, are cold. Similar observations have also been made on ascothoracids, of which mention will be made later. It would be particularly interesting to obtain information on the development of the eggs in such species as *Sacculina abyssicola* Guerin-Ganivet, the host of which lives at a depth of 1,967 to 2,131 fathoms, or *Trachelosaccus hymenodorae* (Sars) occurring on a crab brought up from more than 1,639 fathoms.[1]

Sacculina gregaria Okada & Miyashita is found on *Eriocheir japonicus* de Haan and, consequently, has passed with its host from brackish water into fresh water. It is, however, unable to reproduce under

eggs and shed its own larvae. In this way, the life cycles of both the parasite and the host are synchronized and conditions for infesting new hosts are assured in a particularly favorable manner.

Rhizocephala do not appear to show a marked specificity for their hosts as the same species is frequently found on different hosts. These may either belong to the same genus or to the same family or even to an entirely different group altogether. The

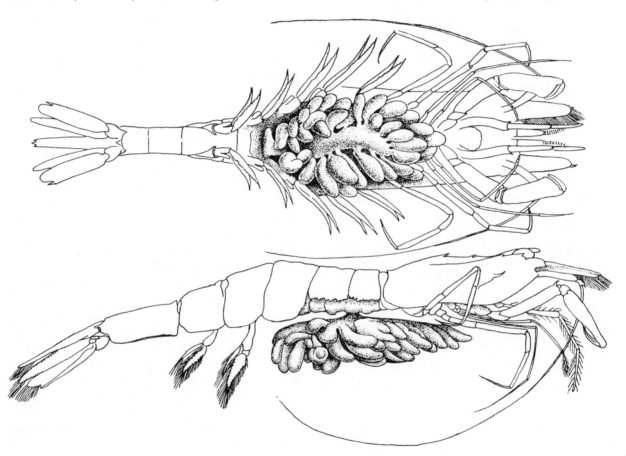

FIG. 76. *Mycetomorpha vancouverensis* Potts on *Crangon communis* Rathb. (Potts).

these conditions; this is only possible when the crab, its host, returns to brackish water to incubate its

[1] The fauna of the Polar seas and of the abysses contain several species in common. It is also known that these waters form an identical biotope since the colder, heavier waters of great depths are not mixed with the warmer, lighter waters (LeDanois). The gigantic size of the Polar isopods is duplicated by the size of those from the abysses. It is probable that the temperature factor is the principal cause of this increase in size in the same way as in land-living animals; the largest specimens of a given species are those that occur in the highest latitudes.

most primitive, that is the admittedly most ancient species of decapods, phylogenetically, such as the peneids represented by the genera *Palinura* and *Astacura* that occurred already in Jurassic times, are entirely free from parasites. On the other hand, the results of many years of research work have lead Perez to consider the *Rhizocephala* as having evolved with their hosts. If this should be the case, we should have to assume that these parasites only appeared at the end of the Mesozoic period, i.e., when their present hosts also originated.

Ascothoracids are very closely related to the cirripeds although some authors treat them as a separate class (Krueger). They are almost exclusively parasitic on echinoderms. Most of the least modified species, such as belong to the genus *Synagoga* Okada, occur on the surface of crinoids, while the species of the genus *Myriacladus* Yoshii are found within the body cavity of starfishes and are extremely modified.

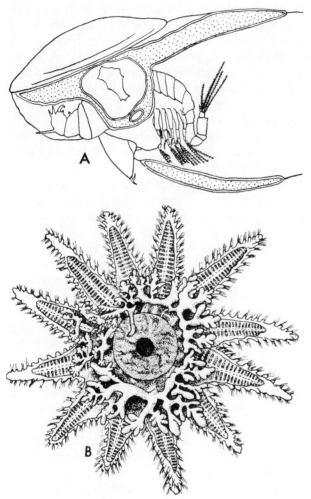

FIG. 77. A. *Myriacladus okadai* Okada male. B. *Dendrogaster murmanensis* Kluge female specimens in an asterid (Korschelt).

The sexes are separate and a marked sexual dimorphism may also occur together with dwarf males that are probably neotenic larvae. The first larval stages are similar to those of all the cirripeds, yet no complete life cycle has been worked out so far. In two species recorded from the Polar seas, namely *Ulophysema, ørsundense* (Brat.) and *Dendrogaster asteri*

cola Knip., development within the egg is prolonged so that the larva upon hatching is a cypris.

In the ectoparasitic genus *Synagoga* that is least modified, the adult female retains the general structure of the cypris while in the entoparasitic forms, and especially in *Myriacladus*, the female undergoes complete metamorphosis. It loses its appendages, legs, antennae, etc., and the gut develops in an extraordinary manner, branching out into the body cavity of the starfish (Fig. 77). Nothing is known of the manner in which the female enters the starfish nor of the way in which metamorphosis occurs. The males of this species, although equally endoparasitic, fail to grow and retain the characters of the larval cypris; they should, consequently, be considered as neotenic.

REFERENCES

DAY, J. H. 1939. A new cirripede parasite, *Rhizolepas annelidicola* nov. gen. et sp. *Proc. Linn. Soc.*, London, 151:64–79, 6 figs.

DELAGE, Y. 1884. Evolution de la Sacculine (*Sacculina carcini* Thomps.) crustacé endoparasite de l'ordre nouveau des Kentrogonides. *Arch. Zool. Exp.*, (2) 2:417–736, 9 pls.

FOXON, G. F. H. 1940. Notes on the life history of *Sacculina carcini* Thompson. *J. Mar. Biol. Assn.*, 24:253–64.

JOHNSTONE, J. 1927. *Anelasma squalicola* (Lovén), its general morphology. *Proc. Trans. Liverpool Biol. Soc.*, 41: 29–91, 8 figs., 1 pl.

KRUEGER, P. 1940. Cirripedia. *Bronn's Kl. Ord. Tier.*, 5 (3), 560 pp., 391 figs.

PEREZ, CH. 1931. Les rhizocéphales parasites des Pagures. *Verhand. Schweiz. Naturf. Gesell.* 112:261–76, 4 figs.

REINHARD, E. G. 1942. The endoparasitic development of *Peltogaster paguri*. *J. Morph.*, 70:69–79, 6 figs.

———. 1942a. The reproductive role of the complemental males of Peltogaster. *Ibid.*, 70:389–402, 8 figs.

SMITH, G. 1906. Rhizocephala. *Fauna et Flora Neapl.*, vol. 29, 122 pp., 24 figs., 8 pls.

ISOPODA

Parasitic isopods constitute one of the most interesting groups of parasites known, since, apart from a purely morphological transformation due to parasitism, the epicarids provide definite evidence that the sexes are determined epigamically and that their life cycle comprises two hosts.

Gnathids and cymothoids are only temporary parasites, the former during their larval stages and the latter in the adult stage only, whereas entoniscids are parasitic in both the larval and adult stages

Adult gnathids are usually found in plankton or in

mud dredged from the bottom. They possess neither a mouth nor a gut and never ingest any food when adult. The larvae, on the other hand, are temporary parasites on fishes, feeding exclusively on blood. There exist such morphological differences between the larva, the male, and the female, that each was formerly referred to a distinct genus, namely *Pranzia*, *Anceus*, and *Gnathia* (Fig. 78).

Pranzia larvae fix themselves to the fins of a fish and gorge themselves with blood to such an extent that the last three thoracic segments are completely obscured and reappear only after the meal is digested. After each meal the larva molts and thus goes through three distinct larval phases. After the third molt, it becomes adult. The mouth parts of both the male and the female are completely atrophied, but

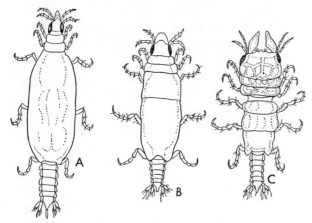

FIG. 78. *Gnathia maxillaris* Sars. A. Larva. B. Adult female. C. Adult male (Sars).

the male retains a pair of powerful mandibles, with which it burrows into the mud. These small burrows are located so that they are uncovered at low tide, and each contains both a male and a female. Nourishment accumulated by the larval instars is sufficient for the female to produce her eggs and to incubate them until they hatch, after which the female dies.

Cymothoids are ectoparasitic on fishes and occasionally also on cephalopods, and attach themselves either to the surface of the gills or to the interior of the mouth. No sedentary forms are known except perhaps the species belonging to the genus *Ichthyoxenos* that occur within cavities in the host's skin, and each cavity always contains both a male and a female. Cymothoids are frequently found free in plankton and do not appear to be attracted by

any particular host, since the same species is frequently found on very different species of hosts.

Sexual dimorphism also appears to occur here to a certain extent in that the male more closely resembles the last larval stage than it does the female (*Cerathoa*) and that the latter, in genera such as *Agarna*, *Livoneca*, and *Irona*, is distinctly asymmetrical. For these reasons, it is not possible to attribute these differences to a parasitic mode of living since both the male and the female are temporary parasites. Moreover, protandrous hermaphrodites are also found among the cymothoid genera *Cymothoa*, *Nerocila*, *Anilocra*, and *Ichthyoxenos* in which the functional male possesses a rudimentary ovary that develops normally after the final molt, and the male thus becomes a female.

Several of the above characteristics are also found in entoniscids although in a somewhat more pronounced fashion.

The life cycle of all epicarids involves two hosts although in a few cases the first host may not be necessary since the larva that emerges from the egg appears at a more advanced stage of development (*Entoniscoides okadai* Miyashita). The larva that hatches normally is known as an *epicaridium* and resembles a very small isopod whose mouth parts are adapted to piercing and sucking. Moreover, these larvae possess clawlike appendages with which they attach themselves to the surface of free-swimming copepods. Here they undergo six successive molts while feeding on the copepod and pass through two distinct larval stages known as the *microniscus* and the *cryptoniscus* stages that were formerly considered as being two different types of parasites (Fig. 79). The cryptoniscid larva abandons the copepod and goes in search of a decapod crustacean living on the bottom of the sea. At this stage, variations in the life history occur according to whether the larvae belong to the bopyrines or to the cryptoniscines (the two suborders of the entoniscids) (Fig. 80).

In the first case, the larva enters either the branchial chamber or the brood pouch of its host and molts. After ecdysis, the larva is found to have lost most of its pleopods and to have retained only the pereiopods: it is now known as a *bopyridium*. Up to this stage of the life cycle, there has been no trace of any differentiation into either the male or the female sex. Both field observations and experimental research show that the first bopyridium larva to at-

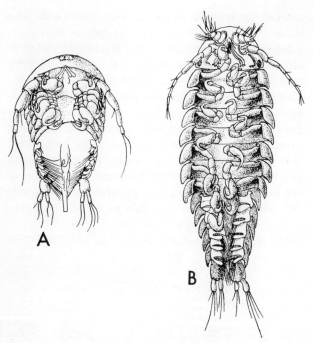

FIG. 79. A. *Cepon elegans* G. & B. microniscus larva. B. *Portunion kossmanni* G. & B. cryptoniscus larva (Giard & Bonnier).

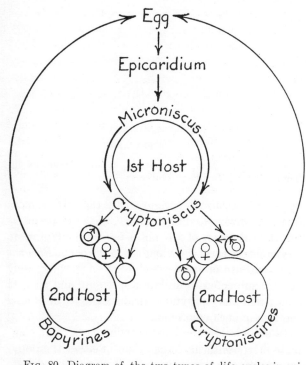

FIG. 80. Diagram of the two types of life cycles in epicarids.

tach itself onto a crab always, and invariably, becomes a female and that the successive larvae, either attached to the same host or to the growing female of their species, all become males.

Should several bopyrid larvae simultaneously enter the branchial chamber of an uninfested crab, they will all become females, but only one of these will develop normally into a mature specimen, the others disappearing without being able to mature. Several males, however, may be present together with a single female, yet here also, only one will remain permanently attached to the female (Figs. 81, 82).

Once permanently attached, the female continues its metamorphosis and molts once more. The body is now much larger, the pleopods are flattened and function as respiratory organs. The whole organization remains that of an isopod but with extraordinarily developed oostegites that form a huge brood pouch. Since the males remain at the bopyrid stage, they should be considered as neotenic larvae, and this accounts also for the extreme sexual dimorphism.

In a series of very ingenious experiments, Reverberi has been able to prove that if a young, presumptive male be removed from the female and placed into the branchial chamber of an uninfested crab, it will grow into a female; the testes will regress and be replaced by ovaries. This has quite recently been confirmed by Reinhard. By rearing two females, *in vivo*, without their host, Reverberi has successfully transformed the smaller one into a male with completely formed testes. This proves that in this case sex is determined epigamically and that the larvae are still ambipotent (Fig. 83).

The life history of the second suborder, the cryptoniscines, is completely different from the cryptoniscus larval stage on. The larvae also enter the branchial chamber or the brood pouch of crabs and all develop in the same manner. They become protandrous hermaphrodites of a delayed type since the males are morphologically distinct from the females. The gravid females are subject to a true degenerative process which is not due to parasitism, but to an excessive production of eggs. Further research may show that in this case also the presence of adult females prevents other males from transforming into females.

The morphological changes that the females of both of these suborders undergo are even more

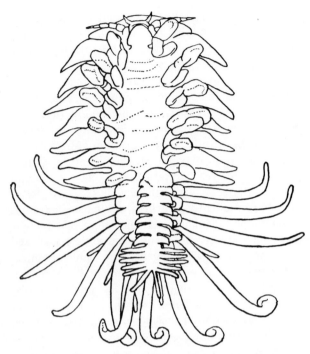

FIG. 81. *Ione thoracica* Montagu male and female (Reverberi & Pitotti).

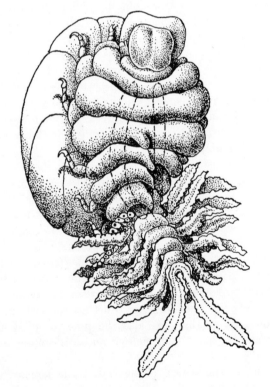

FIG. 82. *Cepon elegans* G. & B. Gravid female with dwarf male (Giard & Bonnier).

marked in cryptoniscines than in bopyrines. The latter contain the least modified species since it is still possible to recognize the typical isopod anatomy, although the number of pereiopods may be very much reduced as in *Branchiophryxus* Caull., for instance. In the genus *Phryxus* Rathke, all the appendages, except one, have disappeared from one side only of the parasite and, consequently, the latter has become completely asymmetrical. It is found that this type of asymmetry is correlative with the location of the parasite within the branchial chamber of the host. The atrophy of the appendages on one side only would indicate that this part had been sub-

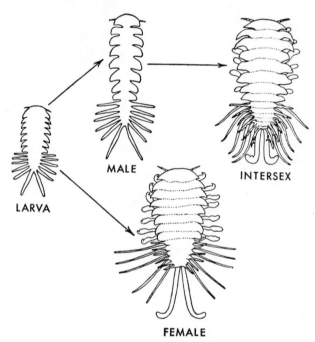

FIG. 83. *Ione thoracica* Montagu, showing larval evolution into male, female, and intersex.

jected to unilateral pressure (Fig. 84). It is more likely, however, that asymmetry, in these species, is primary in origin and is not a parasitic adaptation. Asymmetrical species belonging to the genus *Phryxus* occur within the brood pouch of shrimps where they are not subjected to unilateral pressure and also, as mentioned above, asymmetrical species occur among the free-living cymothoids.

In entoniscids, the female undergoes a more complete morphological change than in either the bopyrids or the dajids (Fig. 85). The pereiopods are completely atrophied whereas the pleopods become excessively developed. Their surface becomes corrugated and they contain numerous blood lacunae; consequently, there is no doubt as to their respiratory function. The development of the oostegites to form the brood pouch is also peculiar, since the anterior pair grows out into a sort of hood around the head of the female. At first attached within the branchial chamber of the crab, the fertilized female takes advantage of its host's molting to push in the walls of the branchial chamber into the body cavity of the crab. The female finally lies within the host's body cavity enclosed in a very fine chitinous membrane that is completely closed from the branchial cavity. A secondary opening appears later when the epicaridian larvae are expelled from the brood pouch

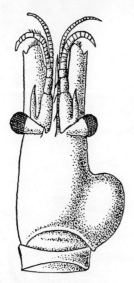

FIG. 84. *Bopyroides hippolytes* Krøy. in the right branchial chamber of its host (Sars).

(Drach). The position of the parasite is somewhat similar to that of certain parasitic snails that have become, secondarily, endoparasites (see page 28). In *Pinnotherion vermiforme* G. & B. that lives in the oyster crab, the posterior end of the parasite, containing the ovary, lies in the abdomen of the host. The males are usually found among the pleopods of the female. It is probable that the males described as occurring in the body cavity of *Pinnotheres* parasitized by *Pinnotherion* had accidentally broken in, since in this host the teguments remain soft during the whole life of the crab.

In cryptoniscine females, the whole body undergoes a complete anatomical degradation that leaves them a bulky sac, distended by an enormous number of eggs. No sooner is the female attached to its

host than it gorges itself and accumulates food reserves in its hepatic diverticula. At this stage, the female still resembles an isopod, but when the hepatic diverticula are completely filled with nourishment and the first eggs appear in the brood pouch, most of the female's internal organs begin to degenerate. Both the mouth and the gut become atrophied, the nervous system disappears, and the entire body becomes progressively distended by the ever increasing mass of eggs, and it loses all semblance of a crustacean. All trace of segmentation disappears although the original position of the segments may sometimes be found on the surface of the body. All that remains of the female isopod is a living shell, distended with eggs, that pulsates regularly. The eggs are liberated by splitting of the body wall, and the female dies (Fig. 86).

It seems that each genus of entoniscids is found on a particular host or group of hosts that appear to be characteristic for the parasites. For instance, *Cabirops*, *Gonomoniscus*, and *Ancyroniscus* are found only on isopods; *Cryptoniscus* on ostracods; *Liriopsis* and *Danalia* on *Rhizocephala* which are parasitic on decapods. Moreover, *Gonomoniscus* occurs on the cryptoniscid genus *Podascon* that is parasitic on an amphipod. In *Ancyroniscus* the anterior extremity of the female emerges inside the brood pouch of its host. The female feeds exclusively on the host's eggs and consequently cannot survive on males. It would be interesting to discover whether the larval forms of this parasite are attracted to female hosts only and if they die when attached to males.

Several authors of the French school who have worked on parasitic isopods have assumed that the relationships between epicarids and their host are very intimate. Giard has, somewhat dogmatically, decreed that any epicarid discovered on a host that has not been recorded previously as harboring these parasites must *ipso facto* belong to a new species. Such a view of host specificity is, of course, much too extreme, and as long as no experimental research work has been done in this field, no definite conclusions are possible. In areas where parasitic copepods are fairly abundant, it seems that such a rigid host specificity does not exist. For instance, *Phryxus abdominalis* Krøy. has been recovered from no less than twenty different species of shrimps belonging to two genera, *Pandalus* and *Spirontocaris*; *Bopyroides hippolytes* Krøy. from eleven species and *Argeia pugettensis*

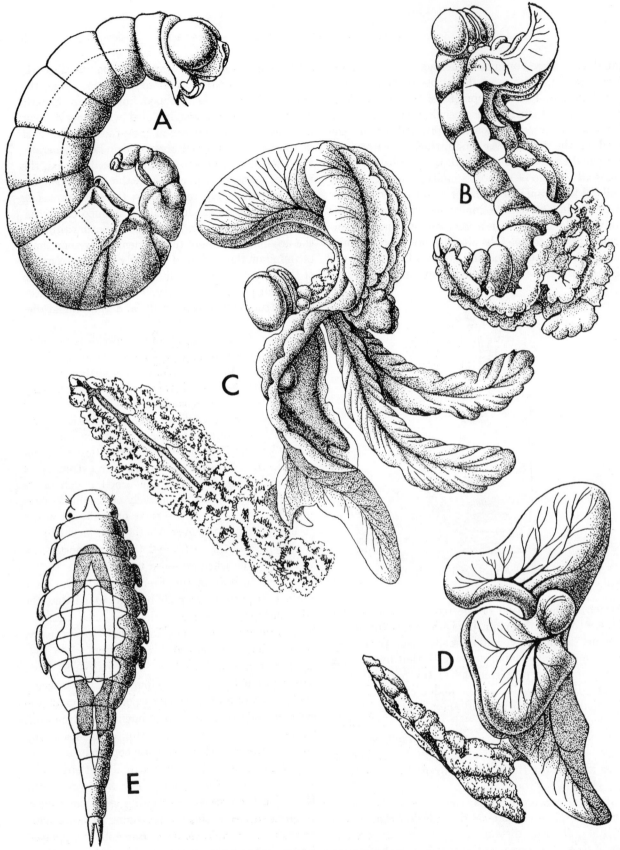

Fig. 85 (*see legend on opposite page*).

Dana from fifteen species belonging to the genera *Crago* and *Neocrangon* (Richardson).

Hemioniscus balani Bucholz is usually found off the coast of France on *Balanus balanoides* L. In the Gironde estuary, it also occurs on *Balanus improvisus* Darw. However off the coast of Roscoff, *Hemioniscus balani* is found only on *Chthamalus stellatus* (Poli), a host that also occurs in the Gironde estuary, but there it is never parasitized by this species (Perez). There is no doubt that a larger number of observations will show that host specificity, while remaining marked, never reaches the point where every species of parasite occurs on a distinct host. Some hosts may exert a stronger attraction than others on the

of the parasites and the frequency of the intermediate host. Reverberi and Pitotti have been able to establish the interesting fact that the larvae of *Ione thoracica* Montagu are found attached to *Acartia clausi*, a species of copepod that occurs at certain seasons in very large numbers in the Gulf of Naples. This species is completely absent from the beginning of December to March, a period during which egg laying has also ceased in the parasites.

There appears to be only a single entoniscid reported so far from fresh water. This is *Entoniella fluviatilis* Miyashita that occurs on *Eriocheir sinensis* M. Ed., a crab capable of living in either salt water or fresh water. The complete life history of the para-

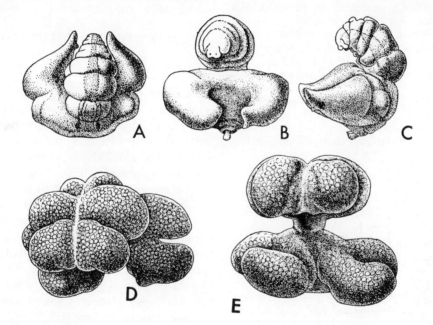

FIG. 86. *Ancyroniscus bonnieri* C. & M. A–C. Adult female. D–E. Gravid female (Caullery & Mesnil).

larval forms. Being attached to planktonic organisms, these are necessarily subordinated to the effects of currents and tides and are thus spread over wide areas. Giard and Bonnier carried out their research work off Wimereux in the English Channel where the tides and currents are more regular than off Roscoff or other Atlantic shores. It is also very probable that there exists a correlation between the life cycle

FIG. 85. *Portunion maenadis* Giard. A–D. Development of a young female into a gravid female, showing the extraordinary development of the oostegites and transformation of the pleopods into respiratory organs. E. Greatly enlarged male (Giard & Bonnier).

site is unknown, as is also the first host. It is obvious that this entoniscid has been carried into fresh water from the sea and that it has been able to adapt itself to its new environment without difficulty.

Apart from the degenerative process that occurs in the females of cryptoniscines, and which should not be considered as being adaptive to parasitism, the other entoniscids all show modifications that are correlative with egg production. Yet these occur also in cymothoids which are not permanent parasites, and cannot be considered as showing adaptations to parasitism. Consequently, we find here a group of parasites that is very much modified morphologically as a result of an enormous egg production due to feeding on the host's blood, but that furnish no evidence of any type of parasitic adaptation.

REFERENCES

ATKINS, D., 1933. *Pinnotherion vermiforme* Giard and Bonnier, an Entoniscid infecting *Pinnotheres pisum*. *Proc. Zool. Soc. London*, 319–63, 14 figs., 6 pls.

DRACH, P. 1941. Nouvelle conception sur les rapports éthologiques des Entonisciens et de leurs hôtes. Critique de la théorie classique ectoparasitaire. *C. R. Acad. Sc.*, 213:80–82.

GIARD, A., & BONNIER, J. 1887. Contributions à l'étude des Bopyriens. *Trav. Inst. Zool. Lille*, 5, 252 pp., 10 pls.
———. 1893. Contributions à l'étude des Epicarides. *Bull. Sc. France et Belgique*, 25:415–93, pls. 5–13.

MONOD, TH. 1933. Tanaidacea et Isopoda. *Mem. Inst. Egypt.*, 21:161–264, 80 figs.

PEREZ, CH. 1924. Sur la specificite du parasitism des *Hemioniscus*. *Bull. Soc. Zool. France*, 48:375–76.

REINHARD, E. G. 1949. Experiments on the determination and differentiation of sex in the bopyrid *Stegophryxus hyptius* Thompson. *Biol. Bull.*, 96:17–31, 4 figs.

REVERBERI, G., & PITOTTI, M. 1942. Il ciclo biologico e la determinazione fenotipica del sesso di *Ione thoracica* Montagu. Bopiride parassita di *Callianassa laticauda* Otto. *Pubb. Staz. Zool. Napoli*, 19:111–84, 27 figs.

RICHARDSON, H. 1905. A monograph on isopods of North America. *U. S. Nat. Mus. Bull.*, vol. 54, 727 pp., 740 figs.

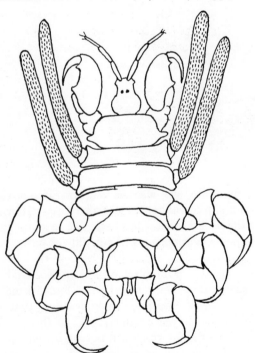

FIG. 87. *Cyamus mysticeti* Lutken (Lutken).

AMPHIPODA

Amphipods are frequently found associating with marine invertebrates without any signs of parasitism. Even species such as *Phronima sedentaria* Forsk., which burrow into colonies of tunicates, are probably only predators.

The so-called whale lice, belonging to the genus *Cyamus* (Fig. 87), occur only on whales and are found to burrow into the epidermis of their host. The body is flattened dorsoventrally, their legs are provided with claws, and their antennae are reduced. Nothing is known of the biology of these forms that appear to show definite signs of being adapted to an ectoparasitic mode of life.

REFERENCES

LUTKEN, C. F. 1873. Bidrag til Kundskab om Asterne af Slaegten *Cyamus* Latr. elle Hvallusene. *K. Dansk Vidensk. Selsk.* (5), 10:231–84, 4 pls.

SUMMARY OF PARASITIC ADAPTATIONS AMONG CRUSTACEANS

From the data reviewed above, it is clear that crustaceans are extremely plastic organisms, susceptible to considerable morphological changes as to their environment and, consequently, what might be regarded as parasitic adaptations cannot always be distinguished from changes that constitute adaptations to environment only.

All the parasitic forms are blood feeders and such a highly nourishing diet has greatly influenced their metabolism, especially that of the females, so that egg production is much greater than in the free-living forms. Consequently, in species that incubate their eggs in special brood pouches, the latter become hypertrophied and distort the whole body of the female (*Isopoda*). Moreover, since these parasites have become permanent and sedentary, they lose most of their locomotory appendages; those remaining are transformed into gills. Yet all these modifications are consequential to parasitism and are not parasitic adaptations.

Then again, the whole life history of parasitic cirripeds indicates that the larval stages have become adapted to parasitism in a manner so teleological that it is difficult, almost impossible, to trace their origin to free-living forms (kentrogon). This is also true for the hermaphroditic adult whose whole existence is intimately adapted to that of its host.

Copepods appear to be intermediate between these two extremes and illustrate almost every phase of both larval and adult adaptations to parasitism on the one side, and extreme bodily transformations as a consequence of parasitism on the other.

From a purely biological standpoint, it is interesting to stress the fact that lability of sex in crustaceans appears to be much more frequent than was formerly supposed, and that sex determination is influenced not only in the parasites but also in the crustacean hosts that harbor the latter. Sex reversal, and consequently the appearance of intersexes in crustaceans harboring parasites, is one of the most interesting aspects of the effects of parasites on their hosts and we will deal with it more fully in a later chapter.

ACARINA

The recent mites and ticks cannot be referred to a common origin in spite of their possessing a fundamental type of anatomy and the six suborders accepted by most authorities cannot be directly related to one another. All the members of these natural subdivisions are extremely widespread and occur in almost every biotope. Curiously enough, most of the species at some stage of their life cycle can be associated with other organisms to which they may attach themselves temporarily. It is therefore natural that many species have become sedentary on their hosts and have evolved into permanent parasites. Only *Notostigmata* and *Holothyroidea* have failed to give rise to parasitic forms as is also the case for Oribatids, included in the *Sarcoptiformes* of which all the other members are parasites. In most cases, the parasites occur on the surface of their hosts but they may also penetrate into the air passages and into the lungs or into the epidermis. *Tetrapodili* occur exclusively in the parenchyma of plants.

The extreme variety of both biological and anatomical types observed in the parasitic species can thus be explained, since distinct groups have, independently, become adapted to similar modes of life. Consequently the result will be a mixture of convergent evolution and original anatomical structure that together give rise to more or less highly specialized organisms (Figs. 88–100).

The life histories of most of the parasitic acari are insufficiently known yet. In cases where definite information is available there apparently exists a great variability both in the nature and the number of larval stages. Incidentally, the latter are in no way related to the mode of life nor can they be considered as eventual adaptations to parasitism.

The primitive type of life cycle contains four larval stages between the egg and the adult. From the egg, there emerges an hexapod larva which passes successively through three nymphal stages, the proto-, deuto-, and the tritonymph. From the last there emerges an adult. Each stage is separated from the preceding one by one or more molts. In contrast to the larval stage, both the nymph and the adult are octopod.

The complete life history as outlined above is rarely found; it occurs, however, in *Ornithodorus* Koch (I). [The Roman numerals correspond to the diagram (Fig. 101) which summarizes the seven different types of life histories.] In most other Mesostigmatata, the tritonymphal stage is lost (*Argas* Latr.) (II). In *Liponyssus* Kolen. and *Ixodes* Latr. both the deuto- and tritonymphal stages have disappeared so that the adult emerges from the protonymph (III). In entonyssines on the other hand, the proto- and tritonymphal stages are lacking, and consequently the larva passes directly to the deutonymphal stage (IV). In spinturnicids, a hexapod larval stage is missing, as is also the tritonymphal stage, so that a protonymph emerges directly from the egg and the species may be considered as being viviparous (V). Finally, in rhinonyssines and raillietids there no longer appear to be any nymphal stages and consequently the hexapod larva becomes, directly after molting, an octopod adult (VI). An exceptionally abbreviated life cycle is that of podapolipodids in which the female only is parasitic on insects, yet both sexes are neotenic and, consequently, the adult is hexapod (VII).

All parasitic acari obtain their food in a more or less liquid form, many of the species feeding either on blood or lymph. Bird parasites of the genus *Harpyrhynchus* and no doubt also of other related genera that live in feather shafts and penetrate into the follicles, feed on fat. This is also the case for the larvae and nymphs of *Myobia* from rodents and for all the stages of the genus *Demodex* that occurs in the hair follicles of mammals. No general rule can be found as to the mode of feeding and the nature of the food. Nor does the location either on the surface or within the lungs or air passages of the host influence the method of feeding.

In ticks, a meal of blood always precedes a molt between two successive instars and also egg deposition in the female. Consequently, the life cycle demands at least three successive hosts that may quite well belong to the same species of animal. These

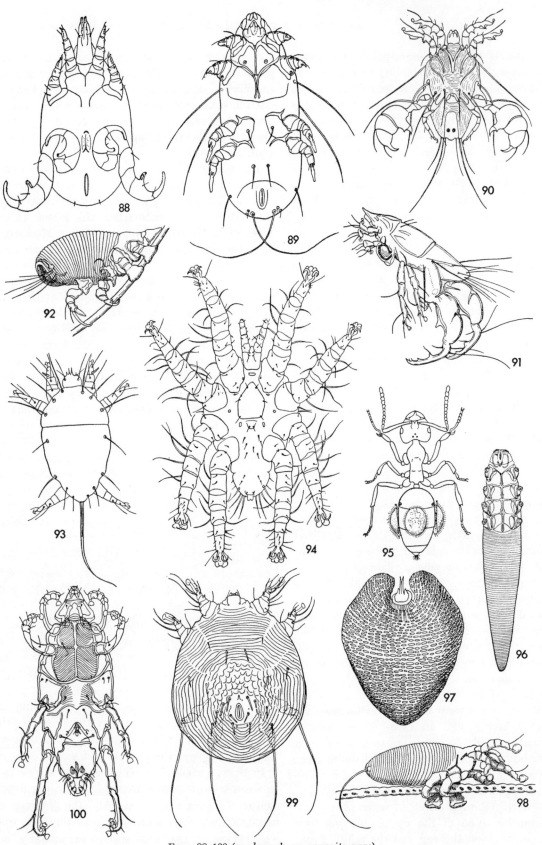

FIGS. 88–100 (*see legends on opposite page*).

hosts will harbor respectively the larva, nymph, and adult (*Amblyomma, Dermacentor, Rhipicephalus*). In *Boophilus*, none of the larval stages ever abandon the first host from the moment the larva has become

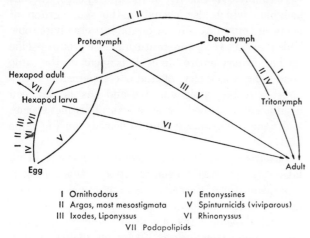

I   Ornithodorus   IV Entonyssines
II Argas, most mesostigmata   V   Spinturnicids (viviparous)
III Ixodes, Liponyssus   VI Rhinonyssus
            VII Podapolipids

FIG. 101. Diagram of the different types of life cycles of parasitic mites.

attached to the moment the female drops off to lay its eggs.

Argasids, on the other hand, are always temporary parasites and abandon their host after each meal.

FIG. 88. *Ewingia cenobitae* Pearse from the gills of a crab, showing the strongly modified third and fourth legs.

FIG. 89. *Laminosioptes cysticola* (Vizioli), a subcutaneous parasite of game birds with much reduced legs (Hirst).

FIG. 90. *Analges chelopus* (Herm.), a bird parasite with a very modified third pair of legs (Berlese).

FIG. 91. *Atopomelus locusta* Trouess. with fourth pair of legs transformed for clinging to its host (Trouessart).

FIG. 92. *Alabidocarpus megalonyx* (Trouess.) with the first two pairs of legs transformed for clinging to the hairs of its host (Berlese).

FIG. 93. *Locustacarus trachealis* Ewing from the tracheae of grasshoppers, showing the reduction in length of the legs (Ewing).

FIG. 94. *Spinturnix araguensis* Vitzth., showing the peculiar hooks with which it attaches itself to the wing membrane of bats (Vitzthum).

FIG. 95. *Trichocyllibia comata* (Leonardi) attached in a symmetrical manner upon the abdomen of an ant (Janet).

FIG. 96. *Demodex folliculorum* Owen with much reduced legs and vermiform body (Hirst).

FIG. 97. *Podapolipus berlesei* Lahille. Dorsal view showing the almost complete reduction of the legs (Lahille).

FIG. 98. *Myocoptes tenax* Michael with third and fourth pairs of legs transformed for attachment to hairs (Berlese).

FIG. 99. *Notoedres cati* (Hering), an itch mite from cats. Dorsal view of a female, showing sculpturing of the cuticle (Hirst).

FIG. 100. *Chirodiscoides caviae* Hirst, showing the striations of the cuticle on the ventral surface of the thorax (Hirst).

All ticks appear to have in common an indifference in choice of host which may be either a mammal, bird, or reptile. *Ixodes ricinus* (L.), for instance, occurs in the adult stage both on birds and mammals, although its larvae and nymphs are found on lizards, passerine birds, rodents, insectivores, and even on bats.

Consequently, such blood-feeding parasites as these are apt to play an important role in the transmission of various microorganisms, passing, as they do, from one host onto another and thus assuring the rapid spread of a disease to animals, usually those that live in herds, for example.

In lymph feeders, the parasitic mite buries its mouth parts in the tissues of the host and injects the contents of its salivary glands. The resulting irritation of the host's tissues causes both lymph and serum to flow toward the site and these are absorbed by the parasite.

Parasitic mites sometimes show a remarkable adaptation to a specialized mode of attachment or to a particular habitat that is reflected in the development of their legs, although these modifications do not necessarily affect the same pair of legs in all cases.

Large clawlike legs occur in *Analges* (Fig. 90) and *Atopomelus* which are ectoparasitic on birds and mammals respectively. In the first case, it is the third pair of legs that is transformed while in the second case, it is the fourth pair that bears claws. In both *Ewingia* (Fig. 88) and *Myocoptes* (Fig. 98), the third and fourth pairs of legs are specialized and are used to attach the mite to branchial filaments in the former genus, or to hairs in the latter genus. *Alabidocarpus* (Fig. 92) from bats is attached to the hairs by highly specialized legs that resemble those of *Myocoptes*, but in this case belong to the first and second pair. In *Demodex* (Fig. 96) from mammalian hair follicles, all the legs are very short. In Tetrapodilids, from plants, the first two pairs of legs only are retained and finally in *Podapolipus berlesei* Lahille, that occurs on a South American species of locust, all the four pairs of legs are lost (Fig. 97).

Without being necessarily associated with any particular type of legs, a cuticular striation is often found on either ventral or dorsal surfaces or simultaneously on both. In *Chirodiscoides* (Fig. 100), that lives on rodents, the parasite clasps a hair and presses it with its legs against the cuticular striations on the ventral surface and these striations prevent the mite from slipping along the hair. Many species that burrow into the epidermis, such as *Acarus, Notoedres* (Fig. 99), and *Knemidokoptes*, possess such cuticular striations on both the ventral and dorsal surfaces of the body. On the dorsal surface, moreover, there exist numerous short spines and setae that help to anchor the parasite into the host's epidermis. Although not provided with cuticular striations but only with dorsal spines and setae, pterygosomids have succeeded in maintaining themselves beneath the scales of lizards, as their body is flattened dorsoventrally and it is wider than it is long.

The tarsal extremities are often modified and adapted to particular habitats as in spinturnicids, for instance. These mites are permanently attached to the patagium of bats to which they are literally hooked by their extremities, each leg bearing a double hook (Fig. 94). Incidentally, this is the only group of parasitic mites in which the species possess two distinct resting positions. When the bat extends its wings, the legs of the mite are extended laterally and when the wings are folded, the legs of the mite are also folded on the ventral surface.

All hydrachnids practice protelian parasitism and their larvae are found attached to aquatic insects or aquatic insect larvae. The adults, of course, are all free-living. Parasitic larvae are more frequent on insects or aquatic larvae of airborne insects which leave the water at a certain stage of their development. Parasitic larval mites remain attached to their host until the latter pupates. They then fall off into the water and become free-living. From this type of life cycle, one might assume that the larvae of hydrachnids must have access to air before becoming adult.

Larvae of *Trombicula autumnalis* Shaw, the so-called harvest mites or chiggers, attach themselves to a large number of different species of vertebrates, including man, where they set up an intense irritation. On the other hand, larvae of the genus *Hannemannia* appear to be specific for amphibians of tropical countries. Their presence on tree frogs causes the epidermis to proliferate, and in *H. hylodeus* (Oud.) to form a wall around the parasite. The larvae of *H. hylae* (Ewing) from the California tree frog, *Hyla arenicolor* Cope, is completely overgrown by the epidermis. In *Endotrombicula penetrans* Ewing, the larva penetrates beneath the epidermis of its host, a species of South African tree frog.

The numerous ectoparasitic species of gamasids show different types of adaptations to parasitism and to various food habits. In a general way, it appears that only the larvae and adult males are lymph feeders, whereas the females feed on blood.

Dermanyssids that live on rodents lay eggs, whereas laelapids, which also occur on the same group of hosts, are either ovoviviparous or entirely viviparous. This is also the case for spinturnicids, a group specific for bats whose entire life cycle is spent on the same host. The specificity of these ectoparasitic forms appears to be highly variable and has as yet been insufficiently studied, because several distinct species and genera may occur simultaneously on the same host.

Laelaps muris (Ljungh) occurs on rodents in all latitudes. One might even question if this species is a parasite, since it appears to be more nearly a commensal that occasionally feeds on blood.

Cavilaelaps de Fons. has been found only on wild guinea pigs; *Hemilaelaps* Ewing on snakes. *Liponyssus* Kolen. seems to be quite specific for bats, yet in tropical countries the species *L. bursa* (Berl.) is a plague in poultry yards. *Bdellonyssus bacoti* (Hirst), which occurs on rats in Egypt, Abyssinia, and the Argentine, has become a parasite of man in Australia and in the United States. *Allodermanyssus sanguineus* (Hirst), a normal parasite occurring on Egyptian rodents, is also found on man in this country (Ewing). *Ophionyssus serpentium* (Hirst) is found on snakes in Europe, India, and Brazil (imported?). Most passerine birds in Europe harbor the species *Dermanyssus hirudinis* (Herm.), but *D. queritus* Vitzth. occurs exclusively on woodpeckers.

Such an erratic type of host specificity, where the same species may occur on a great many different hosts, would indicate that possibly there exist biological species of these parasites and, in addition, that their anatomical structure is relatively simple and in no way affected by parasitism. Such conditions, as also occur in certain species of parasitic nematodes, appear to be particularly favorable to a physiological adaptation to a given host. This, of course, can only be discovered by well conducted experiments. Itch mites (*Acarus, Sarcoptes*) of man and other mammals are all morphologically identical, so much so that several authors consider them as varieties of a single species. A species from a given host, however, manifests a marked specificity toward the latter although transmission from animals to man does sometimes occur. This also appears to indicate that we are dealing with physiological adaptations that are not yet permanently established.

Having apparently become too sensitive to light and a dry atmosphere, some mites have entered into natural cavities of both insects and vertebrates. A need for oxygen excludes their adaptation to intestinal parasitism, although some species are able to pass through the intestine and come out alive, without being able to establish themselves (*Tyroglyphus farinae* L.).[2]

In insects, mites attach themselves to the inner walls of the tracheal tubes which they pierce to suck the haemolymph as in *Acarapsis*, a dangerous parasite of bees. In vertebrates, the genera *Entonyssus* and *Ophiopneumicola* occur in the wall of the lung of African and South American snakes. The parasites are viviparous and their life cycle is shortened because the larvae remain in the uterus until they have reached an advanced stage of development. *Rhinonyssus* is found attached to the mucous membrane of the nares in a large number of birds. A sarcoptid, *Cytodites nudus* Vitzth., is found in the air sacs of game birds, and sometimes migrates into the bronchi and into the bones, causing the bird to suffocate. *Cytodites banksi* (Well. & Wher.) occurs in the lungs of a California ground squirrel and causes small nodules of connective tissue to form around it. Similar nodules, although larger, are sometimes found in the lungs of monkeys harboring a gamasid mite of the genus *Pneumonyssus* Banks.

A very peculiar adaptation is found in *Halarachne* which occurs exclusively in the nasal passages of seals. The females burrow into the mucosa but both the males and the larvae remain attached to the surface of the latter. Since neither of the adult forms is able to maintain its foothold on a wet surface, transmission from one host to another can occur only through the larval forms as these can move about on a slippery surface.

It is obvious that parasitic mites have become adapted to this peculiar mode of life at different times and in different groups, and that convergence has played a large part in certain similarities as already mentioned above. Specialization has followed two directions, one along morphological lines and the

other along physiological lines. In both cases, the result has been to isolate the parasite upon its host. The different races of *Acarus siro* L. (syn. *Sarcoptes scabei* auct.) are an indication of this sort of mechanism. Morphological specialization, such as is found in spinturnicids, for instance, explains both the specificity toward the host and the much greater speciation of the parasites. In every case where parasites are isolated on their hosts by one of the above two mechanisms or by both at the same time, the entire life cycle also occurs on the host. In this case, the mites either attach their eggs to the host or become ovoviviparous and the first larval stage is parasitic. When such isolated genera are compared to related but not so isolated genera, it is found that in the

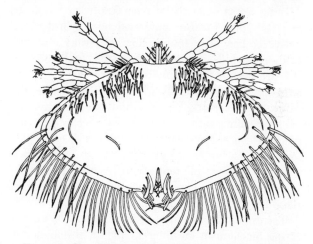

FIG. 102. *Pterygosoma aculeatum* Lawrence from beneath the scales of a lizard, showing the marked flattening of the body and numerous spines (Lawrence).

first case the number of species is always much greater than in the second.

Isolation has also been the cause for an intimate host-parasite relationship in pterygosomids, for instance. The genera and species are absolutely characteristic for lizards, living beneath the scales and attaching their eggs to the epidermis (Fig. 102). Moreover, *Pterygosoma* occurs only on agamids and gerrhosaurids, *Zonurobia* and *Scaphothrix* on zonurids. *Geckobia* is reported from both Australian and African species of geckos and *Geckobiella* from South American species. On the other hand, *Pimeliaphiloides* occurs on both European and South American lizards.

There can be no doubt whatever that pteryogsomids originated on the ancestors of the present-day lizards and, judging from their geographical distribu-

---

[2] These mites can occur in enormous numbers in hoarded foodstuffs, and during World War II we have seen a dog present signs of acute intestinal irritation after having eaten such food. Live mites together with numerous dead specimens were found in the dog's feces.

tion, must have existed at a time before lizards became segregated onto different continents, i.e., somewhere in Secondary times.

Most parasitic mites from birds occur on widely different hosts in no way related to one another. However, both the ostrich and the rhea harbor the same two species, *Paralges pachycnemis* Trouess. and *Pterolichus bicaudatus* (Gervais). These parasites appear never to have been reported from other species of birds and here again we find an isolating mechanism that has certainly arisen in early Tertiary times.

Schizocarpus Trouess. occurs on both the European and American beavers, separated for several thousands of years.

Lung mites, seem to be remarkably well isolated and they also furnish some evidence of host specificity. It has been found, however, that although ixodiorhynchids, pneumophionyssids, and entonyssids are specific for distinct hosts, exchanges of parasites can occur, especially when the hosts are kept in captivity (Keegan). This also indicates clearly that we are dealing with a segregational mechanism that has enabled the parasites to evolve along morphological lines, but this does not seem to be the case for physiological differentiation. In other words, the parasites while remaining physiologically generalized have become morphologically specialized.

Tetrapodilids also give some evidence of an isolating mechanism on different plants although it is quite possible that, in this case, some kind of physiological specialization also exists.

An interesting indication that might lead to the possible origin of certain parasitic mites is found in the fact that bats harbor two species of ixodids, *Argas boueti* Roub. & Bel. and *Ixodes verspertilionis* Koch. The former species occurs on tropical bats and the latter on European bats, yet both possess distinct characters such as are usually found in organisms living in caves, i.e., both the legs and palps are much longer than in other species. Consequently one hesitates to state whether these two ixodids were primitively cave dwellers that have subsequently passed to bats or whether the fact that they live on bats has induced the appearance of troglobiotic characters.

REFERENCES

Ewing, H. E. 1942. A second introduced rat mite becomes annoying to man. *Proc. Helm. Soc. Wash.* 9:74–75.
Keegan, H. L. 1943. Three new ophidian lung mites of the sub-family Entonyssinae Ewing. *Parasitology*, 43:128–33, 14 figs.
Lawrence, R. F. 1935–36. The Prostigmatic mites of South African Lizards. *Parasitology*, 27:1–45, 22 figs.; 28:1–39, 23 figs.
———. 1948. Studies on some parasitic mites from Canada and South Africa. *J. Parasit.*, 34:364–79, 6 figs.
Radford, C. D. 1943. Genera and species of parasitic mites (Acarina). *Parasitology*, 35:58–81.
Roubaud, E., & Colas-Belcour, J. 1933. *Argas boueti*, nouvelle espèce d'ixodide parasite des Chauves Souris au Soudan français. *Parasitology*, 26:472–77, 6 figs., pl. 28.
Turk, F. A 1947. Studies on Acari IV. A review of the lung mites of snakes. *Parasitology*, 38:17–26, 9 figs.
Vitzthum, H. 1935. Milben aus der Nasenhöhle von Vögeln. *J. f. Ornith.*, 83:563–87, 12 figs.
———. 1941. Acarina. *Bronn's Kl. Ord. Tier.*, 5(4):5B, 1011 pp., 522 figs.

INSECTA

Only very few insects are totally parasitic at all stages of their life history and these are practically restricted to the true lice and sucking lice. In *Strepsiptera*, the males alone are free-living and in the adult stage only; all the other stages are parasitic within insects. Larval fleas are mostly free-living and only the adults lead a parasitic life that is rarely sedentary. Nearly all of the other groups of insects contain species that have become adapted to parasitism either in the larval or in the adult stages.

The diptera contain by far the greatest number of different types adapted to parasitism, mostly in the larval stages, on numerous hosts ranging from invertebrates to vertebrates, including man.

Many adult flies feed on blood, either exclusively or occasionally, yet it is doubtful whether they should be considered true parasites, because their contact with the host is usually limited to a very short time. Blood-feeding habits are usually related to some particular physiological act such as egg production or egg laying. Consequently, it occurs much more frequently in females than in males.

It is obvious that blood feeders, passing from one host to another, are thus able to transmit parasites (*Protozoa* and *Filariae*) to uninfested hosts and in this way, play an important role as intermediate hosts.

Insects feeding on blood may become ecologically adapted to certain hosts and give the impression of being physiologically specialized. This has often been claimed as being the case for mosquitoes attacking man, yet these so-called specialized races have always been found capable of feeding on other hosts also, if such are present within their environment. These ecological races, such as also occur in plant-feeding nematodes, have nothing in common with physiological species that are determined genetically.

Larval flies occur in practically every type of environment that is capable of supporting life, except sea water. Those that live in decaying organic matter are more or less preadapted to becoming parasitic, although it must not be forgotten that the environment most suitable for the development of fly larvae is determined by the adult female fly, since the latter lays her eggs only in surroundings or within a host of her choice. Decomposing organic matter emits odors that attract female flies and causes them to oviposit. Consequently, it is easy to understand why fetid wounds or malodorous natural cavities very often contain fly larvae.

That any specific host attraction does not exist, in most cases, is borne out by the facts that maggots of *Sarcophaga*, *Wohlfartia*, *Cochliomyia*, and *Lucilia* occur both on man and on various other mammals, and that there is no specific location for these myiases. This explains, also, the presence occasionally of the larva of *Wohlfartia magnifica* (Schiner) in a hollow tooth. Such nonspecific locations can only be attributed to the particular odor of the site by which the female fly is attracted and induced to oviposit. All these maggots are saprophagous.

Lucilia bufonivora Moniez, however, appears to present quite a different problem since the larvae feed only on living amphibian tissue, especially on toads. The female fly deposits her eggs on the surface of the skin, usually on the back for obvious reasons, and here the eggs hatch within twenty-four hours. Hatching apparently is induced by the chemical action of the skin glands. The first stage larvae migrate along the toad's back, passing between the so-called parotis and the head from where they reach the eye. The toad blinks its eyelids and thus carries the minute larvae to the opening of the lacrymal duct. The larvae penetrate into the latter and thus reach the nasal cavity (Spence).[3] After the second larval stage is reached, the maggots feed on the living tissues and completely destroy the cartilaginous septum of the nasal cavity. The large hole produced in this way is found to be crawling with maggots that only drop off before pupating in the soil. When toads, frogs, salamanders, and newts are placed with female flies, the flies oviposit almost exclusively on toads. This indicates that the flies are attracted by the particular odor of the toads. It is clear the *L. bufonivora* has become ecologically as well as physiologically specialized on account of its larvae feeding on living tissues, while all the other species belonging to this genus feed on purulent tissues.[4]

The maggots of *Chrysomyia bezziana* (Villn.) can thrive only in wounds on living animals even though these become infected and purulent. All attempts to breed these maggots on carcasses have failed and it appears that this species, the only one so far belonging to the genus, has become an obligatory parasite of mammals.

African flies belonging to the genus *Auchmeromyia* possess larvae that are blood feeders and, consequently, are intermittent and always temporary parasites. *A. luteola* (Fabr.) is associated with man, its larvae, the so-called Congo floor maggots, living during the daytime in the sandy floor of native huts and emerging only at night to gorge themselves with blood. Should the bed be slightly raised above the ground then the maggots are unable to reach the human host. In the laboratory it is possible to rear these larvae on other hosts. In the field, on the other hand, they apparently seem to be associated with certain types of hosts only and are adapted to animals with very scant hair. *A. luteola* (Fabr.) associates with man, *A. boueti* (Roub.) with the aardvark, and *A. choerophaga* (Roub.) with wart hogs. Both of the last two species have become segregated ecologically, since wart hogs are known to use the abandoned lairs of the anteaters as dens. As the maggots occur in the sandy soil of these lairs, they have become adapted secondarily to wart hogs. It is more than likely, on the other hand, that anteaters are the original hosts from which both *A. luteola* and *A. choerophaga*, closely related to *A. boueti*, have been derived. *A. choerophaga* may also be reared experimentally on both man and pigs.

The ecology of all parasitic fly larvae is governed by the necessity for the larva, at a given stage, to have access to air. This is usually obtained by piercing the host's skin or by a secondary communication

[3] The writer has been kindly authorized by Dr. L. Taylor, Director of the Veterinary Laboratory of the Ministry of Agriculture, Weybridge (England), to make use of these very interesting observations that will shortly be published by their author, veterinarian Tom Spence, entomologist at the Laboratory.

[4] *L. sericata* (Mg.) was formerly used to clean out infected wounds since it only fed on purulent matter and never on live tissues.

between the larva and the host's tracheal system when the latter is an insect. Consequently, the respiratory adaptations of the parasitic larvae are the cause for their migration through the host's body and it is easy to understand that the reaction of the latter will differ according to whether the host is an invertebrate or a vertebrate. Most parasitic maggots are metapneustic in the first larval stage, i.e., possess a single pair of spiracular openings located at the posterior end of the larva. The subsequent larval stages are all amphipneustic and, consequently, a second pair of spiracular openings appears in the first thoracic segment. At this stage, also, there is an increase in the metabolic rate that causes the maggot to feed actively. Subsequently, it damages the host's tissues, since the perforation it makes to bring its posterior spiracular openings into contact with air, permits a secondary infection of the surrounding tissues if the host is a vertebrate.

The eggs of *Cordylobia anthropophaga* (E. Bl.), known as the Ver de Cayor, are deposited on the surface of the skin of a great number of mammals, including man. The first stage larva burrows deep into the epidermis. On reaching the second larval stage, the larva seeks air and pierces the skin with its posterior extremity. The resulting infection causes a furuncular nodule from which the third stage larva escapes before pupating in the soil.

Fly maggots belonging to the genus *Dermatobia* are also obligatory skin parasites of mammals and their life history is very similar to that of *C. anthropophaga*, but the adult female fly shows a peculiar type of behavior that is unparalleled in other species. Instead of laying its eggs upon the host, it lays them on the body of another species of fly, usually a bloodsucker. Consequently, it is the latter that carries the eggs onto the host (Fig. 103). In other words, the eggs of this parasite are deposited by proxy! For *D. hominis* (L.) this transport host is a mosquito, *Janthinsoma lutzi* Theob. or an anthomyid, *Hylemyia heydeni* (Neiv. & Gom.) and for *D. cyaniventris* (Macq.) a species of *Stomoxys*. The chances for spreading the eggs over a greater number of hosts are naturally increased since the female *Dermatobia* does not lay all of its eggs on the same host. It would be interesting to find out whether eggs are always deposited on female mosquitoes or whether they also occur on males—in other words, whether there exists a specific attraction to female mosquitoes only. It is probable that the eggs attached to transport hosts break off and fall onto the skin when the abdomen of the fly becomes distended with blood.

Botflies are provided with rudimentary mouth parts and a more or less atrophied gut and, consequently, do not ingest any nourishment. Their adult life is short, limited as it is to copulating and ovipositing, since the female already contains completely formed eggs on hatching from the pupa. The eggs are attached to hairs of mammals and the larvae become obligatory parasites. According to the greater or less extended migration through the host's body, it is possible to consider different types of life cycles.

Oestrus ovis L. and *Rhinoestrus purpureus* (Br.) possess the simplest life cycle. The female fly deposits her eggs at the entrance of the host's nostrils, on sheep in the first case and on horses in the second. The larvae, on hatching, penetrate into the nasal passages and from there, enter the frontal sinuses, to the walls of which they attach themselves. On completing their larval development, the maggots loosen their hold, fall into the nasal passages, and are expelled when the host sneezes. As is the case for all myiases, pupation occurs outside the host on the ground.

Horse botfly larvae occur in the digestive tract of equines and furnish some evidence that each species possesses a particular mode of entrance into the host. This is also in accord with the observation that the adult female fly oviposits in definite regions of the horse. The eggs are laid on the lips by *Gastrophilus haemorrhoidalis* (L.), on the cheeks by *G. inermis* (Br.), under the lower jaw in *G. nasalis* (Clark), on the legs and sides of the chest by *G. intestinalis* (de Geer) and finally, any convenient place near the horse, or on its skin by *G. pecorum* (Fabr.). Curiously enough, the nearer the eggs are laid to the horse's mouth, the smaller their number: 160 to 200 for *G. haemorrhoidalis* as compared to 2300 to 2500 for *G. pecorum* (Dinulescu).

Botfly eggs deposited on the head region hatch spontaneously and the first stage larvae make their way into the mouth of the horse. On the other hand, eggs deposited on other parts of the horse's body or on inanimate objects can hatch only under the combined influence of the horse's tongue and saliva with which they are carried into the mouth. Regardless of the way the first stage larvae reach the mouth, they all burrow into the mucosa of the tongue or the palate and tunnel their way through until they reach the pharynx. The second larval stage is now reached.

The maggots emerge from the mucosa and attach themselves on the surface, close to the epiglottidean region. They finally pass down into the intestine and each species takes up its abode in a particular region. *G. haemorrhoidalis* and *G. intestinalis* in the stomach, *G. inermis* in the rectum, *G. nasalis* in the duodenum. Another species, *G. meridionalis* (P. & Ew.), occurs in the same part of the intestine as *G. nasalis* but

whereas, *G. haemorrhoidalis*, on leaving the stomach, reattaches itself to the mucosa surrounding the anus. Here it remains for a few days before dropping off and pupating. The various species of botflies are ecologically associated with the horse and other equines. Experimental evidence shows that this association is due to the female flies being attracted by equines rather than other hosts. Horse botfly maggots

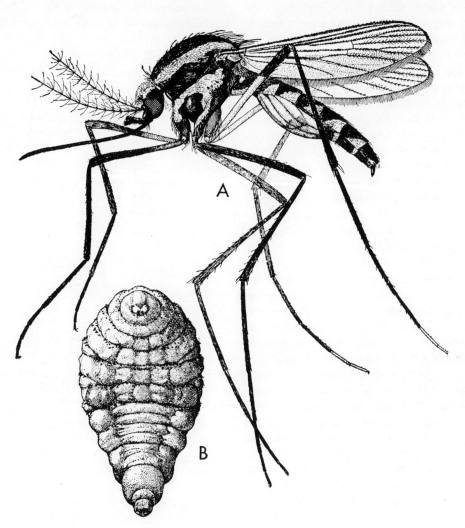

FIG. 103. *Dermatobia hominis* (L.). A. Ova deposited on the abdomen of a mosquito. B. Mature larva ready to break out through the skin of the host (Sambon).

burrows deeply into the walls of the duodenum, forming very characteristic growths, consisting mainly of connective tissue, around the parasites. *G. intestinalis* and *G. inermis* abandon their host before pupating and are evacuated with the feces,

have been successfully reared in dogs and guinea pigs.

The maggots of ox warbles, *Hypoderma bovis* (de Geer) and *H. lineatum* (de Vill.), undertake extensive migrations through the host from the point of their ingress to their final location on either side of the spine. In *H. bovis*, the female fly deposits her eggs on the hocks of the hind legs. The larvae hatch spontaneously and burrow into the skin until they reach the loose connective tissue surrounding the ischiatic nerve, which they follow up as far as the sacral region, from where they pass into the subcutaneous connective tissue. At this stage the larva has increased in size and its postabdominal spiracles open on the surface so that the second stage larva pierces the skin to gain access to the surface. Here also an abscess forms subsequently, and the full-grown larva emerges from the opening and pupates in the ground (Gebaur). Although the life history of *H. lineatum* is not yet known in all its details, it appears that the larvae also bore into the skin and reappear several months later in the pharyngeal region from where they pass down toward the diaphragmatic end of the esophagus. Leaving the latter, they are said to pass outside the pleura and into the intercostal spaces from where they reach the subcutaneous tissue of the dorsal region (Warburton).

Larval migrations are also known to occur in maggots that parasitize invertebrates. This is particularly well demonstrated by the larva of the cluster fly, *Pollenia rudis* Fabr., which develops in a common earthworm *Allolobophora chlorotica* Sav. (Keilin). The female of this fly deposits its eggs in the soil and the first stage larvae soon hatch. The tiny maggots penetrate into the male sexual openings of the earthworm and enter either the seminal vesicles or the coelomic cavity in a region comprising the ninth to twelfth segments. The larva remains motionless for at least eight months and is gradually surrounded by a cyst formed by phagocytic activity of the host's blood. If several larvae penetrate simultaneously, they are all surrounded by phagocytes and all except one are destroyed. On approaching the end of the first larval instar, the maggot awakens from its torpor and breaks through the surrounding tissues, migrating toward the anterior end of the earthworm. It advances with its posterior end directed forward until it reaches the prostomial region; breaking through the body wall, the larva extrudes its spiracular openings and immediately starts to feed actively on the surrounding tissues. As the larva increases in size, the tissues of the host that enclose it gradually disintegrate, exposing the maggot. The latter continues to feed on the earthworm and finally devours the whole posterior extremity before penetrating into the soil and pupating (Fig. 104). It is interesting to note that the third stage larva has become entirely saprophagous, feeding on partly de-

stroyed and decomposed host tissue, and that it is possible to maintain such larvae entirely on decomposed fragments of earthworms.

A somewhat similar type of life history occurs in *Melinda cognata* Meigen, a calliphorine fly that deposits its eggs in snails, *Helicella virgata* Da Costa, where the maggots feed on the living tissues and finally devour the dead and decomposed snail.

The entomobius larvae of tachinids gain access to the body cavity of their hosts in different ways.

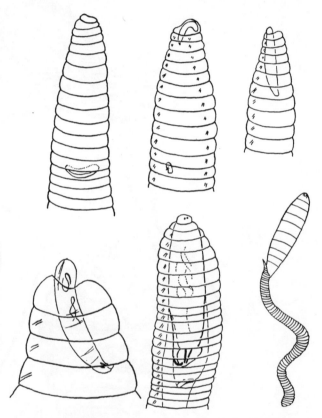

FIG. 104. Various stages of the larval development of *Pollenia rudis* Fabr. in an earthworm (Keilin).

The eggs may be directly inoculated through the skin by the female fly (*Compsilura concinnata* Meig., *Cermomyia survicauda* Fall., *Conops flavipes* L., etc.) (Fig. 105) or be deposited on the surface of the body, the first larva penetrating into the host through the egg shell (*Tachina larvarum* L., *Meigenia floralis* Meig., *Sarcophaga acridiorum* Weyenb., etc.). In the third case, the eggs are deposited by the adult female upon leaves on which the host feeds. The larvae thus hatch within the host's gut and penetrate into the body cavity (*Frontina lacta* Meig., etc.). During their initial larval stages, all these maggots feed on the host's haemolymph. Conopids that are parasitic in *Hymenoptera* establish a communication between their spiracular openings and a large trachea of the host, whereas, in all the other cases, the larva pierces the host's skin and establishes a secondary opening through which it thrusts its spiracular openings. At

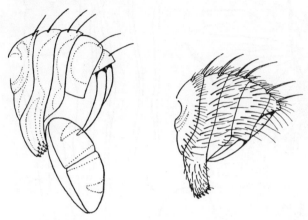

Fig. 105. *Neocelatoria ferox* Walt., a tachinid fly with an oviscapt capable of piercing the integument of other insects (Walton).

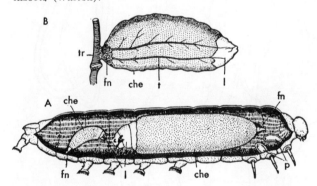

Fig. 106. Parasitic dipterous larvae showing mode of attachment and the chitinous sheath secreted around the parasite by the host. A. *Panzeria rudis* Fall. in the body cavity of a caterpillar. B. Larva of *Hyria tibialis* (L.), showing mode of attachment of host's trachea. che.—chitinous envelope. fn.—respiratory funnel. l.—larva. p.—undeveloped larvae. t.—tracheae of parasite. tr.—trachea of host (Prell; Pantel in Keilin).

the same time, the tissues of the host react to the presence of the larva and form around the latter a very thin chitinous envelope that is attached to the respiratory opening by a distinct funnel-shaped portion. The larvae feed only on haemolymph during the first larval instars but later on they become sarcophagous and destroy their host (Fig. 106).

Cryptochaetum striatum Thorpe presents an interesting adaptation to larval parasitism. This species of fly deposits its eggs in half-grown scale insects belonging to the species *Aspidoproctus maximus*. The first stage larva is devoid of a mouth, tracheae, or spiracles but is provided with a pair of long caudal processes that contain blood. The second stage larva has both a mouth and tracheae, the latter penetrating into the caudal processes which have grown to be about five times as long as the body of the larva (Fig. 107). In the third stage larva, these processes increase to at least ten times the body length and are packed with tracheal filaments. The postabdominal spiracles open out at the end of two pronged organs that are thrust through the body cavity of the scale into the brood pouch where they receive air. Pupation occurs within the host (Fig. 108).

Dipterous larvae in aquatic insects are not frequent, yet some species have also succeeded in adapting themselves to this environment. *Ginglymia acrirostris* Towns. is found in the body cavity of an aquatic lepidopterous larva, *Elophila fulicalis* Clemens. The latter lives in swiftly running streams under a thin and irregular web of silk and is provided with gills. At the time of pupation, the web of silk is replaced by a thick rooflike covering of silk, open at both ends, and although the pupa is beneath the surface of the water, its back is surrounded by air. A full-grown larva of *Ginglymia* thrusts its powerful spiracles through the skin of the pupa, between the fourth and fifth abdominal segments, so that the openings are located beneath the silken canopy in contact with air (Lloyd) (Fig. 109).

All entomobius larvae are at first parasites and then become predators, as is clearly seen from the above examples. This is no doubt also true for all dipterous larvae from vertebrates, although in this case, the difference in size is so great that nobody would consider larval flies as predators. This is, however, the case from a physiological standpoint and there does not exist any major difference between the adaptation of these larvae to a parasitic mode of life on vertebrates or on invertebrates. It is necessary to stress the fact that in vertebrates the external manifestations caused by these parasites are entirely secondary and are in no way related to the life history of the maggot, but are reactions of the host's tissues to concomittant infections.

Evidence shows in several ways that pupiparous flies are somewhat preadapted to becoming true para-

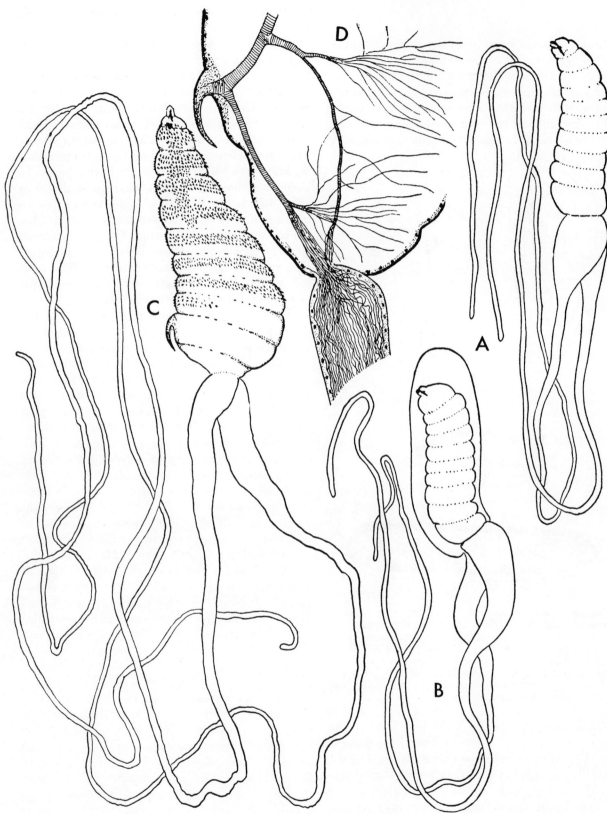

Fig. 107 (*see legend on opposite page*).

sites. Both the males and the females are obligatory blood feeders and the fact that the wings tend to regress and even become completely atrophied contribute to isolating these flies on their host. As may be gathered from their name, the larval stages are spent within the uterus of the female where they

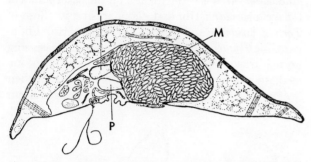

FIG. 108. Pupa of *Cryptochaetum striatum* Thorpe with tracheal "spine" piercing the brood pouch of *Aspidoproctus maximus* Newstead. P.—pupa of the parasite. M.—marsupium of the host with ventrally placed opening (Thorpe).

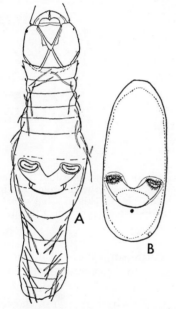

FIG. 109. *Ginglymia acrirostris* Towns. A. Tracheal openings of the parasitic larva thrust through the skin of the host, an aquatic caterpillar. B. Pupa of the host with tracheae of the parasite protruding through the integument (Lloyd).

feed on a particular glandular secretion provided by the so-called "milk glands." Pupation takes place

---

FIG. 107. *Cryptochaetum striatum* Thorpe. A. Second stage larva. B. Transition from second to third stage larva showing molt. C. Third larval stage. D. Spiracle and tracheal supply of caudal process (Thorpe).

immediately after birth and in some cases even the pupa is attached to the host.

Pupiparous flies constitute an heterogeneous group of polyphyletic origin in which it is possible to recognize two principal trends represented on the one hand by hippoboscids and on the other, by strebilids and nycteribids (Fig. 110). The latter occur exclusively on bats whereas the former are associated with both mammals and birds.

In both *Hippobosca* and *Lynchia*, the wings have remained normal. They are mostly atrophied in *Stenopteryx* and *Crataerhina* and completely lost in *Melophagus*. *Lipoptena* possess wings on emerging from the pupa, but they are lost as soon as the fly arrives on its host. Progressive atrophy of the wings

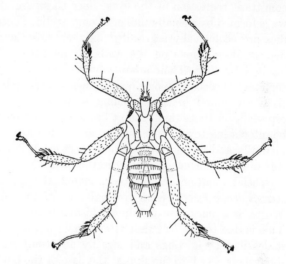

FIG. 110. *Nycteribia biarticulata* Herm., a pupiparous, wingless, dipteran from bats (Falcoz).

is accompanied by a parallel, though partial, regression of the eyes. Normal in *Hippobosca* and *Lynchia*, they become smaller in the other genera. Isolation upon the host is favored in both *Melophagus* and *Lipoptena*, since these attach their pupae to the hairs of the host, sheep in the former and red deer in the latter case. Yet although keds are absolutely specific for sheep, the deer louse fly occurs also on other hosts and even on man. Consequently one may assume that the persistence of wings in the freshly emerged flies has prevented the formation of isolated populations that could become ecologically segregated on particular hosts. This is substantiated by other examples as, for instance, in the genera *Stenopteryx* and *Crataerhina* that both possess rudimentary, functionless wings, and that are strictly adapted to their hosts, swallows and swifts, respectively. However, morphological isolation is not the only factor responsible for host specificity, and in certain cases, it is probable that there are also physiological factors that govern these adaptations. For instance, *Lynchia*, which possess normal wings and which deposit their eggs in the nest of the host, occur exclusively on pigeons whereas *Hippobosca*, that possess the same anatomical and biological characters, are found on different species of mammals and even of birds.

As stated above, strebilids and nycteribids occur exclusively on bats, the former on New World bats and the latter on Old World bats. We also find here a progressive atrophy of the wings but without a concomittant regression of the eyes, since these are always formed by a small number of ommatidia. These flies are ecologically segregated on their hosts and deposit their pupae on the walls of the caves inhabited by bats. Their adaptation to bats is very certainly of secondary origin since their nearest relatives are found in cave-dwelling forms and more especially in those that inhabit bat guano. It would be interesting to test this type of adaptation experimentally and to find out whether there exists some sort of physiological specificity in this case.

Special mention should be made of the genus *Ascodipteron* Adens. from tropical bats of the Old World, as a marked sexual dimorphism is found here. This is due to the fact that after copulation the females lose their wings and legs by autotomy and force their way into the skin at the base of the bat's ear. The hinder end remains close to the surface so that pupae are produced normally (Fig. 111). Nothing is known of how the female feeds, but nourishment must be absorbed in some way since the entire body swells up, becomes pear-shaped, and loses all trace of its segmentation. No host reaction has been recorded.

Hymenopteran larvae occur in a very great number of insects, spiders, and millipedes, and consequently their choice of hosts is much larger than is the case for larval dipterans. The eggs are deposited within the host after the latter's skin has been pierced by the ovipositor of the female. Certain of the larvae, however, on hatching emerge from their host and remain on the latter as ectoparasites, whereas the greater number pursue their development within the host. The fact that a given larva may be either ecto- or endoparasitic, according to the host on

which it is found, would indicate that the nature of the host is responsible for the biology of the larva. Braconid larvae, belonging to the species *Dentrosoter protuberans* Nees, occur on the surface of the larva of *Myelophilus* (coleoptera), but inside the larva of *Scotylus* (coleoptera). The larvae of *Onchophanes lanceolator* Nees is ectoparasitic on the caterpillars of *Cacoecia sorbiana* Hb. and endoparasitic in those of *Tortrix viridana* and *Sesamia aspidiana* Hb. Endoparasitic *Hymenoptera* L. larvae, although possessing normal tracheae, do not attempt to enter into immediate contact with the respiratory organs of their host as do the diptera. Respiratory exchanges occur

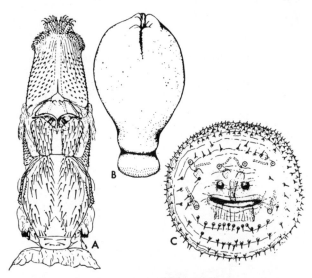

FIG. 111. *Ascodipteron africana* Job. A. Head and thorax of a young female, showing the autotomized wings. B. Adult female extracted from the skin of a bat's ear. C. Posterior extremity of gravid female protruding through the opening (Jobling).

through the entire surface of the cuticle, which is extremely thin in this case and enables the larvae to utilize the oxygen present in the haemolymph of the host. All parasitic hymenopteran larvae begin as parasites and finally become predators, eating their host.

Only a single case is known of an adult hymenopteran that feeds on the blood of its host, an insect. This is *Riela manticida* Kieff., the female of which is found at the base of the wings of the praying mantis where it is seen to gnaw through the chitinous veins and to feed on the blood. On reaching its host, the female of this species cuts off its own wings at the base and attaches itself to the thorax of a mantis

(Fig. 112). The point at which it is attached is about the only place where it can escape being brushed off by the formidable front legs of its host. The eggs of the mantis are laid within a foamy mass that later hardens to form an egg capsule, and as soon as egg laying begins the parasite allows itself to become engulfed within this mass and lays its own eggs among those of the host. Should the parasite alight on a male instead of a female mantis, its life cycle is interrupted since it will never leave its host, even during copulation, when it might pass from the male onto the female (Chopard).

An extremely interesting problem of parasitic adaptation is that of the *Strepsiptera* in which a marked sexual dimorphism is found; the males are

The minute larvae of *Eoxenos laboulbenei* Peyerimh. measure only 200μ in length. They penetrate between the abdominal segments into the body cavity of thysanurans of the species *Lepisma aurea* Duf., *L. crassipes* Esch., and *L. wasmanni* Moniez. Here they grow into the second larval stage and the latter, after ingesting nourishment, molts into a third larval stage that is easily recognizable on account of the larvae being rolled up within the host (Fig. 113). The lateral edges are folded toward the ventral surface so that the larva appears somewhat cigar-

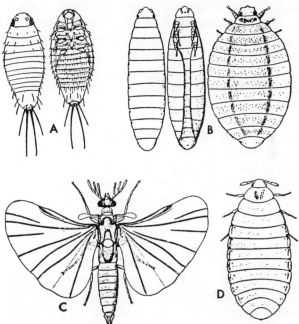

FIG. 113. *Eoxenos laboulbenei* Peyerimhof. A. First stage larvae. B. Larvae from body cavity of a thysanuran showing the sides rolled in and expanded after the larva escapes from the host. C. Adult male. D. Wingless, adult female (Silvestri).

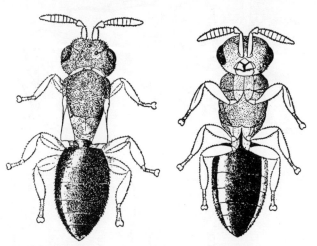

FIG. 112. *Riela manticida* Kief., female specimens, dorsal and ventral view, showing the autotomized wings (Chopard).

winged and the females wingless. Although male strepsipterans possess only one pair of wings they are in no way related to the *Diptera* since in the latter, the anterior pair of wings is retained whereas in the former, the posterior pair is retained and the anterior pair replaced by a pair of balancers.

The life history of strepsipterans contains both free-living and parasitic stages, the latter occurring exclusively within other insects, and whenever the latter are holometabolous, the parasite is obliged to adapt its own life cycle to that of its host since otherwise it perishes.

The less specialized strepsipterans known as mengeids were first recorded from amber collected in the Tertiary beds of the Baltic, although their discovery as living organisms is of comparatively recent date.

shaped. At this stage, the third stage larva emerges from its host and it is observed that the latter hardly ever contains more than two or three larvae. The host dies when the larvae have emerged. As soon as the third stage larva emerges, the lateral edges of its body that were folded over flatten out and the larva appears as in figure 1138. Pupation occurs on the ground, and whereas winged males emerge from their pupa, the females are wingless. From now on, the digestive system is atrophied, and the rest of the life cycle is spent on reserve materials only. Although the female possesses a vaginal pore, fertilization takes place in any part of the body where the male pierces the cuticula with its copulatory apparatus. Impregnation consequently is "hypodermic." The vaginal pore in the female is apparently used only to bring forth the larvae. These, as soon as they emerge, seek a new host. This life history is further complicated by the recent discovery of parthenogenetic females that do not emerge from the pupal molt, although the vaginal pore opens out on the surface. It is also found that the males are not attracted to the parthenogenetic females and completely ignore them. Moreover, the life cycle of *Eoxenos laboulbenei* shows that *Thysanura* are infested in the autumn and consequently that the larvae pass the winter within their hosts, whereas the parthenogenetic females, protected by the pupal molt, are capable of passing the winter in the free state and consequently their larvae will attack new hosts in the spring.

The life cycle of the more specialized strepsipterans, i.e., stylopids, is apparently less complicated since the third larval stage never occurs. The minute, first stage larvae are extremely agile, their legs are terminated by small suckers, or by claws, and their whole body is covered with stiff hairs. These larvae enter into the nests of their hosts either by dropping in from above, or by phoresy, attaching themselves to the host as it comes to feed on plants and flowers. This second alternative would seem to be the usual one, since the female parasitized by strepsipterans loses partly or wholly its nest building instinct owing to the atrophied condition of its ovaries, and the almost complete depletion of its reserve materials on which the parasites have fed.

The genera *Stylops* and *Hylecthrus* are associated with solitary bees, the former with andrenids and the latter with prosopids into whose cells they allow themselves to be walled. The genus *Xenos*, on the other hand, is associated with social wasps of the genus *Polistes* in which all the cells may be parasitized.

The first stage larvae penetrate into the host larva where they feed abundantly and molt into the second stage. The latter is completely devoid of legs as of other appendages and lives freely within the body cavity of its host, accumulating reserve materials at the host's expense. The life cycle of the parasite is synchronized with that of the host in such a way that the second larval instar of the parasite is reached at the point where the host larva is about to undergo

its nymphal molt. While the teguments of the host nymph are still soft, the larval parasite pierces them between two abdominal segments and protrudes its anterior end. At this stage it molts and becomes a nymph. Consequently, when the adult hymenopteran emerges from its nymph, its abdominal segments are pierced by the parasite. The males of the latter emerge immediately after their nymphal molt, whereas the females remain within the host's body, enclosed by both the larval and the nymphal skins (Fig. 114). On the ventral surface of the female, these are slightly detached from the adult cuticula, thus

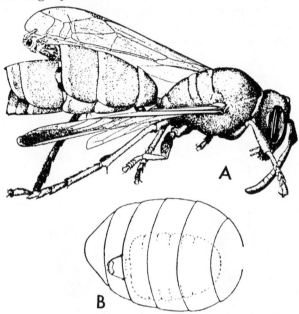

FIG. 114. A. *Polistes gallicus* L. with a male *Xenos vesparum* hatching from the puparium. B. Abdomen of *Andrena vaga* Panz. with adult female of *Stylops* sp. (Ulrich).

forming a spacious pouch into which oviducts open and in which both fertilization of the ova and their incubation take place. This marsupial pouch is completely closed until after copulation has taken place. It then communicates with the surface of the body by a slit located behind the cephalothorax, at the bottom of which a hole is torn by the male copulatory organ. Here also fertilization is hypodermic and the number of larvae produced is something extraordinary. *Stylops* gives birth to more than two thousand larvae and *Xenos* as many as five to six thousand.

A single host may harbor simultaneously several parasitic larvae, yet if the latter have not reached their complete development at the time that the host undergoes the nymphal phase, they will die since they are then unable to pierce the much tougher cuticle of either the nymph or the adult.

The synchronizing of the host's and the parasite's life cycles stands out in a particularly clear manner if different hosts are compared. For instance, prosopids hibernate in the larval stage and andrenids in the nymphal stage, and their parasites, in the first case *Hylecthrus*, hibernate in the first larval instar, and in the second case *Stylops* hibernate as nymphs. In *Polistes*, only the adult female hibernates and its

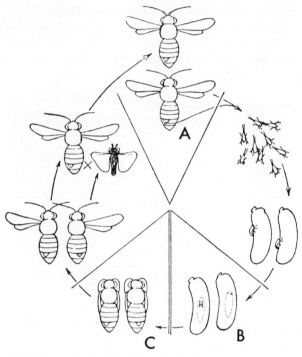

FIG. 115. Diagram of life cycles of strepsipterans, showing the three ways in which the parasites are able to hibernate in their hosts. A. In the adult (*Xenos*). B. In the cell of the host larva (*Hylecthrus*). C. In the pupa of the host (*Stylops*) (Ulrich).

parasites, belonging to the genus *Xenos*, also hibernate as adult females (Fig. 115).

Should the host produce several generations a year, it is found that the parasite also adapts itself and produces several generations. In the case of *Homoptera* (cicadas), where no nymphal stages exist, all the stages of the parasite may be found together. The teguments no doubt being less tough than in *Hymenoptera*, the second larval instar of the parasite can always pierce the cuticula of its host, whatever the stage of its development.

Consequently we find that in the less primitive strepsipterans the life cycle is shortened and that the third larval instar is dropped out. Moreover, it is interesting to remark that mengeids, the more primitive forms, are associated with the more primitive insects that usually spend their entire existence on or in the ground, whereas stylopids are associated with higher insects. So far, no stylopized hymenopterans have been found in amber and this might indicate that they became parasitic only in later times, and consequently stylopids, would be more recent, as parasites, than mengeids.

The larvae of coleopterans belonging to the rhipidiphorids are predaceous on the brood cells of hymenopterans, into which they are carried through phoresy. They even may become hyperparasites, as for instance *Macrosiagon pectinatum* Fabr. that preys on hymenopteran larvae, which are themselves parasitic in lamellicorn beetles.

Rhipidius pectinicornis Thunb. in the larval stages occurs within the body cavity of oriental cockroaches from which it emerges before pupating.

Only a single ectoparasitic coleopteran has been described, so far, in which both the adult and the larval stages never leave their host. This is *Platypsyllus castoris* Ritsema that occurs in the fur of both the American and European beavers. Its body is flattened; there are no wings and only a rudimentary pair of elytra. The femurs are also flattened, the eyes have disappeared, and the head bears a ctenidium along its posterior edge. Since this parasite is closely associated with its hosts, it appears probable that it had already become adapted to them in Tertiary times when both the European and the American beavers lived on the same continent.

Polyctenids (*Hemiptera*) and arixeniids (*Dermaptera*) (Fig. 116) are closely associated with bats and show evidence of a series of adaptations to parasitism that are all the more curious since these insects are the only members of their orders that have adopted this mode of living. In polyctenids, the legs and wings are foreshortened and the eyes have disappeared, adaptive characters that recall those of *Platypsyllus*. The morphological characters of arixeniids, on the other hand, recall the structures peculiar to cave-dwelling species and it is even doubtful whether these are true parasites or not. This point will be discussed later in a general review of adaptive characters in insects (see page 92).

The fur of mammals may, under certain circumstances, become a very peculiar environment for a large number of different organisms, both animal and vegetable. This is especially the case for the fur of sloths in which occur such unexpected species as butterflies. The entire life cycle is spent in this very specialized environment where caterpillar, pupa, and moth occur all together and never leave their host. Three species of pyralids have been reported from the fur of sloths. The caterpillars and the imagos apparently feed on the sebaceous secretions and perhaps also on the hairs but not on the lichens that also occur in this biotope. *Bradypodicola hahneli* Spuler

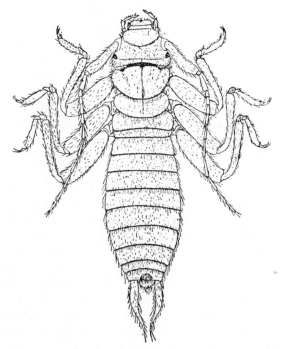

FIG. 116. *Arixenia esau* Jordan, a parasitic earwig from bats, showing the typical troglobiotic aspect of both the legs and the antennae (Jordan).

on *Bradypus sp.*, *Cryptoses choloepi* Dyar on *Choloepus hoffmanni* Peters, and *Bradypophila garbei* Ihering on *Bradypus marmoratus* Gray, all show a flattening and a broadening of the femurs as well as a very dense hairy covering of the head and thorax. The thorax is distinctly flattened in *Bradypodicola*.

Taxonomically, these three species of pyralids are related to the wax moth, *Galleria*, whose imagos and caterpillars live in beehives and feed on wax. They are consequently adapted to a relatively high though constant temperature and degree of moisture, as well as to a specialized diet. It is consequently easy

to understand how species that have arisen from this group have been able to adapt themselves to surroundings where they find the above conditions and also an abundance of fatty secretions. The specificity of this form of parasitism is strict, since the host is unable to clean its fur and rid it periodically of its various parasites.

Fleas are bloodsuckers and permanent parasites in their adult stages, whereas the larval stages are not parasitic and feed on organic detritus. Fleas live in nests of birds and holes of mammals and pass onto their hosts to feed, becoming sedentary and permanently attached in only a few cases such as the South American parrot sticktight flea, *Hectopsylla psittaci* Fr., that is introduced with its host into zoological gardens and is able to pass onto several other species of

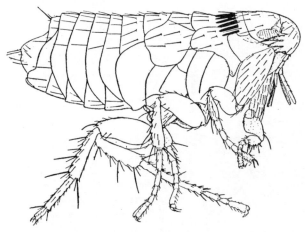

FIG. 117. *Palaeopsylla klebsiana* Dampf, a fossil flea from Baltic amber.

birds including tame pigeons. In this species, as also in the jigger flea, *Tunga penetrans* L., that burrows into the epidermis of man, only the female flea becomes sedentary. The body of fleas is curiously adapted to parasitism in that it is laterally compressed. The segments and the legs bear numerous spines and stiff hairs that enable the flea to pass forward through fur and feathers but make it difficult and nearly impossible to move backward. The pronotum bears a series of large spines, directed backward, known as a ctenidium that also enables the flea to maintain its hold on the host.

The genus *Palaeopsylla* Wag., first discovered in Baltic amber, is found today on insectivores, moles, and shrews (Fig. 117). Ischnyopsyllines are specific to bats and coptophyllines to jerboas. Bird fleas have arisen from mammalian species and are consequently more recent in origin and also less adapted to their hosts (see page 157). *Ceratophyllus* occurs in birds' nests, *C. garei* Rothsch. on many different species of birds, but particularly on those nesting upon the ground. *C. gallinae* Schr. lives on fowls and on many other species of birds also, yet *C. styx* Rothsch. is specific to the sand martin, *C. rusticus* Wag.; *C. farreni* Rothsch. to the swallows; and *C. hirudinis* Curt. to the martin, a distribution that appears to indicate very clearly that these fleas are segregated upon their hosts since the latter are rarely found nesting together or even in the same regions.

Both biting lice and sucking lice are entirely parasitic in all stages of their life cycle. They are admirably adapted for this mode of living as their body is flattened dorsoventrally; the segments are provided with stiff hairs directed backward and the short, yet broad legs are terminated by claws.

Biting lice are primarily bird parasites that have become adapted secondarily to mammals. As all the stages of their life cycle are passed upon the same host, it is easy to understand that the parasites must be fairly closely adapted to the latter and that such associations have in time become permanent. The food of these *Mallophaga* is necessarily specialized even when several species are found together on the same host. For instance, on fowls the wing louse, *Lipeurus caponis* (L.), occurs only on the wings and feeds on hooklets, barbs, and barbules of the feathers. The large fowl louse, *Goniocotes gigas* Tasch., the fluffy louse *G. hologaster* Nitzsch, and the shaft louse, *Menopon gallinae* L., all feed exclusively on barbs and barbules, whereas the chicken body louse, *Eumenacanthus stramineus* (Nitzsch), gnaws into the quills of young feathers and also feeds on blood (Crutchfield & Hixon). Both on birds and on mammals, *Mallophaga* are extremely sensitive to changes of temperature and degree of humidity, these factors appearing almost more important than the nature of the food. This is borne out both by attempts to culture these parasites (see page 160) and also by the fact that stragglers are of frequent occurrence. These may either pass from one host to another through direct contact or after the death of the original host; also by transfer through hippoboscid flies to the body of which the *Mallophaga* attach themselves and are thus carried onto other hosts (Fig. 118). Such phoresy does not necessarily imply that the biting lice transferred onto another host will be able to establish

themselves definitely, but many such cases of phoresis have been reported (Clay & Meinertzhagen).

True lice, *Anoplura*, are all bloodsuckers and are very closely adapted to their hosts. They occur exclusively on mammals where they seem to have become very specific and eventually can be utilized for studying phylogenic relationships among hosts (see page 160).

Adult insects that live in fur or among feathers of their hosts appear to possess a certain number of characteristics in common that cannot all be attributed to convergence. One of the most important of these is the flattening of the body in the dorso-

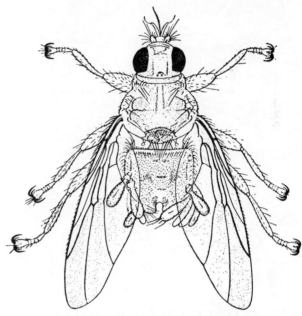

FIG. 118. A louse fly, *Ornithomyia avicularia* (L.), carrying on its abdomen specimens of *Mallophaga* (Warburton).

ventral direction as occurs in biting lice, true lice, hippoboscids, nycteribids, *Platypsyllus*, butterflies, polyctenids, and arixeniids. In fleas only is the body compressed laterally, and this might indicate that these parasites became adapted originally to mammals, since a laterally compressed organism can move about in fur more easily than an organism that is flattened dorsoventrally.

Polyctenids and arixeniids belong to the *Hemiptera* and *Dermaptera*, respectively, i.e., groups in which the body is naturally flattened in all of the free-living species, and consequently this cannot be a case of convergence due to parasitism. It is, however, possible that such conditions preadapted these species to adopting a parasitic mode of life.

The flattening of the body is evidently a consequence of parasitism in *Platypsyllus*, hippoboscids, nycteribids, and parasitic *Lepidoptera*, since it is never found in any other species of these groups of insects. Since neither true lice nor biting lice possess any free-living relatives, it is not possible to say whether the shape of their body is a consequence of their mode of life or whether it existed primarily and enabled them to become parasites. However, the flattening of the body alone is not sufficient to indi-

ture in biting lice would indicate an avian origin for the latter. True lice, on the other hand, are provided with powerful claws that are particularly well adapted to seizing hairs and enable the parasite to maintain a firm hold on its host (Fig. 120). Consequently, we find that, in this case, parasitic adaptation has evolved along different lines.

We have already discussed wing atrophy among parasitic dipterans and remarked that the only pupiparous flies that attach their pupae to the surface of their hosts are those in which the wings have disappeared completely, either through atrophy or autotomy, while the other hippoboscids and nycteri-

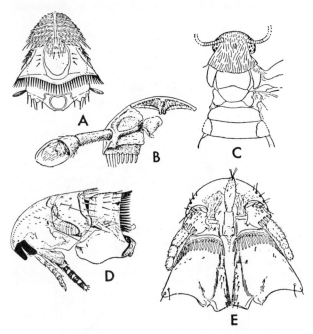

FIG. 119. Converging types of ctenidia in parasitic insects. A. *Strebla* (dipteran). B. *Platypsyllus* (coleopteran). C. *Bradypodicola* (lepidopteran). D. *Ischnopsylla* (aphanipteran). E. *Eoctenes* (hemipteran) (Baer).

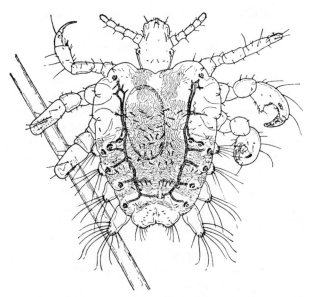

FIG. 120. Crab louse, *Phthirius pubis* L., showing mode of attachment to hair. The diameter of the opening that results from the claw closing onto the tarsus corresponds approximately to the diameter of a pubic hair (Denny).

cate an ectoparasite since these also show other attributes. Of these attributes, one of the most important, and also the most incomprehensible from an evolutionary standpoint, is the ctenidium, formed by a series of thick, short, and sometimes flat spines that are inserted behind the head and are known to exist in fleas, nycteribids, strebilids, polyctenids, and *Platypsyllus* (Fig. 119). In *Bradypodicola* the ctenidium is replaced, functionally, by a dense covering of scales, all of which are lying in the same direction. It is interesting to observe that the majority of ectoparasites that possess a ctenidium occur in the fur of mammals and that the absence of this struc-

bids lay their eggs in the nest of birds or on the walls of caves in which bats live. This may, perhaps, account for the parallel atrophy of both the wings and the eyes in hippoboscids, a consequence of both a parasitic and a troglobiotic life. Nycteribids that live on bats possess rudimentary eyes and these are completely absent in both polyctenids and arixeniids. In this case, however, we are dealing with species that have arisen from cave-dwelling ancestors and parasitism cannot be responsible for their atrophy or disappearance. This is also borne out by the general aspect of these forms, by the length of their appendages, and in arixeniids by the length of the antennae. It is possible that arixeniids are not true ectoparasites since they occur in a cutaneous pouch located on the ventral surface of the larynx of a tropical species of bat (*Chiromeles* Horsf.). Incidentally, this is one of the few species of bats that is almost completely devoid of hairs and this also might explain the peculiar location of the parasite. On the other hand, it is within this pouch that the droppings of the young bats accumulate so that it would finally appear that we are dealing with a highly specialized guanophilic organism rather than with an ectoparasite. The fact that *Arixenia* lays eggs and is not viviparous, as all the other species associated with bats, would also seem to confirm this view.

From the above it is easy to observe that ecto-parasitic insects have not evolved along identical lines and that they have also arisen during different

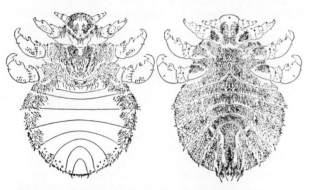

Fig. 121. *Lepidophthirius macrorhinus* End., ventral and dorsal views, showing distribution of the minute scales that retain air when the host, a seal, dives (Enderlein).

periods in the history of their hosts. Several cave-dwelling species were probably preadapted to living on animals that occur within caves and that emerge only in the evening or at night when the surrounding conditions resemble mostly those found in caves. Other forms have become adapted by various means that may sometimes appear to be identical, such as the flattening of the body and the appearance of a ctenidium, for instance. An interesting case of local adaptation to parasitism is found in two species of seal lice. *Lepidophthirius* End. and *Antarctophthirius* End. occur in the fur; their bodies, especially the dorsal surface, are covered with tiny scales that retain air when the host dives (Fig. 121). On the other hand, *Echinophthirius* End., which is attached in the immediate vicinity of the nostrils and is enclosed within these when the seal dives, is not provided with such scales.

We have seen, previously, that maggots do not furnish any evidence of a specific parasitism and that their presence within a given host is caused essentially by the attraction that this host exerts on the female fly. The nature of the attraction has not yet been worked out in detail and is certainly complex. Radiant heat and moisture must play an important part in such attractions as certain odors do also. With regard to the latter, some very interesting experiments have been carried out on ichneumonid flies (Thorpe). *Nemerites canescens* (Grav.) is strongly attracted by the odor of the larva of *Ephestia kuhniella* (Zell.), its normal host. It is, however, possible to rear the larval ichneumonids, experimentally in the caterpillars of *Meliphora* and *Galleria*. The adult insects which emerge from *Ephestia kuhniella* are not normally attracted to the caterpillars of either *Meliphora* or *Galleria*, but if bred on the caterpillar of these species, they are subsequently attracted to them. Moreover, an ichneumonid "conditioned" with *Meliphora* is hardly attracted to *Ephestia*, its original host. Consequently, the nature of the food eaten by the larvae has modified the behavior of the adult insect toward its usual host.

Drosophila larvae bred in a medium containing peppermint and then washed before pupation give rise to flies that are attracted to this odor which normally repels them. Similar experiments have been carried out on a large scale with free-living insects feeding on particular host plants, and here also it is possible after one generation to modify their behavior toward their original food plant. We have evoked a similar reason previously to explain, tentatively, why *Lucilia bufonivora* is attracted to toads and, apparently, to toads only (page 79).

Blowflies, belonging to the species *Lucilia caesar* (L.) and *L. sericata* (Meig.) have become a serious menace to Merino sheep in Australia. The eggs are laid mostly at the base of the tail and the maggots burrow into the tissues. In a series of recent experiments, Cragg and Ramage have been able to determine experimentally what attracts adult flies to the sheep and induces oviposition.

Under the conditions in which the experiments were conducted, sulphydryl compounds were found to play an important part in blowfly attack and, also, that attraction is not completely dependent on some factor produced by the living animal, since oviposition can be induced on a clipped fleece that is kept moist and impregnated with ammonium carbonate and indole.

It is, however, probable that the factor provided for by the living animal is precisely the degree of moisture that appears to be indispensable. Cysteine results from the breakdown of wool fibers with the production of sulphur under the influence of bacterial agents. It is most likely that these thrive only under given conditions of moisture.

The amount of sulphur present need not be great, since a solution containing 0.1 per cent ammonium carbonate, to which is added 0.001 per cent ethyl mercaptan is sufficient to induce oviposition.

It would be interesting to breed maggots in media containing these substances and then to test the attractions shown by the adult blowflies.

It has already been stated that horse botflies fix their eggs to the hairs of the host and that *Gastrophilus pecorum* attaches them either to surrounding objects or more rarely to the skin, not to the hairs, of the horse. In this case, the egg is provided with a small stalk that spreads at its base, enabling the egg to remain firmly in position. The eggs of this species, moreover, have also been observed on the host, but never on the hairs. Instead, they are attached directly onto the surface of the skin. As this mode of attachment is also found in *Gyrostigma pavesii* (Corti), a rhinoceros botfly, it might be interpreted as being a preadaptation to mammals whose skin is almost hairless.

Tachinids and hymenopterans parasitic in insects have certainly been adapted to parasitism for a very long time, as fossil insects, occurring in the Quercy phosphorites and belonging to species that are usually associated with decomposing cadavers, have been found to contain a nymph of a braconid (Handschin). This would indicate that such forms of parasitism had become established by mid-Tertiary times.

REFERENCES

BRUMPT, E. 1934. Recherches expérimentales sur la biologie de la *Lucilia bufonivora*. *Ann. Parasit.*, 12:81–97, 6 figs.

CHOPARD, L. 1923. Les parasites de la Mante religieuse.

I. Riela manticida Kieff. *Ann. Soc. Entom. France*, 91: 249–64, 16 figs.

CLAY, TH., & MEINERTZHAGEN, R. 1943. The relationship between Mallophaga and Hippoboscid flies. *Parasitology*, 35:11–16.

CRAGG, J. B., & RAMAGE, G. R. 1945. Chemotropic studies on the blow-flies *Lucilia sericata* (Mg.) and *Lucilia caesar* (L.). *Parasitology*, 36:168–75.

CRUTCHFIELD, C. M., & HIXON, H. 1943. Food habits of several species of poultry lice with special reference to blood consumption. *Florida Entom.*, 26:63–66.

DEORAS, P. J. 1941. Structure of Hemimerus deceptus Rehn var. ovatus; an external parasite of Cricetomys gambiense. *Parasitology*, 33:171–85, 29 figs.

DINULESCO, G. 1932. Recherches sur la biologie des Gastrophiles. Anatomie, Physiologie, Cycle évolutif. *Ann. Sc. Nat. Zool.* (10), 15:1–183, 42 figs., 8 pls.

GEBAUR, O. 1940. Das Verhalten der Grossen Dasselfliege (*Hypoderma bovis* de Geer) im Tierversuch und die perkutane Invasion der Larve des ersten Stadiums. *Zeitschr. f. Parasitenk.* 11:391–99, 7 figs.

HANDSCHIN, ED. 1944. Insekten aus den Phosphoriten des Quercy. *Abhand. Schweiz. Paleont. Gesell.*, 64:1–23, 7 figs., 3 pls.

KEILIN, D. 1944. Respiratory systems and respiratory adaptations in larvae and pupae of Diptera. *Parasitology*, 36:1–66, 54 figs., 2 pls.

MATHYSSE, J. G. 1946. Cattle lice. Their biology and control. *Bull. Cornell Univ. Agric. Exp. Sta.*, vol. 832, 67 pp., 41 figs., 4 pls.

MEIXNER, J. 1933. Strepsiptera Kirby. *Handb. Zool.*, 4: (12); *Insecta*, 2:1349–82, figs. 1393–1423.

PANTEL, J. 1898. Le *Thrixion halidayanum* Rond. Essai monographique sur les caractères extérieurs, la biologie et l'anatomie d'une larve parasite du groupe des Tachinaires. *La Cellule*, 15:1–290, 6 pls.

THORPE, W. 1938. Further experiments on olfactory conditioning in a parasitic insect. The nature of the conditioning process. *Proc. R. Soc. B.*, 126:370–97.

———. 1941. The biology of *Cryptochaetum* (Diptera) and *Eupelmus* (Hymenoptera) parasites of *Aspidoproctus* (Coccidae) in East Africa. *Parasitology*, 33:149–68, 26 figs.

ULRICH, W. 1943. Die Mengeiden (Mengenillini) und die Phylogenie der Strepsipteren. *Zeitschr. f. Parasitenk.*, 13:62–101, 11 figs.

WARBURTON, C. 1922. The warble-flies of cattle. *Hypoderma bovis* and *H. lineatum*. *Parasitology*, 14:322–41, 3 figs.

WILSON, F. H. 1934. The life-cycle and bionomics of *Lipeurus heterographus* Nitzsch. *J. Parasit.*, 20:304–11, 1 fig.

———. 1939. The life-cycle and bionomics of *Lipeurus caponis* (Linn.) *Ann. Entom. Soc. Am.*, 32:318–20.

Nematoda

From a purely biological standpoint, such as we have adopted here, nematodes form the link between free-living groups that contain parasitic forms and those that are entirely parasitic. Although parasitic nematodes, on account of their economic importance, are sometimes considered as a distinct group, it should be borne in mind that this is not the case and that the number of free-living species is very much greater than that of the known parasites.

From a purely taxonomic standpoint, it is not possible to separate the free-living forms from the parasitic species. All nematodes are grouped into a single system in which several families that are entirely parasitic are placed next to others that contain both free-living and parasitic species or only free-living species.

Nematodes have invaded and become adapted to every known biotope.

"They occur in arid deserts and at the bottom of lakes and rivers, in the waters of hot springs and in the polar seas where the temperature is constantly below the freezing point of fresh water. They were thawed out alive from Antarctic ice. . . . They occur at enormous depths in alpine lakes and in the ocean. As parasites of fishes they traverse the seas; as parasites of birds they float across continents and over high mountain ranges" (Cobb.). We might add that insects and mammals carry them to the four corners of the earth and that no living thing—man, beast, or plant—is safe from their attack.

When organisms present such a vast distribution and such possibilities of adapting themselves to very different environments, it is not surprising to discover that their morphology shows generalized characters. This is especially true for most of the free-living species as also for those parasitic in invertebrates. The more specialized forms occur among the parasites of higher vertebrates, but without its being possible to attribute the specialized characters directly to parasitism.

Apart from certain structures immediately related to the mode of feeding, the anatomy of nematodes is fundamentally similar throughout the entire phylum. For further details the reader is referred to the work of Chitwood *et al.*

The writer knows of no single group of organisms that is so perfectly preadapted to becoming parasitic as are the nematodes. To their morphological character must also be added their saprophagous and predatory habits that cause them to search for food of all kinds. From a physiological standpoint, it seems that the nematodes predatory on plants show a marked tendency toward splitting up into distinct races that are specialized as to their food habits. Such races are not genetically determined, but are physiologically adapted. They may also be reversible and consequently play an important role in agriculture (Steiner). It is quite possible that such physiological races exist also in other groups of nematodes and especially among the parasitic species, where their presence can be discovered only by carefully conducted experiments.

It is usual for the productivity in parasitic forms to be much greater than in the corresponding free-living forms. In nematodes, this is not the case and when the parasitic and free-living species are compared as to productivity, no apparent difference can be found. It is true that a female *Ascaris* is able to produce something like twenty million eggs, but this is attributable to its large size and not to its being parasitic. Certain parasites in vertebrates show an enormously developed uterus. This occurs in *Tetrameres* and *Simondsia*, but also in *Sphaerularia*, from insects and *Heterodera* in plants (Fig. 122).

It is in the life histories of the parasitic species that signs of adaptation to parasitism become evident although even here, in the light of more recent work on life histories of species predatory in insects, this distinction is not so clear-cut as might be supposed.

As was first determined experimentally by Mau-

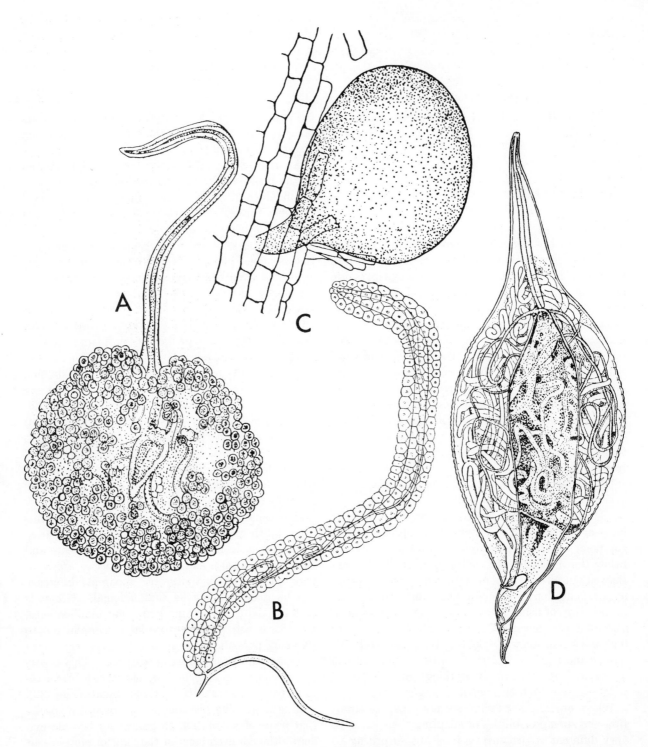

Fig. 122. Unrelated species of female nematodes, showing deformation of the body by the gravid uterus. A. *Simondsia paradoxa* Cobb. B. *Sphaerularia bombi* Dufour (the body of the worm appears as an appendage of the uterus). C. *Heterodera schachti* Schmidt. D. *Tetrameres fissispina* (Dies.) (Cobbold; Goodey: Leuckart: Travassos).

pas, and later extended by other authors, all nematodes on hatching from the egg pass through a given number of larval stages that are each separated by a single molt. He also established the fact that in free-living nematodes, the third larval stage is often ensheathed within the preceding molt and is thus able to resist a sudden change in environment that would destroy the other larval stages. In parasitic nematodes, this third larval stage corresponds to the infestive larva which will become an adult worm only when introduced into the final host.

The number of larval stages in both free-living and parasitic nematodes is four and, consequently, the life cycle may be represented somewhat diagrammatically in the following way where L = a larval stage and M = a molt.

$$\text{egg} \rightarrow L_1 + M_1 \rightarrow L_2 + M_2 \rightarrow L_3 + M_3 \rightarrow L_4 + M_4 \rightarrow \text{adult}$$

Experimental work has shown that in several species of parasites from vertebrates, there are less than four molts between the larva hatching from the egg and the adult worm and, consequently, that the life cycle is shortened. Such cases are not exceptions to Maupas' rule but are due to the fact that certain species molt once (ascarids) or even twice (syngamids) while in the egg so that in the first instance, the larva that hatches is already in the second stage and in the second case, in the third stage.

The infestive larval stage, henceforth designated as L_3, when ensheathed within the preceding molt, is not necessarily immobile but may move about actively, migrate from the soil onto grass (trichostrongylids), or penetrate actively into the skin of the final host (ancylostomids). It is particularly interesting to observe that this larval stage occurring both in free-living and in parasitic nematodes corresponds, from a biological standpoint, to the dissemination phase that enables free-living species to be carried by the wind, when their environment dries up, and parasitic species to await a favorable occasion for passing into the final host. In certain species that live in dung the cuticle of the second larval stage is covered with an oily secretion that consequently surrounds L_3 and enables this larva to attach itself to the body of insects such as aphodids, that are dung feeders. In *Rhabditis coarctata* Leuck., the ensheathing molt shrinks in a very characteristic fashion and the larvae are attached to the surface of the dung beetle, *Aphodius fimentarius* L. (Fig. 123). In the genus *Cheilobius*, which occurs in decomposing vegetable matter, the third stage larvae

are coiled like a watch spring and become affixed by a short stalk to staphilinids (Bovien). Consequently, the life cycle of such species contains a phase during which the larvae are phoretic on insects, and are

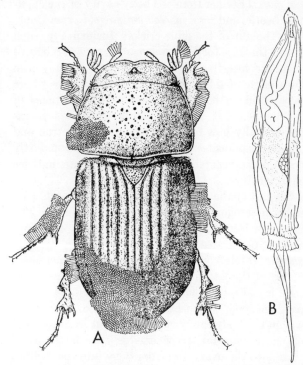

Fig. 123. *Rhabditis coarctata* Leuck. A. Third stage larvae encysted upon the body of a dung beetle, *Aphodius fimentarius* L. B. Third stage larva showing the characteristic wrinkling of the cystic sheath (Triffit & Oldham).

thus disseminated by the latter and are also assured of finding a fresh supply of their staple food. Phoresis may even become compulsory so that the life cycle may be completed, as for instance in certain species of the genera *Neoaplectana* and *Cheilobius*, in which the duration of the third larval stage is dependent on the food supply. If food is lacking, this larval stage remains encysted until an insect carries it to a fresh supply. Masses of L_3 larvae are sometimes found beneath the elytra of coprophagous and xylophagous beetles, where they are agglomerated by their oily secretions, and have often been misinterpreted as belonging to the life cycle of nematodes that occur within the body of such beetles.

There is no proof, so far, that the nematodes described as parasitic in insects are true parasites; in fact this may be the case for mermithids only. All the other species are predators, that enter either passively, as an egg, or penetrate actively into larval or adult insects upon the dead bodies of which they feed. Certain of these species even reproduce within their host and the latter is finally completely invaded by the worms. This is the case for *Neoaplectana glaseri* Steiner from the body cavity of the Japanese beetle, and for *Cephalobium microbivorum* Cobb. from the gut of the mole cricket. Incidentally, such is also the case for *Probstmayria vivipara* (Probstm.) from the intestine of the horse and probably also for other atractids from the rectum of reptiles where they occur in enormous numbers at all stages of development. It would be interesting to test experimentally how far these nematodes are true and obligatory parasites, or only forms that live on partly decomposed vegetable matter such as occurs in these environments.

Several of the species associated with insects possess a heterogonic generation in their life cycle. The female of *Heterotylenchus aberrans* Bovien, after copulation, penetrates into the maggot of a fly, *Hylemya antiqua* (Meig.) where it remains during metamorphosis of the latter. Within the adult fly, the nematode lays its eggs and from these hatch, *in situ*, a parthenogenetic generation that also reproduces within the body cavity of the host, but from the eggs of which bisexual larvae emerge. The latter penetrate into the ovary and from there into the oviduct through which they escape from the body cavity. This bisexual generation becomes adult in the soil and fertilized females seek a fresh maggot to penetrate (Fig. 124).

Only two genera of rhabditoidids have been able to adapt themselves to vertebrates, *Rhabdias*, to amphibians and reptiles, and *Strongyloides*, to mammals. Curiously enough, in both of these are found heterogonic generations as mentioned above in *Heterotylenchus*.

In *Rhabdias*, the hermaphroditic females occur in the lungs of their host and the bisexual generation is free-living. The latter, however, does not always occur regularly, and in some species this type of development appears to be related to certain nutritional requirements (Chu). The L₃ larvae penetrate through the skin into the lymph ducts and are carried passively into the lungs (Fuelleborn). In *R. fuscovenosa*, from grass snakes, the larvae penetrate into their host via the gut and pass directly from the latter into the lungs (Goodey). Since heterogonic L₃ larvae are also able to penetrate into snails and probably into other invertebrates also and remain

encapsulated without molting, it is probable that these invertebrates constitute paratenic hosts (Fuelleborn).

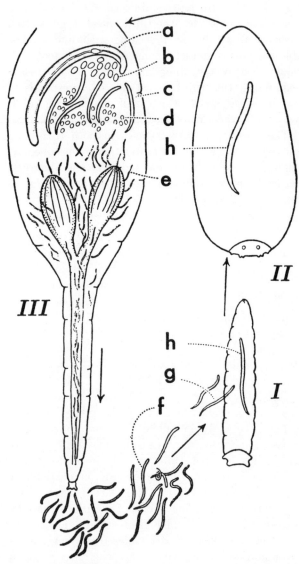

FIG. 124. Diagram of the life cycle of *Heterotylenchus aberrans* Bov. a. Parasitic female of the bisexual generation. b. Its eggs. c. Females of the parthenogenetic generation. d. Eggs of the latter. e. Larvae escaping through the ovaries and the oviduct. f. Free-living, bisexual generation. g. Fertilized females penetrating into the larvae of the host. h. Adult females of the bisexual generation. I. Larva. II. Pupa. III. Adult of the onion fly, *Hylemya antiqua* (Meig.) (Bovien).

In *Strongyloides stercoralis* (Bavay) and other species, the parthenogenetic female occurs in the wall of the host's gut and the heterogonic generation is found in the feces after they have been evacuated.

Here also, the L_3 larva penetrates through the skin, although it may also be carried directly to the mouth, and in either case ultimately enters the blood stream. The larvae migrate via the lungs into the intestine. Under certain conditions that have not yet been established for all the species and that might even be associated with certain races of parasites, the heterogonic generation is suppressed and the L_3 larvae, formed in the feces, penetrate directly through the skin of the host.

From a purely biological standpoint, it is possible to group the different types of life cycles occurring in nematodes from vertebrates into distinct categories. These are based on the presence or absence of a free-living larval form, of an intermediate host, or of a paratenic host, and on the way in which the infestive larva reaches the organ parasitized in the final host.

Such a classification of biological facts bears no relationship to the taxonomic arrangement of the parasites, but it yields a clearer view of both the possible complications and simplifications of their life histories and can thus be used as examples of parasitic adaptations.

According to their life histories, it is possible to group the parasitic nematodes from vertebrates into two principal categories, monoxenous nematodes possessing only one host and consequently no intermediate host although eventually a paratenic host may occur, and heteroxenous nematodes with two or more hosts and consequently with an intermediate host and also a possible paratenic host (Seurat). A third category, autoheteroxenous nematodes in which the final host invariably becomes the intermediate host for the next generation, as in *Trichinella* for example, was first proposed by the writer.

I. MONOXENOUS NEMATODES

A Free larval stage:
  a. gut parasites:
  1. *L_3 ensheathed in soil; no migration.*
    The eggs hatch on the ground; ensheathed L_3 climb up on grass blades and are swallowed by the host; adult in intestine (*Trichostrongylus* spp. and *Haemonchus* spp. from ruminants).
  2. *L_3 ensheathed in soil; migration through host.*
    The L_3 larvae although ensheathed remain very mobile and penetrate into the skin of the host. Having reached the lungs via the blood stream, the larvae pass into the bronchi and the windpipe and reach the intestine (*Ancylostomatidae* from man and carnivora).
  a′. lung parasites:
  1. *L_3 ensheathed in soil; migration through host.*

The eggs are swallowed together with mucus from the bronchi and are ejected and hatch in the soil where also the L_3 larvae occur ensheathed within the two preceding molts. These larvae migrate onto grass blades and are thus swallowed by the final host in which they reach the lungs by migrating from the gut via the blood stream. In very heavy infestations larvae occur in almost every organ, but become adult only in the lungs (*Dictyocaulus arnfieldi* (Cobbold) from equines).
  2. *L_3 ensheathed in soil; migration through host; paratenic host optional.*
    The eggs hatch in the bronchi and the L_1 larvae pass out with the feces. L_3 is found ensheathed in the soil but if eaten by earthworms, survives a long time in these. Although the paratenic host is not necessary in this case, it enables the L_3 larvae to survive during the winter or even during a drought. The rest of the life cycle is the same as above (*Dictyocaulus viviparus* (Bloch) from cattle).
B. No free larval stage:
  b. gut parasites:
  1. *L_3 contained in egg; no migration.*
    The first larval stage molts twice within the egg so that the latter is infestive when swallowed. L_3 may sometimes hatch and is found in such cases to be ensheathed in the preceding molt and able to remain alive in the soil for a considerable time. When the eggs or the ensheathed larvae are swallowed by the final host, the larvae become adult in the gut (*Oswaldocruzia filicollis* (Goeze) from amphibians).
  2. *L_2 contained in egg; migration through host.*
    The larva develops within the egg, outside the host's body, as far as the L_2 stage. When the egg is swallowed, it hatches within the intestine of the host and the larva penetrates into the wall of the gut, enters the blood stream and is carried to the lungs. Here it molts and L_3, breaking into the bronchi, passes up the windpipe and again into the intestine to become adult (*Ascaris lumbricoides* (L.) from man).
  3. *L_2 contained in egg; no migration.*
    The larvae develop into L_2 within the egg outside the host but do not hatch until the egg is swallowed. The larvae penetrate into the mucosa of the gut where they molt and then return into the lumen to become adult (*Ascaridia* spp. from game birds).
  4. *L_1 contained in egg; slight migration.*
    The first stage larva is formed within the egg outside the body of the host and can survive a long time inside the egg. When this is swallowed, the larva hatches and undergoes all of its molts in the host's gut. The worms migrate from the gut into the gut wall or into other organs where they become adult (*Capillaria* spp. from birds). In cases where the worms become adult in organs that are no longer related to the gut, as the liver, spleen, etc., the ova can be liberated only after the death of the host, either by decomposition of the body or if the host is eaten by another animal. In this case, the eggs will pass through

TABLE 2. Location of Various Stages in the Life Cycle of Nematodes

egg	L_1	L_2	L_3	intermediate host	paratenic host	migration	adult	species
soil	soil	soil	soil	—	—	—	gut	Trichostrongylus spp., Haemonchus spp.
soil	soil	soil	soil	—	—	skin..blood..lungs	gut	Ancylostomatidae
soil	soil	soil	soil	—	—	gut.........blood	lungs	Dictyocaulus arnfieldi
bronchi, gut	soil	soil	soil	—	optional; earth-worms	gut.........blood	lungs	Dictyocaulus viviparus
soil	egg	egg	egg	—	—	—	gut	Oswaldocruzia spp.
soil	egg	egg	egg	—	optional; earth-worms, insects	gut.........blood	lungs	Syngamus spp.
soil	egg	egg	lungs	—	—	gut..blood...lungs	gut	Ascaris lumbricoides
soil	egg	gut	gut	—	—	gut..............	various organs	Trichuroidea
soil	egg	egg	gut wall	—	—	—	gut	Heterakis spp., Ascaridia spp.
uterus	uterus	uterus	gut	—	—	—	gut	Probstmayria, Tachygonetria
gut	soil	mag-gots	mag-gots	necessary	—	—	stomach	Habronema spp.
gut	soil	snails	snails	necessary	—	gut ....blood	lungs	Protostrongylus spp.
water	egg	water	cope-pod	necessary	optional; fish	—	stomach wall	Spiroxys spp.
water	egg	water	cope-pod	necessary	necessary; fish	gut...body cavity	stomach	Gnathostomum spp.
uterus	water	cope-pod	cope-pod	necessary	—	gut.................	subcut. connect. tissue	Dracunculus spp.
uterus	water	cope-pod	cope-pod	necessary	optional; fish	—	gut	Camallanus spp.
soil	egg	earth-worms	earth-worms	necessary	—	gut..........blood	lungs	Metastrongylus spp.
soil	insect	insect	insect	necessary	—	stomach...........	esophagus wall	Gongylonema spp.
uterus	blood	insect	insect	necessary	—	blood..............	connect. tissue	Filaroidea
uterus	lymph	connect. tissue	muscle	necessary	—	gut................	gut wall	Trichinella

the intestinal tract of this animal and survive. They can become embryonated in the soil only and must therefore be swallowed by another host when the L_1 larva is formed within the egg.

5. *Viviparous; no migration.*

The third stage larvae are formed in the uterus of the female worm and immediately become adult after molting, without leaving the intestine of the host (*Probstmayria vivipara* (Probstmayr) from equines and *Tachygonetria vivipara* (Wedl) from lizards). As already mentioned, it is doubtful whether these are true parasites. No other case of any metazoan parasite developing *in situ* within its host is recorded.

b'. lung parasites:

1. L_3 *contained in egg; migration through host; paratenic host optional.*

The infestive larva is formed within the egg outside the body of the host. Several alternatives may occur. If the eggs are swallowed they hatch in the host's gut and the larvae pass by way of the blood stream to the lungs where they become adult. In hot weather, the eggs may hatch in the soil and the ensheathed larvae are swallowed directly. Finally, both the eggs and the ensheathed larvae may be swallowed by paratenic hosts such as earthworms and insects. In this case, the latter play an important part in spreading the infestive larvae over a much wider area. (*Syngamus* spp. from birds and mammals).

II. HETEROXENOUS NEMATODES

C. With free larval stage:

c. gut or stomach parasites:

1. *Egg hatches in soil; L_1 eaten by intermediate host; no migration.*

The egg hatches either in the soil or in the host's intestine but, in either case, L_1 is found free in the feces. The first larval stage is eaten by fly maggots and passes from the gut of the latter into the body cavity. The larvae molt twice and when the adult fly emerges from the pupa, L_3 migrate into the proboscis from which they escape when the fly alights on the wet surface of a horse's mouth, and pass into the intestine to become adult. Should the L_3 larvae be deposited on mucosae other than the mouth, or on sores, they penetrate into the submucosa where they cause an inflammatory reaction. They neither grow nor migrate from the place on which they have been deposited by the fly (*Habronema* spp. from equines).

2. *Viviparous; L_1 in water, eaten by intermediate host; paratenic host optional; no migration.*

Camallanus spp. from the gut of fishes are viviparous; consequently the L_1 larvae are eliminated into the surrounding water. They are swallowed by copepods and pass into the body cavity of the latter to grow into L_3 larvae. If an infested copepod is eaten by a fish, the larvae escape and become adult. According to some authors, *C. sweeti* Moorthy can re-encapsulate in a paratenic host, a fish, before becoming adult. In *Procamallanus cearensis* Pereira *et al.*, on the other hand, it appears that the larvae cannot pass beyond

the L_2 stage in the copepod and that the paratenic host thus becomes a true second intermediate host in which it attains the L_3 stage.

3. L_2 *in water, eaten by intermediate host; paratenic host optional; no migration.*

The eggs of *Spiroxys contorta* (Rud.) from turtles become embryonated outside the host and the larva molts once inside the egg. L_2 is consequently free and is eaten by a copepod in the body cavity of which is formed L_3. When such a copepod is eaten by a turtle, the larvae escape and burrow into the wall of the stomach where they become adult. An optional paratenic host exists here also and may be fish, tadpoles, frogs, newts, or even dragonfly nymphs and sometimes small turtles.

4. L_2 *in water, eaten by intermediate host; paratenic host necessary; migration in final host.*

Gnathostomum spinigerum Owen occurs in tumors of the stomach wall in mammals. The eggs escape into the lumen of the stomach when the wall of the tumor breaks down. L_1 is formed within the egg and molts before hatching so that L_2 is free in the water where it is eaten by a copepod. In the body cavity of the latter, L_3 is formed within six days. Curiously enough, all attempts to infest final hosts (cats) with such copepods have failed. When fish eat infested copepods, the L_3 larvae are found encysted on the peritoneal surface of the gut and when these are fed to cats they migrate through the intestinal wall and penetrate into the wall of the stomach from the peritoneal surface. It would therefore seem that the paratenic host has become indispensable and, consequently, that the life cycle requires two intermediate hosts. Further research will be necessary to verify this apparently exceptional life history.

c'. lung parasites:

1. L_1 *in soil, penetrates into intermediate host; migration through final host.*

Protostrongylus spp. occur in the lungs of artiodactyls. The eggs hatch in the soil and L_1 larvae penetrate into the foot of snails where they enter the mucous glands and molt twice. When the intermediate host is eaten by the final host, the larvae migrate out of the intestine, through the blood stream and into the lungs. *P. rufescens* (Leuck.) is reported from both sheep and rabbits yet the sheep strain cannot become adult in rabbits nor the rabbit strain in sheep (Joyeux & Gaud).

c". connective tissue parasites:

1. L_1 *in water, eaten by intermediate host; migration through final host.*

The Guinea worm, *Dracunculus medinensis* (L.), is viviparous and the L_1 larva is expelled into the water where it is swallowed by a copepod, in the body cavity of which it reaches the L_3 stage. When infested copepods are swallowed by man or other mammals, the larvae migrate from the intestine into the connective tissue where they become adult after about twelve months. The gravid females pass into the subcutaneous connective tissue and finally pierce the skin where it has been softened by soaking in water. The female worm remains in the final host even when dead, and is usually calcified.

D. No free larval stage:

d. gut wall parasites:

1. *Eggs eaten by intermediate host; migration through final host.*

The eggs are embryonated when passed out of the host but do not hatch. They are eaten by an insect in the body cavity of which they pass into the L_3 stage after two successive molts. In *Gongylonema pulchrum* Molin, from pigs, the first intermediate host is a cockroach, *Blatella germanica* L. The larvae are liberated in the stomach of the final host and immediately burrow into the wall of the esophagus where they become adult.

d'. lung parasites:

1. *Eggs eaten by intermediate host; migration in final host.*

The eggs are embryonated when passed out from the host and are eaten by earthworms in the case of the species of *Metastrongylus* from the pig. When infested earthworms containing L_3 larvae are swallowed, the larvae migrate from the gut, via the blood stream, into the lungs.

d''. connective tissue parasites:

1. *L_1 in blood stream or subcutaneous tissue eaten by intermediate host; migration through final host.*

In this group belong all of the *Filariidae* reported from man and other animals. The female worms are viviparous or ovoviviparous and the embryos pass into the blood stream or, in the case of *Onchocerca*, remain in the subcutaneous tissue. Blood-feeding insects ingest infested blood and the microfilariae pass from their gut into the body cavity where finally the L_3 larvae accumulate either in the labrum or the sheath of the maxillae. When the insect pierces the skin of the final host, these organs are compressed and burst under the strain of filariae larvae. The latter, thus liberated on the surface of the skin, penetrate into the capillaries and wander into the connective tissue of the different regions where they become adult.

III. AUTOHETEROXENOUS NEMATODES

This category contains exclusively *Trichinella spiralis* Owen, a nematode that occurs in all mammals, at least experimentally, but more frequently in man, pig, carnivores, and rodents. The fertilized female worms burrow into the intestinal mucosa. They are viviparous and the larvae pass into the lymphatics from where they spread through the entire organism, but more especially to the striated muscles. The larvae penetrate into the muscle fibers and cease their migrations; they increase in size and their presence causes the host tissues to react and enclose the larvae within a cyst. Within this cyst, the larvae may remain alive for several years. Infection of a new host takes place when the latter eats infested muscle. Curiously enough, no molts have ever been observed in *Trichinella* larvae, yet the encysted stage only is infestive. Transmission of *Trichinella* must originally have been favored by cannibalism such as occurs normally among rodents.

The above grouping of the various types of life cycles is not complete as to the migrations within the final host. In several cases the actual route of migration is not yet known definitely, although numerous pathological reactions occur along the course followed by the worms (see page 177). Adult nematodes parasitic in vertebrates occur in various organs of their host, yet each species of worm possesses a definite localization: the gut throughout its entire length from the esophagus to the rectum; the lungs, bronchi, and trachea; the kidneys and bladder; the various connective tissues of the gut wall; blood vessels and heart; organs such as the liver and the spleen; and the peritoneal and subcutaneous connective tissues. Consequently, it is easy to understand that to reach the outside eggs or larvae must be voided either into the gut or onto the surface of the skin, and that arthropods feeding on blood will be able to remove from the capillaries any larvae that would otherwise be condemned to permanent seclusion. In only a few cases, for instance when larvae encyst in the host's tissues or eggs accumulate in a deep-seated organ, must the host be eaten or eventually disintegrate after death to make the larvae or the eggs accessible to other hosts.

Parasitic nematodes are obviously polyphyletic, which accounts also for their extremely varied modes of adaptation to their hosts and for the many ways in which the larvae gain access to them. The reasons for such migrations may be a matter for speculation, yet when the problem is approached from an experimental angle or by reasoning from data available, some interesting information may become evident.

When first stage larvae of *Strongyloides stercoralis* (Bavay) are deposited on the skin of laboratory animals, rabbits for instance, they penetrate into the skin but do not migrate far from their original site and undergo two molts. If such L_3 larvae are fed to a suitable host, they will become adult in the gut without migrating (Fuelleborn). Consequently it has become possible to create an intermediate host within this life cycle.

Third stage larvae of dog hookworms, *Ancylostoma braziliense* de Faria and *Uncinaria stenocephala* Railliet, may penetrate accidentally into the epidermis of man, yet do not migrate to the lungs. They move around within the epidermis and cause the so-called creeping eruption, yet they retain their power to infest a normal host *per os*. On the other hand, L₃ larvae of *U. stenocephala*, when swallowed by a dog, do not migrate from the gut but become adult *in situ* (Fuelleborn). This, moreover, appears to be the normal mode of infestation.

Consequently, these two series of experiments show that, in the first case, migration through the host's body can be theoretically replaced by an intermediate host, and in the second case, that in a normal host, migration may be suppressed in favor of direct development, but that this property is partly retained in an abnormal host.

Adult nematodes occur in the lungs, bronchi, and trachea of their hosts, and from a theoretical standpoint it would be interesting to find out whether such a localization is primary or secondary. The problem remains unsolved as to whether these worms have not yet reached the stage of gut parasites, or whether they have passed beyond this stage and evolved in a new direction.

All lungworms first enter the gut in the larval stage and migrate secondarily into the lungs via the blood stream. L₃ is ensheathed in the soil (*Dictyocaulus*), remains within the egg (*Syngamus*), or is formed in an intermediate host that has eaten the egg or into which the larvae penetrate (*Metastrongylus, Protostrongylus*). Moreover, in both cases in which no intermediate host exists, an optional paratenic host may occur in which L₃ can survive for a considerable time. Curiously enough, the above lungworms all belong to the same suborder *Strongylina* and are placed within closely related families.

Strongylines contain species that occur in most orders of vertebrates except fishes and are consequently bound to land vertebrates only.

Lungworms are found exclusively in mammals and their presence in the form of morphologically specialized species in porpoises, whales, and sea lions is of especial interest, since neither cetaceans nor pinnipeds harbor adult strongyles in their gut.

All intestinal species of strongylines whose life history is known enter the gut either as third stage larvae and become adult without migrating, or penetrate into the skin and migrate via the blood stream and the lungs into the gut. As mentioned above, lungworms have two types of life histories: either the third stage larva is free-living or contained within a paratenic host (*Dictyocaulus, Syngamus*), or the life

cycle contains an intermediate host (*Metastrongylus, Protostrongylus*). No skin-penetrating larvae have been reported so far for lungworms.

Parasitism of cetaceans and pinnipeds by strongylines must have occurred at a time when these mammals were still terrestrial or led a semi-aquatic life since, otherwise, they could not have had the occasion to become infested. Lungworms from seals are closely related to those from carnivores, whereas those from whales and porpoises must have been isolated within their hosts at an earlier date as they show a marked tendency to becoming morphologically specialized if one judges by the gradual reduction of the copulatory bursa of the males. Although seals return to land during the mating season, it is more than probable that they acquire their lungworms through an intermediate host since, in captivity, they do not become infested even when kept in the same enclosure with infested individuals (Dougherty & Herman).

To discover what is the most primitive type of life history in strongylines, it is necessary to compare the larval development with that of free-living worms, and consequently the most nearly original type will be found where L₃, although ensheathed, is free-living. Such larvae may enter the gut in either of two ways: L₃ may penetrate into the skin of the host and be carried through the blood stream, reach the lungs, break through the alveoli and enter the gut via the trachea; or L₃ may be swallowed by the final host and become adult in the gut without migrating. At first sight, this latter possibility appears to be the simplest mode of entrance, yet *Strongyloides*, one of the most primitive nematodes parasitic in vertebrates, and, in spite of its name, only very distantly related to strongylines, follows the skin route with subsequent migration through the blood and the lungs into the gut (Fig. 125). On the other hand, judging from the data available, it would seem that this primitive mode of access to the gut is being gradually lost, since in many species of ancylostomids infestation occurs directly through the mouth without subsequent migration. In *Ancylostoma duodenale*, both modes of infestation have been retained and the skin route appears to be more frequent than the direct route. In *Oswaldocruzia* the indirect route is entirely lost and only the direct route retained. In *Dictyocaulus*, the larvae enter via the gut but migrate subsequently to the lungs. *D. viviparus*, moreover, may have an optional paratenic host in its life history.

A subsequent modification of this primitive type

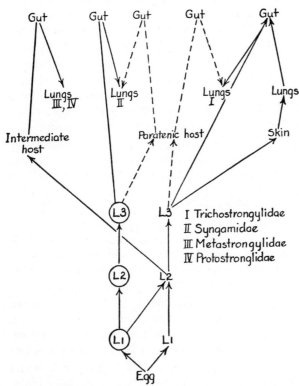

FIG. 125. Diagram of the passage of strongylines into the lungs.

of life cycle occurs when L_3 ceases to be free-living and remains within the egg or hatches under certain conditions only (temperature). When swallowed with the egg, the larvae hatch in the host gut and migrate via the blood to the lungs and bronchi. Here, also, a paratenic host is a secondary acquisition. In this case, it enables L_3 to survive adverse conditions and it has also been found to have a neutralizing effect on the various strains of *Syngamus* from different hosts (Clapham).

The fact that L_3 is no longer free-living nor formed within the egg must be interpreted as a more recent acquisition that may have interesting consequences in regard to its life history. The egg either contains a first stage larva that does not hatch, or should it hatch, the larva molts once only. In both cases the larvae cannot survive for a long time and must either be eaten or penetrate into an intermediate host where they can reach the L_3 stage. When the

intermediate host is eaten by the final host, the larvae migrate from the gut via the blood stream into the lungs.

It is clear that in strongylines, the habit of living in the lungs is a secondary acquisition and that these forms have derived from forms living originally in the gut. Moreover, as the accompanying diagram shows, four different groups of lungworms appear to have arisen independently. Curiously enough, these four groups correspond to four distinct families as recognized by taxonomists.

In no other group of nematodes is it as yet possible to furnish an analysis of the probable lines of evolution followed by the species as in the above mentioned suborder. The migration of ascarids has been interpreted in different ways, and for instance in *Ascaris lumbricoides* it might be due to the disappearance of an intermediate host. However, migration does not occur in all of the species and only partly in others closely related. In *Toxascaris* and *Ascaridia* the L_2 larvae that hatch from the egg in the gut of the host burrow deeply into the mucosa where they remain until they have molted again; the L_3 larvae then return into the gut lumen and become adult. Migration through the lungs also occurs in *Ascaris columnaris* Leidy, *Parascaris equorum* (Goeze), *Neoascaris vitulorum* (Goeze), and *Toxocara canis* (Werner), although in the latter species L_3 larvae are sometimes found encysted in mice and other hosts. Consequently, the failure of certain larvae to penetrate into the capillaries might be due to the fact that they are too large to be swept along by the blood stream (Chandler, Alicata, & Chitwood).

Oxyuroids, although taxonomically related to ascaroids, appear to have evolved on totally different lines. Their direct life cycle and their location in the end gut of their host, where in some cases (see page 101) they multiply without ever leaving the gut, appear to relate them to free-living species. Their presence in enormous numbers in reptiles and in all of their hosts in a region of the gut, where fermentation takes place, seems to indicate that physiologically they are much closer to saprophagous forms than to true parasites.

Spiruroids and filarioids are obviously derived from distinct groups although certain cases of convergence are apparent. The Guinea worm, for instance, closely resembles a filarioid, yet its life cycle shows that it is a spiruroid, invading its host via the gut and passing secondarily into the connective tissue. In contrast, filarioids never pass through the gut and always penetrate via the skin where they are deposited by the intermediate host.

Host specificity in parasitic nematodes will be discussed in a special chapter, but it does not furnish much additional evidence of the different ways in which these worms have become adapted to parasitism. Of polyphyletic origin, the parasitic species appear to have evolved to a certain extent on morphological lines, although no fundamentally new types, distinct from the free-living forms, have occurred. Their possible evolution along physiologically specialized lines will be examined together with the problem of host specificity.

REFERENCES

BAER, J. G. 1946. Le Parasitisme. 232 pp., 135 figs., 5 pls. Lausanne et Paris.

BOVIEN, P. 1937. Some types of associations between nematodes and insects. *Vidensk. Medd. Dansk Naturh. För.*, 101:1–114, 31 figs.

CHANDLER, A. C., ALICATA, J. E., & CHITWOOD, M. B. 1941. Parasites of vertebrates. *Introduction to nematology*, pp. 267–301, figs. 179–200.

CHITWOOD, B. G. 1941. Life history. General discussion. *Introduction to nematology*, pp. 242–45.

CHITWOOD, B. G., & M. B. 1937. Introduction. *Introduction to nematology*, pp. 1–6, 2 figs.

CHRISTIE, J. R. 1941. Parasites of invertebrates. *Introduction to nematology*, pp. 246–66, figs. 165–178.

CHU, T. 1936. Studies on the life history of *Rhabdias fuscovenosa* var. *catanensis* (Rizzo 1902) new rank. *J. Parasit.*, 22:140–60.

CLAPHAM, PH. 1939. On flies as intermediate hosts of *S. trachea. J. Helm.* 17:61–64.

———. 1939. Three new intermediate vectors for *Syngamus trachea. Ibid.*, 17:191–92.

DOUGHERTY, E. C. 1944. The Lungworms (Nematoda: Pseudalidae) of the Odontoceti. Part I. *Parasitology*, 36:80–94, 13 figs.

———. 1945. A review of the genus *Crenosoma* Molin, 1861 (Nematoda: Trichostrongylidae); its history, taxonomy, adult morphology and distribution. *Proc. Helm. Soc. Wash.*, 12:44–62, 3 figs.

———. 1946. The genus *Aleurostrongylus* Cameron, 1927 (Nematoda: Metastrongylidae) and its relatives; with descriptions of *Parafilaroides* gen. nov. and *Angiostrongylus gubernaculatus* sp. nov. *Ibid.*, 13:16–26, 2 figs.

———. 1949. A list of the Trichostrongylid lungworms (Phylum Nematoda) and a key to the six genera. *Parasitology*, 39:218–21, 2 figs.

———. 1949a. The phylogeny of the nematode family Metastrongylidae Leiper (1909): a correlation of host and symbiote evolution. *Ibid*, pp. 222–34, 27 figs.

DOUGHERTY, E. C., & HERMAN, C. M. 1947. New species of the genus *Parafilaroides* Dougherty, 1946 (Nematoda: Metastrongylidae), from sea-lions with a list of the lungworms of the Pinnipedia. *Proc. Helm. Soc. Wash.* 14:77–87, 3 figs.

FUELLEBORN, F. 1928. Ueber den Infektionsweg bei *Rhabdias bufonis* (*Rhabdonema nigrovenosum*) des Frosches nebst Versuchen ueber die Lymphzirkulation des letzteren. *Centralbl. Bakt. Parasit. Orig.* 109:444–62, 1 pl.

GOODEY, T. 1924. The anatomy and life history of the nematode *Rhabdias fuscovenosa* (Railliet) from the grass snake *Tropidonotus natrix. J. Helm.*, 2:51–64.

JOYEUX, CH., & BAER, J. G. 1934. Les hôtes d'attente dans le cycle évolutif des helminthes. *Biol. Med.*, Paris, 24:1–25, 6 figs.

JOYEUX, CH., & GAUD, J. 1946. Recherches helminthologiques marocaines. *Arch. Inst. Past. Maroc.*, 3:383–461, 21 figs.

MAUPAS, E. 1899. La mue et l'enkystement chez les nématodes. *Arch. Zool. Exp.* (3), 7:563–628, 29 figs., pls. 16–18.

SEURAT, L. G. 1920. Histoire naturelle des nématodes de la Berbérie. *Alger*, vi + 221 pp., 34 figs.

STEINER, G. 1925. The problem of host selection and host specialization of certain plant infesting nemas and its application to the study of nemic pests. *Phytopathology*, 15: 499–534, 8 figs.

YORKE, W., & MAPLESTONE, P. A. 1926. The Nematode parasites of Vertebrates. 536 pp., 307 figs. London and Philadelphia.

Pentastomida

Pentastomids occupy a relatively isolated place among invertebrates. The presence of a non-segmented body cavity, but of metamerically arranged muscles, and that of a chitinous tegument with numerous glands, have made it difficult to assign pentastomids to any certain position among what might eventually be considered as related groups. Most recent authors (Heymons) consider them as being intermediate between annelids and arthropods, and nearer to the former than to the latter. The complete absence of both circulatory and respiratory systems on the one hand, and the structure of the nervous system with its numerous nerves leading to sensory organs on the other do not aid much in determining the possible taxonomic position of this group. If, however, the developmental stages and postlarval stages are examined, it appears clear that pentastomids cannot be related to annelids. In the course of its larval development, a pentastomid passes through three stages that are usually clearly defined. First, the so-called primary larva (embryo) is formed within the egg and second, after hatching and molting several times it becomes quiescent, encysted within the tissues of an intermediate host. The third larval stage, sometimes known as the migratory larval stage, corresponds to the infestive larva and will subsequently become adult when eaten by an appropriate final host (Fig. 129).

Such a succession of larval stages is highly reminiscent of the larval development of arthropods and bears no relationship to the so very characteristic transformations of the annelid larvae. The formation of the embryo together with the very first developmental stages have not been observed in many cases, yet in *Armillifer armillatus* (Wym.) these stages have been described as closely resembling the initial stages in arthropods. Considerably more research

work will be necessary both on the formation of the embryo and on the postembryonic development, before a definite solution can be reached.

The anterior region of the semisegmented body is usually recognizable by the presence of two pairs of powerful hooks situated on either side of the mouth opening. The latter is maintained open by a chitinous ring, and leads directly into an esophagus without any trace of movable parts. The gut is straight and opens at the posterior end of the body.

The two pairs of hooks are sometimes borne on pedunculated appendages, capable of independent movements, but are never segmented (*Cephalobaena, Raillietiella*). The hooks possess an autonomous musculature that enables them to be withdrawn into the teguments. In the genera *Sebekia*, *Leiperia*, and *Linguatula*, each hook is double in both pairs, while in the genus *Porocephalus* only the more laterally placed pair of hooks is double (Figs. 126, 127).

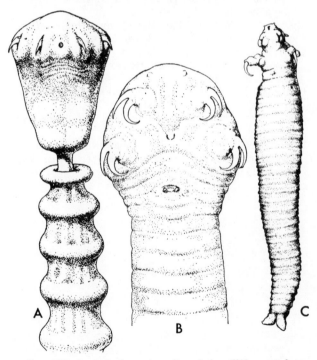

FIG. 126. A. Anterior extremity of *Armillifer annulatus* (Baird). B. Head of *Leiperia gracilis* Hey. & Vitzth. C. Entire specimen of *Raillietiella mabuiae* Hey. (Heymons).

106

The sexes are separate and in most cases sexual dimorphism is not marked except in the genus *Armillifer* where the difference in size and also in shape of the female contrasts with the smaller male (Fig. 128).

The anterior region of this larva bears a curiously shaped perforating apparatus located in front of the mouth. The latter leads into a simple sac-shaped gut that does not open at the posterior end of the

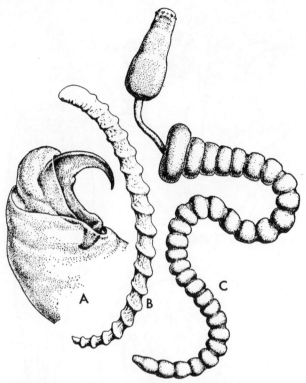

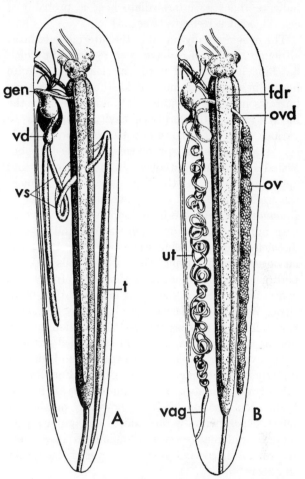

FIG. 127. A. Claw of *Cephalobaena tetrapoda* Hey. B. *Armillifer armillatus* (Wyman). C. Female of *Armillifer pomeroyi* Woodb. (Heymons).

FIG. 128. *Waddycephalus teretiusculus* Baird. A. Male. B. Female. fdr.—frontal glands. gen.—male sexual pore. ov.—ovary. ovd.—oviduct. t.—testis. ut.—uterus. vag.—vagina. vd.—vas deferens. vs.—seminal vesicle (Spencer in Heymons).

From a biological standpoint, pentastomids are unique among parasites, since the adults occur only in the lungs and air passages of vertebrates and, moreover, since the hosts most frequently parasitized are reptiles. A single species, *Reighardia sternae* (Dies.), has been recorded from air sacs in birds, and four very closely related species of the genus *Linguatula* from the nasal passages of carnivores. Curiously enough, larval stages of nearly all the known genera occur in a very great number of vertebrates including fishes, birds, and mammals, yet all of these hosts belong to either terrestrial or fresh-water faunas.

The number of eggs laid by a single female can be enormous; it has been estimated that a female of *Linguatula serrata* Froehl. is capable of producing several million eggs. The larvae that hatch from the egg bear two pairs of mobile appendages, each of which is terminated by a retractile, chitinous hook.

larva. Here there is usually found a "caudal" appendage that sometimes bears spines (*Porocephalus*). The body cavity of the primary larva contains several groups of glandular cells that open on the ventral surface in front of the mouth, and at the base of the anterior pair of appendages.

In certain cases, the eggs appear to be very resistant to definite changes in the surrounding medium. It has been ascertained experimentally that those of *Kiricephalus coarctatus* (Dies.), a parasite of the Indigo snake, *Drymarchon corais couperi* Holbr. in this country, are killed within forty-eight hours when exposed to a temperature of 37° C., but, on the other hand, are able to survive freezing and a temperature as low as 5° C. for over sixty days. This would tend to indicate that the intermediate host is probably a cold-blooded vertebrate (Keegan).

The eggs normally hatch in the intermediate host, although several cases have been reported in which hatching has occurred partly in either the definite host or in eggs maintained outside the host. The larva burrows into the intestinal wall, and either via the blood stream or the peritoneal cavity gains access to various tissues. The larva now enters into the quiescent stage, loses its appendages, and becomes encysted in the host's tissues. It grows slowly and apparently feeds on the fluids that pass through the walls of the cyst. After several molts, eight in *Linguatula serrata*, the body is found to be covered with numerous rows of minute spines and to give distinct evidence of being segmented (Fig. 129). The larva now escapes from the cyst and falls into the peritoneal cavity where it moves about freely and continues to feed on the fluids and cells that occur there. When such a larva is swallowed by an appropriate host, it reaches its final destination by migrating up the esophagus and into the nasal passages in carnivores, or by piercing the gut wall and entering directly into the lung in reptilian hosts. For *Linguatula serrata*, the natural intermediate hosts are usually herbivorous mammals. It is, however, possible to infest experimentally rats, mice, and guinea pigs. Twenty different species of mammals have been recorded as harboring the larval forms of this species in nature.

Larval development of *Porocephalus clavatus* (Wyman), a species occurring in the lungs of South American snakes, has been obtained experimentally in mice but not in guinea pigs, rabbits, dogs, or pigeons. The natural host for this larva appears to be the opossum.

This type of life cycle appears to be that most commonly found, although several authors, particularly Heymons, consider that direct development without an intermediate host can also occur. Their conclusions are based on finding larval pentastomids free or encysted in the tissues or the body cavity of snakes that simultaneously harbor the adult forms in their lungs. Yet very definite evidence has been furnished that *Kiricephalus coarctatus* (Dies.) cannot

develop directly, even when eggs are fed to experimental hosts over a period of several months (Keegan). It is, however, necessary to draw attention

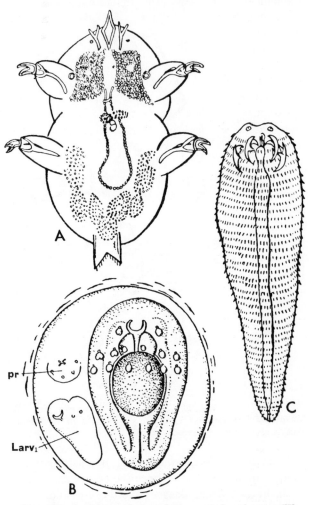

FIG. 129. A. Primary larva of *Porocephalus clavatus* (Wyman). B. Encysted larva of *Linguatula serrata* Fröhl. C. Mature larva of *Linguatula serrata* Fröhl. Larv.₁—preceding molt. pr.—first molt (Heymons).

to the fact that absolutely nothing precludes the final host from being also an intermediate host. The presence of larval forms of the identical species found in the lungs may be explained in different ways. In a normal infestation, some of the infestive larvae swallowed by the snake may not find their way to the lung but remain within the body cavity without growing. A snake harboring pentastomids may readily swallow eggs produced by its own parasites, and the larvae encyst in the tissues as in a normal intermediate host. In other words, this would imply a possible mechanism analogous to autoheteroxenous nematodes of the *Trichinella*-type.

On the other hand, if, as is postulated, a final host is continually able to reinfest itself with eggs from its own parasites and the larvae would be able to develop into adults *in situ*, this would invariably lead to such massive infestations that the existence of both the host and the parasite would be menaced.

It is particularly interesting to record that no larval pentastomid has ever been found in an invertebrate and that, on the other hand, many species of warm-blooded animals can act as intermediate hosts for reptilian parasites. This is particularly evident in the genus *Armillifer* which occurs almost exclusively in African boas and vipers, and of which the larval stages have been found in no less than forty-two different species of mammals belonging to all the orders that occur in the bush, and consequently, never in perissodactyles or in elephants!

On comparing a list of pentastomid parasites with their hosts, it is found that many genera have been reported from hosts that are today widely separated and live on different continents. *Sebekia* occurs in both African and Asiatic crocodiles and also in South American alligators. *Leiperia* and *Alofia* occur only in African and South American crocodiles. *Sambonia* is found in varanids from Africa, Asia, and Australia; *Porocephalus* from African and South American snakes; *Kiricephalus* in both American and Indo-Malagasy colubrids. The genus *Reighardia*, with its single species *R. sternae* (Dies.), is found in terns and gulls from lakes and rivers throughout the world. Finally, *Linguatula* is found in both African and South American felines.

On a closer examination of the species, it is observed that 43 per cent of the genera and 42 per cent of the species have been reported from snakes and 22 per cent of the genera and 28 per cent of the species from crocodiles. Lizards harbor 14 per cent of the genera and 18 per cent of the species, and tortoises, birds, and mammals each harbor 7 per cent of the genera. There is, consequently, not the slightest doubt that the typical hosts for pentastomids are reptiles with a total of 87 per cent of the genera and 90 per cent of the species.

From the data collected above, it is clear that pentastomids have been associated with reptiles for a very great length of time and that they must have existed during Mesozoic times, when reptiles were much more widely distributed than they are today. It is usually assumed that snakes arose from a varanid-type of ancestor in early Cretaceous times, whereas both lizards and crocodiles existed in the Triassic period and, consequently, are the older hosts (Romer).

Reptiles originated as terrestrial vertebrates, some of them, like the crocodiles, becoming adapted later to fresh water. Assuming that the Mesozoic ancestors harbored pentastomids, these must necessarily have completed their life cycle in reptiles only and consequently, the latter became infested by eating their congeners and, later perhaps, by eating fishes, as do the present-day crocodiles. It is more than likely that the carnivorous dinosaurs, the dominant land reptiles of Mesozoic times, also harbored pentastomids and that the present parasites are derived from these distant ancestors. That the parasites have not evolved to a great extent since is borne out by the presence of identical genera occurring today on distinct continents. It is more than probable, however, that the number of species was much greater than it is today and that many of them must have died out at approximately the same time that their hosts became extinct.

As mentioned above, snakes are more recent than the other reptiles and consequently must have become parasitized also at a later date. The fact that today they harbor the largest proportion of both genera and species would indicate that they were better equipped to eat the first mammals that appeared in late Mesozoic times than the ruling reptiles from which they had originated, but which soon disappeared after the advent of mammals. This would explain why the present-day snake pentastomes are found as larval stages in mammals, whereas the other reptilian forms occur in fish and to a lesser extent in small reptiles and mammals.

The adaptation of pentastomids to mammals, and especially to felines, necessarily occurred at a much later date but appears to have remained an isolated success that, so far, has not been repeated in other carnivorous mammals. This is also true for their adaptation to birds, although it is not clear why other birds that live in the same environment as gulls and terns and also feed on fishes, are not parasitized.

Consequently, host isolation and ecological segregation as to food habits appear to be the chief reasons for host specificity in pentastomids. The true nature of this specificity, of course, can only be discovered experimentally and so far no experiments have been made.

The fact that pentastomids have not been able to evolve to a very large extent in either mammalian or avian organisms in the course of time is no doubt due to their being insufficiently adapted to such a form of parasitism. Their chitinous teguments, on which is spread a secretion from the hypodermal glands, and the presence of numerous sensory organs in their skin are reminiscent of free-living organisms, especially since no respiratory organs are present. The absence of mouth parts would also imply that their nourishment must have been either liquid or semisolid.

Accidental ingestion of such free-living organisms by reptiles would cause the former to escape from the gut by the shortest way, i.e., by piercing the gut wall, since they are well-equipped for tearing the tissues. In this way, the pentastomids would fall into the lungs or air sacs where they would find conditions not very different from those in the external environment. The passage to warm-blooded vertebrates has been less successful as is witnessed today by the very small number of species that have survived in so different a habitat. The anatomical structure of birds enabled pentastomids, escaping from the gut, to enter the air sacs where the genus *Reighardia* is established today. In mammals, both the structure of the lung and its location within the pleural cavity, separated from the peritoneal cavity by the diaphragm, would render such a passage from the gut into the lungs impossible. Migration from the intestine into the mouth and into the nasal passages in mammals is consequently a secondary acquisition, a location that enables the parasites to escape from too high a temperature and at the same time to have access to air.

It is therefore clear that conditions of so non-specialized a nature as occur in the lungs of reptiles have saved pentastomids from extinction and, consequently, this archaic group owes its present-day existence to having adapted itself to parasitism.

REFERENCES

HEYMONS, R. 1935. Pentastomida. *Bronn's Kl. Ord. Tier.* 5 (4), vol. 1, 268 pp., 148 figs.

KEEGAN, H. L. 1943. Observations on the pentastomid *Kiricephalus coarctatus* (Diesing) Sambon, 1910. *Trans. Am. Micros. Soc.*, 62:194–99, 4 figs.

PENN, G. H. 1942. The life history of *Porocephalus crotali*, a parasite of the Louisiana muskrat. *J. Parasit.*, 28:277–83, 2 figs.

ROMER, A. S. 1945. Vertebrate paleontology. viii + 687 pp., 377 figs. Chicago.

STILES, CH. W. 1891. Bau und Entwicklungsgeschichte von *Pentastomum proboscideum* Rud. und *Pentastomum subcylindricum* Dies. *Zeitschr. f. wiss. Zool.*, 52:85–157, pls. 7–8.

Acanthocephala

Acanthocephalans form a clearly defined group of parasitic organisms that does not appear to possess the slightest phylogenic relationship with any other phylum. Although, superficially, they sometimes resemble roundworms, no anatomical evidence exists for assuming them to be related. Nor can they be referred to flatworms, even to ancestral forms, on account of the structure of the oocyte and the mode of segmentation of the egg. All flatworms have ectolecithal eggs, whereas in acanthocephalans vitelline materials are regularly distributed throughout the ovoplasm. Following the fourth cleavage of the embryonic cells, the cell walls disappear and the embryonic mass becomes syncytial. This syncytial condition is retained throughout the subsequent stages and consequently occurs in both the larvae and the adults. The number of nuclei is constant in a given species, although in several cases they break up subsequently into a considerable number of fragments. At no stage of development is there ever found a gut or any trace whatever of a digestive system. A proboscis, armed with several rows of hooks, is situated at the anterior end of the body and there are sometimes spines, arranged symmetrically, on the body surface (Fig. 130). The sexes are always separate; the females are usually somewhat larger than the males and the males possess an evaginable copulatory apparatus that is withdrawn into the end of the body (Fig. 131). Eggs are always numerous and are provided characteristically with four membranes, the two outer ones of which form the eggshell proper. Within the egg is formed an embryo which gives rise to the first stage larva, known as the *acanthor*. The latter bears a group of peculiarly shaped hooks, inserted at the anterior end of the larva. Here, also, is attached a set of muscles by which the proximal end of each hook is attached to the body wall. Conse-quently, when the muscles contract, the hooks are drawn in and their extremities point *forward*. By operating these hooks, the acanthor is able to pierce the tissues of the intermediate host (Figs. 132, 133).

The life cycle of acanthocephalans is interesting in more ways than one, but especially since no single free-living stage has ever been reported and, conse-quently, the eggs never hatch normally outside the body of the host It is true, however, that under certain artificial conditions, such as drying and re-wetting the eggs, they may be induced to hatch spontaneously and liberate the acanthor. Yet such artificial hatching is possible only in certain cases and exclusively with eggs removed directly from the body cavity of the female, and never with eggs recovered from the feces of the host. This implies that the outer egg membranes must undergo some kind of chemical or physical alteration after the eggs have been expelled into the gut lumen of the host, making the shell tougher and more resistant to environmental conditions.

In spite of the great number of larval forms reported from different hosts, the life cycle of acanthocephalans is not yet sufficiently known in all its details. An arthropod intermediate host is essential in all cases that have been studied so far and a paratenic host occurs frequently. Although the latter is usually optional, it appears in many cases, from a purely ecological standpoint, to have become obligatory.

When eggs are swallowed by an appropriate intermediate host, an arthropod, the acanthor is liberated from its envelopes and pierces the gut wall, remaining at first attached to the outer surface of the intestine beneath the peritoneum. The acanthor undergoes a distinct metamorphosis of which different stages have been recognized (see Meyer), but the final outcome of which is the transformation of the embryo into an infestive larva, the so-called juvenile. Once the acanthor has pierced the host's gut and is located beneath the peritoneum, it loses its larval hooks and enters upon the so-called acanthella stage, during which it gradually builds up the future organs of the adult, especially the proboscis together with its hooks

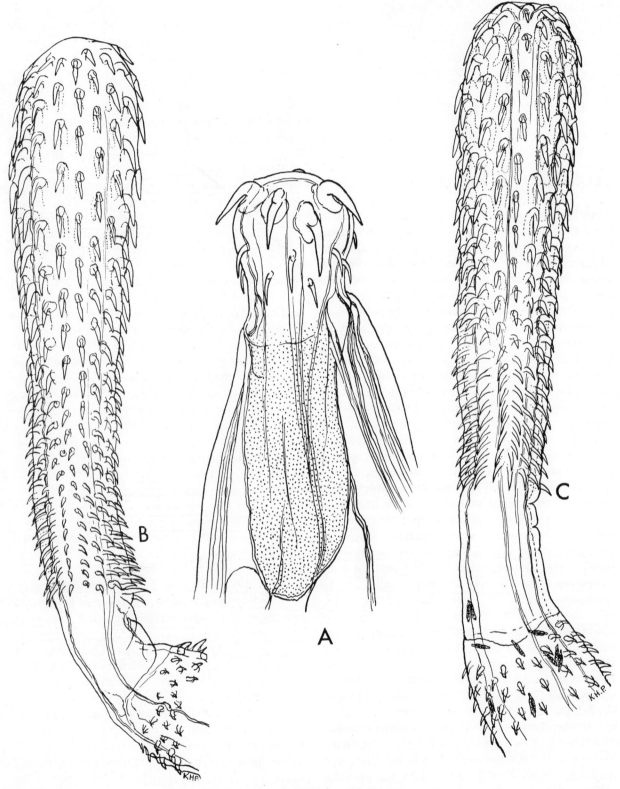

Fig. 130 (*see legend on opposite page*).

which are definitely formed in the larva and have already attained their full size within the intermediate host. When the proboscis is fully formed, the larvae have usually become detached from the surface of the gut and are found free in the body cavity of the intermediate host. Metamorphosis is now completed and the larvae retract their rostellum completely within the body, the skin of which has become greatly thickened. At this stage also the integumentary vascular system first appears. The acanthellas have now reached the stage in which rudiments of all the organs are formed and here it is easy to distinguish the sexes from one another. It is a young acanthocephalan, a juvenile, i.e., an infestive larva. Consequently, the life history of acanthocephalans may be divided into four distinct phases: within the egg the acanthor is formed, it emerges within the gut of the intermediate host, loses its larval hooks, and becomes an acanthella that progressively develops into a juvenile. In the most direct life cycles, the intermediate host is eaten by an appropriate definitive host; the juvenile is liberated and immediately attaches itself by its proboscis to the intestinal mucosa and becomes adult, *in situ*.

Curiously enough, although the proboscis penetrates deeply into the mucosa and sometimes even into the submucosa of the host, there is hardly any trace of inflammation. This is, of course, the case for all normal infestations because in heavy infestations such as occur in domestic animals the picture is different and necrosis of the host's tissues may result.

Adult acanthocephalans have been reported only from vertebrates where species occur in nearly all of the known classes. From a purely ecological standpoint, vertebrate hosts may be divided into two groups according to their food habits, namely, those that feed on aquatic organisms and those that feed only on terrestrial plants and animals. Curiously enough, this somewhat summary classification, that is based entirely on host habits, corresponds also to the major taxonomic subdivisions, all the "terrestrial" forms occurring in the *Archiacanthocephala*, whereas the "aquatic" forms are reported exclusively for the *Palaeacanthocephala, Gyracanthocephala* and *Neoacanthocephala*. Moreover, in land acantho-

cephalans the eggs possess a thick, heavy shell, whereas in aquatic species the shell remains thin

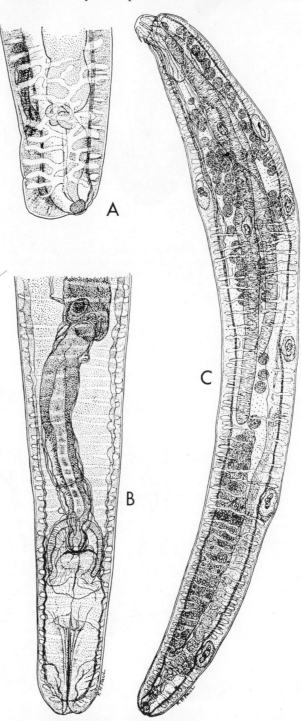

FIG. 130. A. Proboscis of *Neoechinorhynchus emydis* (Leidy). B–C. Proboscides of *Illiosentis cetratus* V. Cl. (Van Cleave).

FIG. 131. Lacunar system in the hypodermis. A. *Neoechinorhynchus crassus* V. Cl. B. *Neoechinorhynchus agilis* (Rud.). C. *Neoechinorhynchus rutili* (Müll.) (Van Cleave).

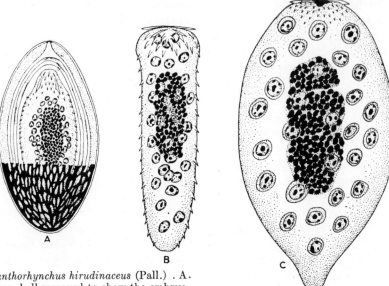

FIG. 132. *Macracanthorhynchus hirudinaceus* (Pall.) . A. Egg with part of outer shell removed to show the embryo. B. Freshly hatched acanthor. C. Acanthor beginning to develop in body cavity of beetle larva (Meyer).

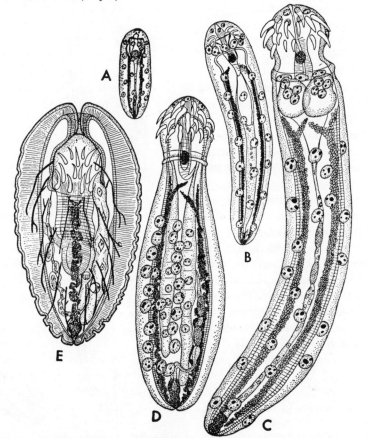

FIG. 133. *Macracanthorhynchus hirudinaceus* (Pall.) larvae from the body cavity of a beetle larva. A–D. Successive stages of acanthellae. E. Encysted infestive larva (All drawings are to the same scale.) (Van Cleave).

(Van Cleave). Consequently, it is easy to understand that in the first case, intermediate hosts will be terrestrial arthropods (insects or insect larvae) and that in the second case, they will belong to the aquatic fauna (isopods, amphipods, ostracods, etc.). The presence of juveniles of the genus *Neoechinorhynchus* has been reported from the foot of snails belonging to the genera *Campeloma* Raf., *Pleurocera*, and *Ceriphasia*, in this country where they have evidently become re-encapsulated subsequent to the arthropods being eaten by the snail. Experimental development of *Neoechinorhynchus emydis* (Leidy) occurs in ostracods (Lincicome) and consequently snails harboring these juveniles are paratenic hosts in which the acanthocephalan larvae are found encysted around the mouth and in the foot.[1]

In most cases, however, the paratenic host is a vertebrate that feeds on the arthropod intermediate host and in the gut of which the juvenile is unable to become adult. Re-encapsulation has been demonstrated experimentally with juveniles obtained from grass snakes, *Coelopeltis monspessulana* Boul. and fed to a tree frog, *Hyla arborea* L. from the body cavity of which the juvenile was later recovered (Joyeux & Baer).

Numerous juveniles of species parasitic in fishes have also been reported from the body cavity of their hosts. It appears that the same fish may be both final and intermediate host. The fish becomes a potential intermediate host if the larval acanthocephalid has not reached full development in the normal intermediate host. Eggs of *Leptorhynchoides thecatus* (Linton) fed to amphipods give rise to infestive juveniles in thirty-two days. When such larvae are fed to small black bass, they attach themselves to the intestinal mucosa and become adult. If, however, larvae less than thirty-two days old are fed to black bass, they do not remain in the gut, but pass through the wall and re-encapsulate in the body cavity (DeGuisti). Consequently, in this case, it is found that an appropriate final host may also become a potential intermediate host. Incidentally, this appears also as a case of double insurance for the

parasitic larva of finding a suitable host, since the small specimens of black bass are eaten by the larger ones.

On the other hand, many of the "aquatic" vertebrate hosts feed only occasionally on invertebrates, their usual diet consisting of small vertebrates. Whereas whales feed on plankton, seals and water birds eat fishes. Consequently paratenic hosts would greatly increase the chances for a life cycle being completed in the latter vertebrates.

Species of the genus *Centrorhynchus* frequently occur in birds of prey, and juveniles have been recorded from frogs, snakes, and even from small mammals, i.e., vertebrates that normally feed on insects and that consequently become potential intermediate hosts. In this case, however, the final host would only exceptionally feed on insects whereas the above paratenic hosts may constitute the staple food of birds of prey. Such is also the case for juveniles of the genus *Oncicola*, the adults of which occur in carnivores although the juveniles have been recovered from armadillos and opossums. Many other similar instances could be cited in other groups, showing that the paratenic hosts have become practically indispensable for completion of the life cycle.

There is no doubt about acanthocephalans having originated as parasites of fishes (see page 167) and that the original life cycle contained a single, invertebrate intermediate host. The fact that juveniles are able to re-encapsulate in vertebrate hosts that feed on arthropods has rendered possible the adaptation of acanthocephalans to such hosts as reptiles, birds, and mammals. In other words, the paratenic hosts have become ecological intermediate hosts. The adaptation to land vertebrates must have occurred in a similar fashion, yet the passage from an aquatic vertebrate to a terrestrial one is not clear. One might imagine that a land vertebrate, eating an aquatic vertebrate harboring juveniles, would become infested and that subsequently, the eggs of the acanthocephalans would be eaten by land arthropods, perhaps at first by isopods in which development may continue. A very interesting indication of such a mechanism can be found in *Acanthocephalus ranae* (Schrank), a species occurring in amphibians and of which the intermediate host is an aquatic isopod, *Asellus aquaticus* L. The passage from semi-aquatic vertebrates, such as amphibians, to a completely terrestrial form would be represented by *Plagiorhynchus formosus* Van Cleave from passerine birds, the inter-

[1] It is interesting to observe that a Limnaeid snail has also been reported by Meyer as harboring the European species *Neoechinorhynchus rutili* (Müll.) that occurs in fishes and the juveniles of which are also formed in ostracods. Snails apparently frequently feed on ostracods, as may be surmised from the discovery of tapeworm cysticercoids that normally develop in small crustaceans, in the stomach of Limnaeids (Joyeux, 1929. *Ann. Parasit,* 7:112–15).

mediate host of which is a land isopod *Armadillidium vulgare* (Latr.) (Sinitsin).

The passage from aquatic vertebrates to truly land vertebrates must have occurred at a comparatively recent period, judging from the distribution of the species and the hosts (see page 167).

No evidence can be gained from the life histories of acanthocephalans that might indicate even a distant affinity with other groups. The phylum stands out isolated yet clearly shows the way in which the original species, parasitic in fishes, have been able to pass secondarily into birds and mammals. Moreover, the evidence cited above of immature juveniles passing through the gut wall and re-encapsulating within the body cavity of fish that are also their normal hosts, would indicate a mechanism that apparently also appears in cestodes (see page 146).

The only apparent difference between an immature juvenile and an infestive one resides in the development of the gonad that has reached a more advanced stage in the latter than in the former. Consequently, one might assume that in normal infestations the parasites become adult as their proboscis penetrates into the host's mucosa, whereas in the former instance this does not occur, and the juveniles pass right through the gut wall. This of course does not imply a direct effect of the developing gonads but indicates, nonetheless, that some physiological modification does occur that enables the parasite to find in the host's gut the necessary conditions for its further development. That such conditions may not be very specialized is borne out by the distribution of the parasites in their hosts, and that indicates a closer relationship between hosts having common food habits rather than between those that possess phylogenic relationships.

REFERENCES

DeGuisti, D. L. 1939. Further studies on the life cycle of *Leptorhynchoides thecatus. J. Parasit. Supp.*, 25:22.

Joyeux, Ch., & Baer, J. G. 1934. Les Hôtes d'attente dans le cycle évolutif des helminthes. *Biologie médicale*, 24:1–25, 6 figs.

Lincicome, D. R. 1948. Observations on the life cycle of *Neoechinorhynchus emydis*, an acanthocephalan parasite of turtles. *J. Parasit. Supp.*, 34:25.

Meyer, A. 1932–33. Acanthocephala. *Bronn's Kl. Ord. Tier.* 4 (2), vol. 2, 582 pp., 383 figs., 1 pl.

Sinitsin, D. 1929. Note on an intermediate host for *Plagiorhynchus formosus. J. Parasit.*, 15:287.

Van Cleave, H. J. 1947. A critical review of terminology for immature stages in acanthocephalan life histories. *J. Parasit.*, 33:118–25, 1 fig., 2 pls.

———. 1948. Expanding horizons in the recognition of a phylum. *Ibid.*, 34:1–20.

Trematoda

Both from a morphological and a biological standpoint, it is possible to recognize two distinct groups of trematodes; the *Monogenea*, that are mostly ectoparasitic with direct larval development, and the *Digenea*, invariably endoparasitic with indirect development involving successive larval stages in such a way that from a single egg there finally arises a considerable number of infestive larvae.

The anatomy of monogenetic trematodes is closely related to that of certain rhabdocoel turbellarians and, consequently, differs fundamentally from that of digenetic trematodes. Aspidogastrids appear to constitute an isolated group that combines certain characters of the *Digenea* with a larval development as in *Monogenea*. The presence of these parasites in fresh-water clams and fishes, and in turtles, coupled with morphological and biological characters, appears to indicate a distinct evolutionary trend that has arisen during the past history of flatworms but that does not necessarily imply their having arisen from a common ancestral stock (Baer, 1946). There seems to be equal justification at present for considering these three groups of trematodes either as distinct phyla or as distinct orders of a single phylum.

MONOGENEA

It is difficult to determine the nature of parasitic adaptation in a group such as this, but some sort of evolutionary mechanism may be recognized that influences both the morphology and the life history of these parasites.

Monogenetic trematodes occur almost exclusively on fishes from which at least 95 per cent of the genera have been reported, the remainder being harbored by amphibians and reptiles (turtles). On fishes, the worms are usually attached to the gills or to the surface of the body and, in a few cases only, they have been reported from the cloaca, the ureters, or the body cavity. In amphibians and turtles, the monogenetic trematodes have been reported only from the upper segment of the gut and from the urinary bladder and quite exceptionally from the surface of the body.

The posterior end of the body is usually flattened and is known as the haptor[1] that often forms a complicated disc provided with hooks and suckers enabling the parasite to attach itself onto the host. From a purely morphological standpoint, it is possible to arrange the different types of haptors into a series of increasing complication but this sequence will not necessarily coincide with a phylogenic classification (see Fig. 134).

The eggs are often provided with long filaments by which they remain attached to the gills of the host or to surrounding vegetation, but in many cases no filaments occur and the eggs drop to the bottom.

The development of monogenetic trematodes is direct, and from the egg there hatches a larval form that gradually grows into an adult worm as a result of a very simple type of metamorphosis. Transformation of the larvae into adults always occurs on the host, no intermediate host being involved. The differences in life histories that may occur are mostly due to the rate of development, i.e., the larval stage is reached within the egg before hatching, a free-swimming larva being exceptional.

Although our knowledge of life histories in monogenetic trematodes is far from complete, the life cycles of members of at least eight families have been worked out in recent years so that it is possible to give a fairly accurate account of the principal phases.

Gyrodactylus from fresh-water fishes and *Isancistrum* from cephalopods appear to be viviparous, the larva forming directly within the uterus of the parent individual. Moreover, in both of these genera, the larvae are found to contain an embryo that itself contains a mass of embryonic cells. In other words, there may be as many as four "generations" enclosed

---

[1] The writer adopts the term proposed by Price, 1934 (*Proc. Helm. Soc. Wash.*, 1:34), but only insofar as applied to monogenetic trematodes.

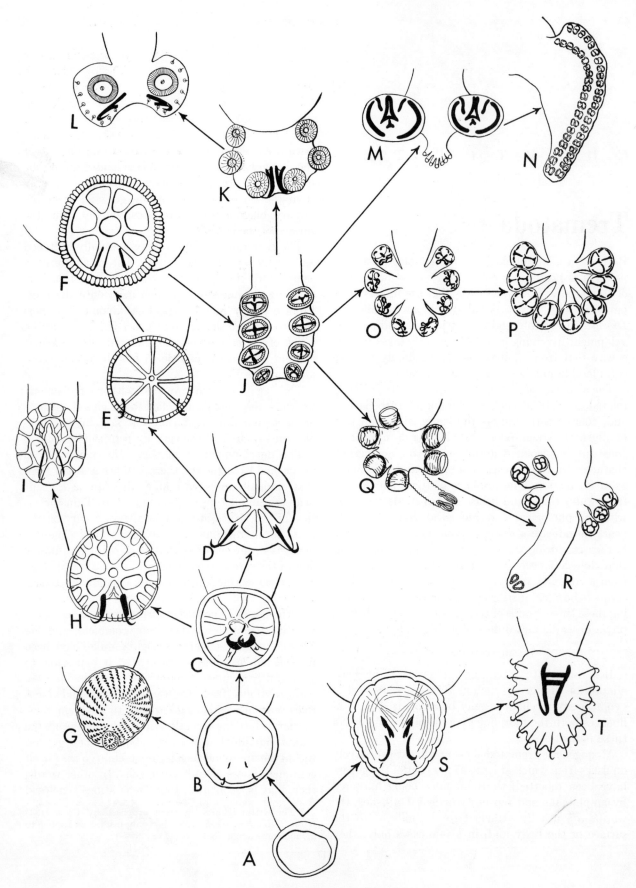

Fig. 134 (*see legend on opposite page*).

one within the other (Fig. 135). There is as yet no completely satisfactory explanation of this phenomenon that may be related both to polyembryony and

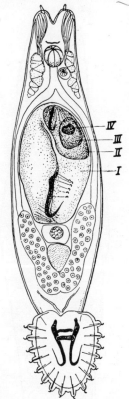

FIG. 135. *Gyrodactylus elegans* Nordm., showing four simultaneous generations I–IV (Fuhrmann).

to progenesis. If it were a case of polyembryony, the larvae would all have to be at the same stage of development since they would have been originally derived from the same egg, unless for some unknown reason there might exist here a differential rate of development. Even if this were the case, there would be no reason for the larvae being located one within another. Progenesis, on the other hand, without the presence of gonads has never yet been observed, and there is nothing to substantiate it in this case. It would be highly desirable for more research work to be executed on this subject which might also eventually shed new light on the development of digenetic trematodes.

FIG. 134. Diagrammatical evolution of the haptor in monogenetic trematodes. A. *Udonella.* B. *Nitzschia.* C. *Trochopus.* D. *Monocotyle.* E. *Tritestis.* F. *Tristoma.* G. *Acanthocotyle.* H. *Merizocotyle.* I. *Thaumatocotyle.* J. *Heterobothrium.* K. *Polystoma.* L. *Sphyranura.* M. *Anthocotyle.* N. *Microcotyle.* O. *Choriocotyle.* P. *Diclidophorus.* Q. *Rajonchocotyle.* R. *Pedocotyle.* S. *Benedenia.* T. *Gyrodactylus.*

Udonella caligorum Johnst. is remarkable among trematodes as it is the only species that occurs on parasitic copepods that are themselves attached to fishes. These worms always occur on caligids (see page 46). The eggs are attached to the host by a long filament ending in a disc. When the young worm hatches it is virtually mature, except for size (Fig. 137). The rate of growth and the time required to be-

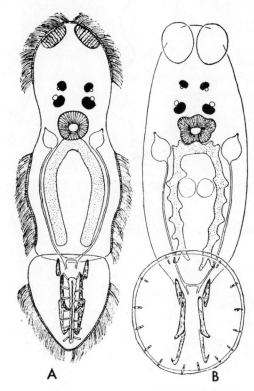

FIG. 136. *Benedenia melleni* (MacCallum). A. Freshly hatched, free-swimming larva. B. Young, immature worm with fully developed haptor (Jahn & Kuhn).

come fully mature have not been determined experimentally (Price, 1938).

Sphyranura oligorchis (Alvey) occurs on the gills and the surface of the body of a mud puppy, *Necturus maculosus* (Raf.). The eggs settle on the bottom as no filaments are present to attach them either to the host or to plants. They apparently have not yet undergone cleavage. Thirty days later the larva is fully formed and hatches. This larva is already in possession of a haptor similar to, although smaller than, that of the adult worm; but there is not yet any trace of either a digestive or a reproductive system. These larvae are very active at first and should they come into contact with a host, they immediately attach themselves to it and apparently migrate to the gills. The completely developed digestive system

must therefore be incubated for a certain time that varies from three to eleven days, at the end of which the egg hatches spontaneously and the larva emerges.

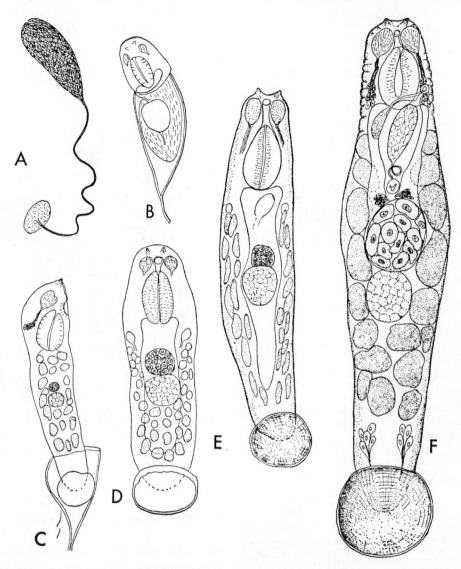

FIG. 137. *Udonella caligorum* Johnst. A. Egg attached to host. B–C. Larva emerging from egg. D–F. Gradual maturation of the worms (Price).

appears five days later and the gonads are mature fifteen days after the larva has become attached. Consequently, the whole life cycle is accomplished within about two months (Alvey).

The majority of egg-laying species, from both marine and fresh-water fishes, appear to have the same type of life cycle. From evidence gathered so far, the eggs never contain a larva when laid and

The larva is ciliated and nearly always possesses one or two pairs of pigmented eye spots that are sometimes retained in the adult or are resorbed. The haptor is distinctly visible, bearing the hooks and hooklets characteristic of the adult but not arranged according to a definite pattern. The digestive organs may be more or less well developed, yet there is never any trace of gonads at this stage. The cilia do not form a continuous layer around the body but are arranged in two and sometimes three bands encircling the larva. These cilia are shed as soon as the larva attaches itself to its host, the haptor then becomes definitely formed, and the genital organs mature gradually until full development is achieved (Fig. 136).

Dactylogyrus vastator Nyb., a gill parasite of carp fry, possesses two kinds of eggs, the production of which is apparently related to the surrounding temperature (Fig. 138). When compared to the normal

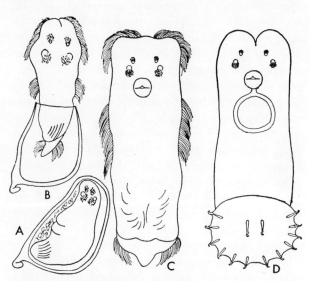

FIG. 138. *Dactylogyrus macracanthus* Wegener. A. Egg. B. Larva hatching. C. Free-swimming larva. D. Young worm attached to host showing development of the gut and haptor (Wilde).

eggs, that develop along the lines mentioned previously, the other type of eggs develop much more slowly and the adult worm usually dies after having produced such eggs. This is especially evident in the autumn, when the fishes lose their parasites and the eggs remain the whole winter in the mud, hatching in the following spring. This also explains why in carp hatcheries, mortality due to these parasites increases after a cold spell, since this coincides with the simultaneous hatching of a great number of these slowly developing eggs (Groben).

Such normal and late developing larvae have so far been observed in the above mentioned species of trematode only, but it is quite possible that the two types may occur in other species also. In *Polystoma integerrimum* Froehl., from the urinary bladder of the European grass frog, a similar mechanism has been observed although it is only indirectly related to the temperature (Gallien) (Fig. 139). The life history of this species is correlated with that of its

host since the grass frog, *Rana temporaria* L., remains in water only during the spawning season. Eggs are voided with urine and develop in the water.

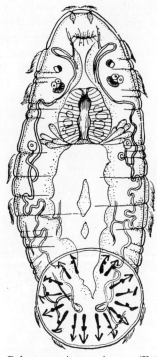

FIG. 139. *Polystoma integerrimum* (Fröhl), a freshly hatched gyrodactyloid larva (Fuhrmann).

The larva that emerges is strongly reminiscent of that described above, with three bands of cilia and a circular haptor. On attaching itself to the gills of a tadpole, the larva gradually acquires its genital organs, losing its cilia at the same time. The haptorial disc breaks up and is replaced by three pairs of suckers between which is located a pair of large hooks. As the gills of the tadpole are resorbed, the young trematode passes into the pharynx through the gut and into the urinary bladder which it enters from the cloaca. From data available, it appears that the trematode becomes sexually mature only when its host is ready to spawn for the first time. In the grass frog, this does not occur before three years and consequently at the end of this time the trematode is also ovigerous. This also explains why adult ovigerous polystomes are found only in the spring, when their hosts enter the water to spawn.

The initial rate of development of the larval trematodes has been found to be correlated with the rate of the tadpoles. When frog's eggs are incubated at

20°C. all the tadpoles that hatch are physiologically similar and develop at the same rate, provided that all other conditions are similar. Tadpoles less than eight days old bear external gills. When such tadpoles are placed with freshly hatched polystome larvae, the latter immediately attach themselves to the gills and undergo accelerated development. They become sexually mature within a very short time and each produces a single egg (Fig. 140). If tadpoles

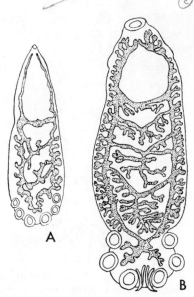

FIG. 140. *Polystoma integerrimum* (Fröhl). A. Neotonic adult. B. Normal adult (Gallien).

more than eight days old are used for this experiment, there is no acceleration in the rate of development of the parasites, the latter proceeding normally, as outlined previously.

The gut of larvae that attach themselves to tadpoles less than eight days old is always filled with blood from the host, and this never occurs when the tadpoles are older and the gills are covered with a thicker skin, since the larvae are unable to pierce the skin to reach the capillaries. It is clear that this neotenic development is primarily due to an excessively rich food supply (Gallien). When larvae hatched from eggs produced by neotenic forms fix themselves to older tadpoles, they undergo the usual slow development of the normal larvae. These results clearly show that there are not two distinct species involved here and that neoteny is not determined genetically, since the conditions are reversible. In the case of *P. integerrimum* the life cycles of both the parasite

and the host have become synchronized as a consequence of the selective influence that tends to eliminate not only the larvae that fail to attach themselves to an appropriate tadpole, but also those that might enter into more or less permanent contact with tadpoles belonging to other species of frogs. Selection is therefore due to ecological factors.

From a purely biological standpoint, this dual type of life cycle is particularly interesting, since the neotenic phase that appears when the first tadpoles are themselves developing enables the parasitic stages to be spread over a much larger area and, consequently, to infest a greater number of individual hosts in which, finally, even the more slowly developing larvae will become adult. Consequently, such intercalary generations play the same role as for instance the free-living, heterogonic generation of *Strongyloides* (see page 98), the schizogonic phase in sporozoans (see page 16), or even the larval stages in digenetic trematodes. None of these mechanisms are homologous, but their ultimate results are identical, yielding an increase in the number of parasitic larvae and, consequently, this should be regarded as an adaptive mechanism.

Diplozoon paradoxum v. Nordm. occurs on the gills of European cyprinids and is well known from the drawings found in all classical textbooks. In many instances, however, the figures are wrongly interpreted.

The egg of this species possess a single, long, coiled polar thread by which it remains attached to the gills. An egg hatches at the end of fifteen days and a larva of the usual ciliated type emerges. Its haptor bears two suckers with which it attaches itself to the host and almost immediately loses its cilia. In due course, the haptor becomes more clearly defined and a small sucker appears on the ventral surface of the larva. At the same time, there appears on the dorsal surface, and more posteriorly located than the sucker, a small fleshy protuberance. When the larva has reached this stage, it is able to remain alive for weeks and even months and was formerly described as an individual attributed to the genus *Diporpa* (Fig. 141). The haptor of the diporpa-stage may become modified subsequently, but there never appear more than two pairs of suckers. Subsequent development of diporpa larvae is possible only after two such larvae have become attached to one another by their ventral suckers and dorsal knobs respectively. To achieve this it is necessary for the larvae to twist themselves one around the other, so that finally one of the individuals is facing ventrally and the other dorsally. At this stage only do the gonads

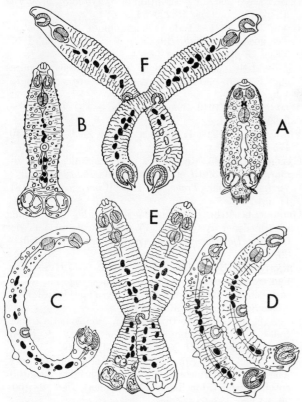

FIG. 141. Development of *Diplozoon paradoxum* Nordm. A. Freshly hatched, free-swimming larva. B. *Diporpa* larva. C–F. *Diporpa* larvae attaching themselves to one another. (Zeller).

first appear, together with two more pairs of suckers on the haptors. If one now tries to separate the two individuals, they are found to be completely fused together, all traces of the suckers having disappeared. Another consequence of this peculiar mode of development is that the vagina of one individual opens in the vicinity of both the uterus and the vas deferens of the other, so that cross-fertilization appears to be almost invariably assured although this is not necessarily the case. This "paradoxical twin" lives for a considerable length of time upon its host, and it is found that its sexual activity decreases and is finally halted in the winter months when ovary and testis are partly atrophied, but reproductive activity is renewed in the following spring. A large number of diporpa-larvae fail to find a partner and consequently die (Zeller). From a morphological standpoint, it is seen that the larvae attach themselves to

one another by a coaptation of the "snap fastener" type. It is utterly impossible to analyze coaptation satisfactorily.[2]

To sum up the life histories of monogenetic trematodes, it is found that development is direct and that the larvae that hatch from the egg gradually become adult worms without there being any intermediate stages. In certain cases, however, development may be accelerated and the parasites may be either viviparous (*Gyrodactylus, Isancistrum*) or emerge as young adults from the egg (*Udonella*). The life history may be complicated by the introduction of neotenic larvae (*Polystoma*) or by the fact that sexual maturity can be attained only after two individuals have become partly fused together, forming a twin organism (*Diplozoon*). No single instance is known, so far, of any trace of an indirect life cycle occurring in monogenetic trematodes. From the study of their life histories, the latter appear more closely related to temnocephalans and to rhabdocoelian turbellarians than to any other group of flatworms (Baer, 1931).

Monogenetic trematodes occur most frequently on the body surface or the gills of fishes, and when present in large numbers they may sometimes cause pathological conditions especially to fishes kept in captivity or in hatcheries. In exceptional cases, the worms may even break through into the capillaries and be swept along with the blood stream as is witnessed by the presence of *Amphibdella torpedinis* Chatin, a species that normally occurs on the body of the electric ray, in the heart and blood vessels of this host. In such cases, however, the parasite does not develop normally and the eggs remain sterile (Ruskowski). Species of the genus *Calicocotyle* are found in the cloaca and cloacal diverticulum of elasmobranchs, whereas the related genus *Dictyocotyle* has been reported by different authors from the body cavity of rays and never from any other part of the body. *Acolpenteron* normally occurs in the ureters and the urinary bladder of fresh-water fishes in this country. Polystomids are particularly interesting as to their location on or within their hosts, since they are the only monogenetic trematodes that have become successfully adapted to vertebrates other than

[2] A coaptation, as defined by the French biologist-philosopher L. Cuénot, consists of the absolute adaptation to one another of two parts of an organism that have arisen both independently and remotely from one another and, consequently, without any reciprocal influence on their respective ontogeny.

fishes, and also to terrestrial forms. When they are found within a host, it is always in a region devoid of digestive glands. For instance, *Polystomoides coronatum* (Leidy) occurs in the mouth, nostrils, and esophagus of turtles; and other species of the same and closely related genera are found in the urinary bladder.[3]

The mode of development of monogenetic trematodes, and the fact that in many cases the eggs remain attached to the host, create favorable conditions for ecological segregation of the parasites upon their hosts. Numerous genera are found, for instance, exclusively on elasmobranchs (*Hexabothrium*, *Erpocotyle*, *Rajonchocotyle*, etc.), others on marine teleosts (*Entobdella*, *Ancyrocotyle*, *Encotyllabe*, etc.), or on fresh-water teleosts (*Dactylogyrus*, *Protogyrodactylus*, *Lepidotrema*, *Diplozoon*, etc.). As mentioned above, *Udonella* occurs only on parasitic copepods. The genus *Gyrodactylus* occurs both on marine and fresh-water fishes. *Diclidophorus* is harbored by species of the cod family and *Kuhnia* by members of the herring family.

The fact that the greater majority of *Monogenea* occur exclusively on elasmobranchs is an argument in favor of their being very ancient parasites. It is interesting to observe that not a single species of monogenetic trematodes has ever been reported from marine turtles. Fresh-water turtles were already separated from the marine species in Mesozoic times and consequently may have acquired their parasites at that period. It is particularly interesting to discover that distinctive fresh-water fishes of Australia harbor an extremely great number of species and genera. These nearly all occur on fishes that have immigrated from the sea at a comparatively recent period (Johnston & Tiegs). In the northern hemisphere, the presence of genera such as *Discocotyle* and *Mazocraes* that are evidently marine on migratory salmonids and on migrating fresh-water herrings shows clearly that these parasites possess a marked degree of euryhalinity.

---

[3] *Oculotrema* (Stunkard) has been described from material collected by the late A. Looss from an hippopotamus in the zoo in Cairo. It was labeled as occurring on the eye. Either this is an accidental infestation introduced into the same enclosure as that in which the hippopotamus lived, or else a mistake has been made in labeling the material. The writer has personally experienced a similar mistake with material from the same collection.

REFERENCES

ALVEY, C. H. 1936. The morphology and development of the monogenetic trematode, *Sphyranura oligorchis* (Alvey, 1933) and the description of *Sphyranura polyorchis* n. sp. *Parasitology*, 18:229–53, pls.

BAER, J. G. 1931. Etude monographique du groupe des Temnocéphales. *Bull. Biol. France et Belgique*, 65:1–57, 3 figs., 5 pls.

———. 1946. La signification des générations larvaires chez les vers plats parasites. *Rev. scientif.*, 84:263–72, 4 figs.

*DAWES, BEN, 1946. The trematoda. xvi + 644 pp., 80 figs., Cambridge.

FUHRMANN, O. 1928. Trematoda. *Handb. Zool.*, 2(2):1–140, 175 figs.

GALLIEN, L. 1935. Recherches expérimentales sur le dimorphisme évolutif et la biologie de *Polystomum integerrimum* Fröhl. *Trav. Sta. zool. Wimereux*, 12:1–181, 11 figs., 4 pls.

GROBEN, G. 1940. Beobachtungen über die Entwicklung verschiedener Arten von Fischschmarotzern aus der Gattung *Dactylogyrus*. *Zeitschr. f. Parasitenk.*, 11:611–36, 8 figs.

JOHNSTON, T. H., & TIEGS, O. W. 1922. New Gyrodactyloid trematodes from Australian fishes, together with a reclassification of the superfamily Gyrodactyloidea. *Proc. Linn. Soc. N. S. W.*, 37:83–131.

PRICE, E. W. 1937. North American monogenetic trematodes I. The superfamily Gyrodactyloidea. *J. Wash. Acad. Sc.*, 27:114–30, 20 figs.; 146–64, 19 figs.

———. 1938. North American monogenetic trematodes II. The families Monocotylidae, Microbothriidae, Acanthocotylidae and Udonellidae (Capsaloidea). *Ibid.*, 28:109–26, 30 figs; 183–98, 17 figs.

———. 1939. North American monogenetic trematodes III. The family Capsalidae (Capsaloidea). *Ibid.*, 29:63–92, 43 figs.

———. 1939a. North American monogenetic trematodes IV. Polystomatidae (Polystomatoidea). *Proc. Helm. Soc. Wash.*, 6:80–92, 1 fig.

———. 1942. North American monogenetic trematodes V. The family Hexabothriidae (Polystomatoidea). *Ibid.*, 9:39–56, 3 figs.

———. 1943. North American monogenetic trematodes VI. The family Diclidophoridae (Diclidophoroidea). *J. Wash. Acad. Sc.*, 33:44–54.

———. 1943a. North American monogenetic trematodes VII. The family Discocotylidae (Diclidophoroidea). *Proc. Helm. Soc. Wash.*, 10:10–15, 1 fig.

*SPROSTON, N. G. 1946. A synopsis of the monogenetic trematodes. *Trans. Zool. Soc. London*, 25:185–600, 118 figs.

ZELLER, E. 1872. Untersuchungen ueber die Entwicklung des Diplozoon paradoxum. *Zeitschr. f. wiss. Zool.*, 22:168–80, pl. 12.

* A complete bibliography will be found in this book.

DIGENEA

Adult digenetic trematodes possess a more homogeneous anatomical structure than do the monogenetic forms. A haptor is never found and, in most cases, there are two suckers. Moreover, all adult digenetic trematodes are normally endoparasitic either in the gut or in natural cavities directly or indirectly in relation with the latter (frontal sinuses, bronchi, lungs, gall bladder and bile ducts, pancreatic

considerable number of larvae. Moreover, no matter how complicated the life cycle, whether fresh-water, marine, or terrestrial, the first intermediate host is invariably a snail, usually a gastropod, sometimes a lamellibranch or a scaphopod, but never a cephalopod nor an amphineuran (Fig. 142).

The miracidium hatches from the egg, either outside the intermediate host or within the gut of the latter when the egg is swallowed. When hatching

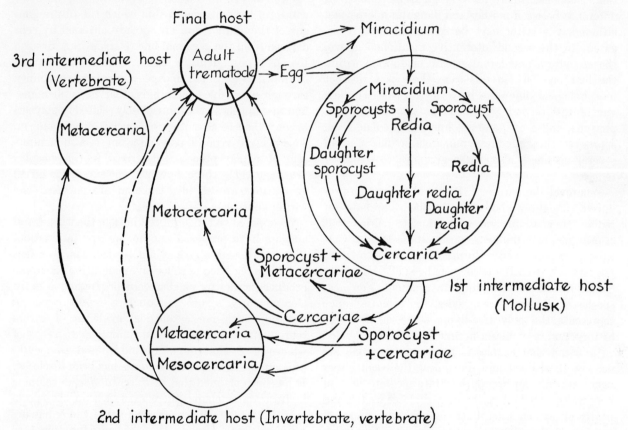

Fig. 142. Diagram of the principal life cycles of digenetic trematodes.

ducts, ureters, urinary bladder, and very rarely in cysts beneath the skin around the cloaca in birds). Occasionally adult trematodes occur in the blood vessels, the eggs being expelled indirectly via the gut or in the urine.

As opposed to monogenetic trematodes, the life cycle of which is direct and relatively simple, that of digenetic trematodes is always indirect, complicated by successive larval forms, of which several are able to multiply individually, thus producing a very

takes place outside the intermediate host, the miracidium enters into the latter via the skin, i.e., penetrates actively into the snail. Whatever the mode of entrance of the miracidium into its host, it always migrates through the body cavity into the region of the body whorl where it penetrates either into the hepatopancreatic gland or into the gonads.

Within the miracidium is located a group of cells usually recognized as germinal cells. The latter soon begin to multiply and give rise to an elongated, sac-shaped organism known as a sporocyst, devoid of cilia, mouth, or gut, but containing groups of cells derived from the original germinal cells. These multiply rapidly and produce within the sporocyst either a second generation of sporocysts or an entirely new type called rediae. In the first case a new generation of sporocysts appears within the original organism and the daughter sporocysts escape from the mother organism by rupturing its walls. It is significant that mother sporocysts do not produce an unlimited number of daughter sporocysts, but only a single generation. There is usually no very great morphological difference between mother and daughter sporocysts, although the latter may be somewhat more elongated. In the second alternative mentioned above, there is also a new larval generation formed within the first one but, in this case, there is a distinct morphological difference between the two. The larvae of this second generation possess a mouth, a pharynx, and a gut, and are known as rediae. Each sporocyst thus produces numerous rediae and in several instances also, these give rise to daughter rediae.

Whatever the nature of the larval generation produced, daughter sporocysts, rediae, or daughter rediae, they all ultimately produce cercariae that appear in great numbers within these larvae. Cercariae are very active forms that, in most cases, migrate out from the tissues of the snail and finally escape into the surrounding environment. For most species of digenetic trematodes, the cercarial stage represents the only free-living stage in their life history, and resembles a minute little fluke provided with a tail that enables it to swim. Cercariae are usually short-lived and die unless they can either penetrate into an appropriate intermediate host or become encysted. Here the cercaria loses its tail and nearly always encysts, its trematodal characters becoming clearly evident during this period. The larva, now known as a metacercaria, represents the infestive stage, and when eaten by an appropriate final host, excysts and becomes adult either *in situ*, within the gut, or in some cases after migrating through the host's body.

The life history of digenetic trematodes as outlined above is approximately identical for all the species so far recorded and, although variations frequently occur, they do not alter in any way the fundamental principles of this cycle.

The nature of the ontogenetical mechanism by which the larvae multiply is still a matter for discussion, although some very good evidence is available for considering this as a particular case of polyembryony. Starting from the egg, it is found that cleavage of the zygote gives rise to both somatic and germinal cells, the former constituting the somatic tissues of the miracidium and the latter remaining in an embryonic state as the primitive germ cells referred to above. Sporocysts and rediae are formed by these cells, some of which become somatic, forming the "shell" of the larva while others remain "germinal." In the subsequent generations, the latter will form the cercariae within which the future gonads of the adult worm are already outlined by cells derived from the germinal line (Cable, Cort, Brooks, Rees). Consequently, there occurs here what is known as germinal lineage, a genetical continuity through successive generations of larvae, a phenomenon that appears to be more closely related to polyembryony than to any other ontogenetical mechanism. This delayed type of polyembryony is also reminiscent of similar processes described in *Gyrodactylus* (see page 117), where, however, the successive larval generations are all identical and are enclosed one within another.

As opposed to the germ cell lineage theory, several authors have proposed another interpretation than that mentioned above. Namely, the larval stages should be regarded as successive generations of larvae produced either by paedogenesis or parthenogenesis. Consequently, sexual reproduction is postulated. So far, no conclusive cytological evidence of sexual reproduction has been forthcoming and no proof whatever of what might be interpreted as oocytes or spermatids within these forms has been disclosed. It has been claimed that in *Bucephalidae*, developing in fresh-water clams, there exist, within the sporocyst, both testes and ovaries and that the rediae are provided with gonads that become functional so that cercariae would result from a fertilized redial ovum and consequently, there would exist in this case, two distinct, successive, adult generations in clams (Woodhead). So far, these findings have never been corroborated so that the question must remain open.

In schistosomatids the sexes are separate in the adult worms, and both males and females occur within the same host. Moreover, it has been proved experimentally that all the cercariae arising from the same egg are always of the same sex and consequently that there are both male and female cercariae. This could not be the case if cercariae were formed either by paedogenesis or parthenogenesis. In the first case, this would imply an equal distribution of the sexes and in the second case, only female cercariae and no males, unless the latter were haploid, but this is evidently not the case from cytological evidence furnished.

Much more careful research work is necessary before any final conclusion can be reached as to the mode of larval multiplication in digenetic trematodes, but so far both cytological and biological evidence appears to favor the view that this is a special type of polyembryony.

The outer cell layer of the miracidium is nearly always ciliated, thus enabling the larva to swim freely when the egg hatches in water outside the intermediate host (Fig. 143). Curiously enough, this

cally at the anterior end of the miracidium. All miracidia possess small, unicellular glands opening into the anterior end. These doubtless secrete enzymes that facilitate penetration of the miracidium into the tissues of the snail. In the case of *Parorchis acanthus* (Nicoll), the eggs hatch while still within the uterus so that this species is practically viviparous.

In the genera *Parorchis* (*Echinostomatidae*), *Stichorchis* (*Amphistomatidae*), and *Typhlocoelium* (*Cyclocoelidae*) that are in no way directly related to one another, the miracidium, while still within the egg, contains a well formed redia in lieu of the usual mass of germ cells (Fig. 145). Development in these

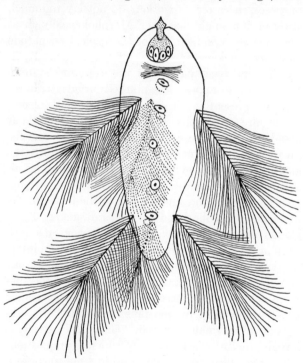

FIG. 143. Miracidium of *Leucochloridomorpha constantiae* (Müll.) with three pairs of plumous appendages (Allison).

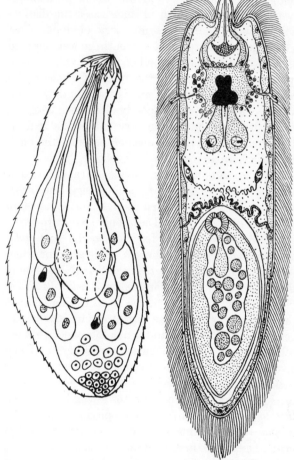

FIG. 144   FIG. 145

FIG. 144. Miracidium of *Halipegus amherstensis* Rankin, showing absence of cilia and presence of spines and large glandular cells (Rankin).

FIG. 145. Miracidium of *Parorchis acanthus* Nicoll with eye spots and penetrating glands, containing a completely formed redia with germ balls (Rees).

ciliated coating is also found in miracidia that remain within the egg and hatch only when the latter is swallowed by the snail. The absence of such a layer of cilia occurs in a very few instances only and, as might be foreseen, only in species which do not hatch outside the first intermediate host, as in *Halipegus*, for instance (Rankin) (Fig. 144). Here the miracidium is protected by a thin cuticula that bears spines, the largest of these being disposed symmetri-

forms has been telescoped, and from a biological standpoint the result is somewhat similar to the development described in *Gyrodactylus*.

There is apparently no ontogenetical difference between sporocysts and rediae (Sewell). The former are capable of producing either daughter sporocysts or rediae, and the latter daughter rediae only, yet cercariae are produced by daughter sporocysts, rediae, and daughter rediae. Not much information is available as to the possible effect of either the snail host or the environing conditions on the production of a second generation of rediae, as for instance in the case of *Fasciola hepatica* L. where daughter rediae appear only during the warmer months of the year. Nor has any evidence been furnished of the same species being capable of giving rise either to daughter sporocysts or rediae, although in some cases the distinction between the two is not very obvious. Most rediae, it is true, possess a mouth, a well marked pharynx and a small gut, all of which are lacking in sporocysts. However, in the redia of *Proterometra macrostoma* Dickerm. the gut is rudimentary, thin-walled, and the pharynx poorly developed. As cercariae develop, the rudimentary gut of the redia is destroyed and the mouth opening becomes the birth pore (Dickerman).

There appears to be some evidence that the number of cercariae produced by a single egg is approximately constant for a given species. For instance, in *Typhlocoelium cymbium* (Dies.) only sixteen to twenty-two cercariae emerge from the redia. In *Cotylophoron cotylophoron* (Fischoed.), there are more than two hundred and in *Parorchis acanthus* (Nicoll) more than a thousand. For *Paragonimus kellicotti* Ward (syn. *westermani* Kerb.) it has been estimated that the number of cercariae produced by the redial generation is about ten to twenty thousand. In most echinostomids and fasciolids, a single germinal line gives rise to more than twenty-five thousand cercariae (Cort). An instance of capacity for cercarial production has been recorded for a winkle, *Littorina littorea* L. infested by an heterophyid, *Cryptocotyle lingua* (Crep.). This snail was isolated for seven years. During the first five years, the snail shed about five and a half million cercariae. After nearly seven years, the number of cercariae shed *daily* was approximately one thousand six hundred. As all possibility of reinfestation had been precluded, this would indicate a heavy initial infestation of the snail. Incidentally, this snail fed exclusively on a diet of *Ulvae* increased in size by 3.5 mm. (Rothschild).

Whereas the first intermediate host of all digenetic trematodes known so far is always a snail, the second intermediate host may belong to almost any group of invertebrates or vertebrates.

Although cercarial ontogeny follows almost identical lines in all the genera, the structure of the cercariae themselves shows a great deal of morphological variation.

Barring a few exceptions, cercariae are able to lead a short, free-living existence and, consequently, one would expect to find them provided with some sort of locomotory organ. This is present in the form of a tail, both the shape and size of which vary greatly, although it has formerly been used for taxonomic purposes, more recent workers do not lay too much stress on this single character. Morphologically, most cercariae show indications of the typical trematode anatomy: suckers, pharynx, bifid gut, genital primordia, and basic pattern of the excretory system, but there also appear less marked larval attributes that are present in all species. In the body of cercariae are numerous though distinct unicellular glands, that may be grouped, for practical reasons, into two principal categories. Several pairs of large glands are usually symmetrically distributed on either side of the mid-line and empty through long, narrow ducts at the anterior end of the larva, in the immediate neighborhood of the oral sucker. These glands are usually thought to secrete a substance enabling cercariae to penetrate into the second intermediate host and also permit them to tunnel out through the snail's tissues into the surrounding medium. The action of these so-called penetration glands is often enhanced by the presence, within the oral sucker, of a small, pointed, "chitinous" stylet, a larval structure the function of which is unquestionable (Fig. 146). In species that do not possess a stylet, the whole anterior region of the cercaria is covered with minute spines that assume the same role as the stylet, by constantly rubbing against the tissues of the intermediate host. The nature of the secretion of the so-called penetration glands has not yet been sufficiently studied. From a purely morphological and an histochemical standpoint, it is found that both the nature and the chemical reaction of the granules enclosed within these cells differ, not only in the different species, but also in the individual glands. There is evidence of at least two distinct kinds of secretion in the penetration glands. More recently, experimental results have been forthcoming that claim to show in cercariae of *Schistosoma mansoni* Samb., a species that penetrates directly into the skin of its host, the presence of hyaluronidase, an enzyme that dissolves hyaluronic acid, one of the principal substrates of connective tissue and also found in the so-called "spreading factor" of certain bacteria (Levine *et al.*)

The other glands occurring in cercariae are much smaller than the penetration glands and are usually located beneath the skin of the cercaria in various

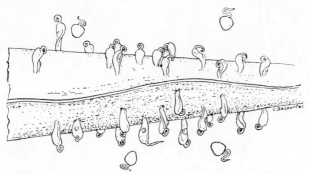

FIG. 146. Cercariae of *Leptophallus nigrovenosus* (Bellingh.) in the act of penetrating into the tail of a tadpole (Brumpt).

parts of the body. The secretion from these glands is a mucoid type of substance that is spread over the surface of the cercaria as the latter wriggles to escape from the snail. It might possibly be a protective coating that would enable the cercaria to withstand the effects of its own penetration glands when the latter pour out their secretion in the presence of an intermediate host. It might also be postulated that such a protective secretion formed around the cercaria before the latter leaves the snail would enable it to withstand the changes that necessarily occur when an organism passes suddenly from a parasitic to a free-living existence (Kruidenier).

As mentioned above, until cercariae are formed, there does not exist any fundamental difference in the life histories of digenetic trematodes. But, with a free-living larval stage in the life cycle, a much greater variety of possibilities is introduced, according to the mode of entry of the cercariae into the second intermediate host and, also, according to

whether or not the presence of the latter is obligatory.

It sometimes occurs that no free-living larval stage is known. In the life history of *Ptychogonimus megastoma* (Rud.) from a shark, the cercariae formed within the sporocyst remain in the latter and thus escape from the scaphopod host. The sporocyst remains on the bottom, animated only by slow muscular contractions. These movements apparently attract crabs which swallow the sporocyst, and in this way the cercariae escape from the partly digested sporocyst and penetrate into the body cavity of the crab where they encyst (Palombi) (Fig. 147). In

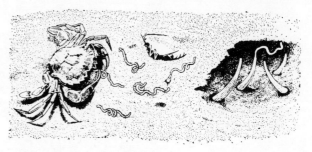

FIG. 147. Sporocysts of *Ptychogonimus megastoma* (Rud), containing cercariae, escaping from the snail host and being eaten by crabs (Palombi).

Plagioporus sinitsini Müll., a parasite of freshwater fishes, the cercariae encyst within the sporocysts and the latter, emerging from the snail, are *eaten* by the final host (Dobrovolny). In the genus *Leucochloridium*, the cercariae also encyst within the sporocyst that lies in the body cavity of a semiaquatic species of snail. As the sporocyst grows, it migrates into the cavity of one of the tentacles and the latter becomes so distended that the sporocyst can be clearly seen through the transparent skin. Since the sporocyst carries numerous pigmented rings on its surface, the snail appears to possess enormous, highly colored tentacles that pulsate rhythmically, owing to the contractions of the sporocysts. Encysted metacercariae are expelled in small clumps through the skin of the snail and become attached to leaves on which the snail feeds (Wesenberg-Lund) (Fig. 148).

Several other instances have been recorded of metacercariae encysting within sporocysts but usually the latter do not belong to the same species of trematode. In such cases, careful observations always show that cercariae liberated from neighboring snails have penetrated both into the snails harboring sporocysts and into the sporocysts themselves.

nism that would protect previously infested snails from a subsequent infestation either by the same or by other species (Cort *et al.*).

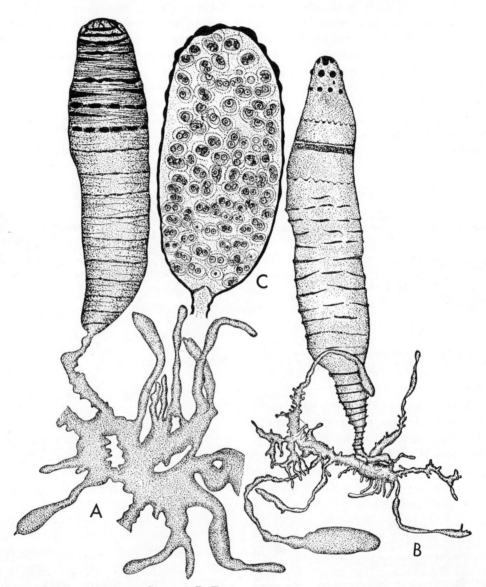

FIG. 148. *Leucochloridium paradoxum* Carus. A–B. Two differently pigmented, branched sporocysts. C. Section of a ripe sporocyst showing encysted metacercariae (Wesenberg-Lund).

Where this is found to be the case, it is sometimes discovered that only the metacercariae that have been formed within the sporocysts survive, whereas the others, formed in the snail tissues, are destroyed. This might indicate some kind of immunity mecha-

The life history of *Dicrocoelium dendriticum* (Rud.), the small liver fluke of cattle and other mammals, also lacks a free cercarial stage. The cercariae that escape from the sporocyst in the snail host, a land species, encyst in the snail's lung but both the stylet and the tail are retained within the cyst. In the lung of the first intermediate host, several such cysts become agglomerated by the mucous secretions always present here, and are finally "sneezed" out from the pneumostome in the shape of a mucoid ball containing numerous encysted cercariae. When such balls are swallowed by an appropriate final host, the cyst dissolves in the intestine and the cercariae are liberated. Penetrating into the gut wall, the cercariae are carried via the blood stream into the liver and here, losing both their stylet and tail, they penetrate into the gall ducts and later into the gall bladder. *Brachylecithum americanum* Denton, a common species of dicrocoelid from passerine birds in this country, develops in two species of terrestrial snails in a way similar to *Dicrocoelium dendriticum*. In this case, however, experimental infestation of definitive hosts with cercarial "balls" failed. Moreover, some evidence appears to indicate that a second intermediate host such as a chrysomelid beetle for instance, might be necessary. Yet, so far, no experimental proof has been forthcoming (Denton).

In the genus *Brachylaemus*, the first intermediate host of which is also a land snail, the cercariae emerge from the pulmonary cavity, as has been observed experimentally, and re-enter via the urinary pore into the kidney of the same snail where they encyst (Joyeux, Baer, & Timon-David). In this case, moreover, when several snails occur close together, cercariae may penetrate into the kidney of other specimens of the same species of snail.

In blood flukes belonging to the families *Schistosomatidae* and *Spirorchidae*, the cercariae are free-swimming, but penetrate directly into the skin and capillaries of the final host and consequently no metacercariae are formed, nor is there a second intermediate host in this life cycle.

Several species of cercariae are known to encyst upon plants (fasciolids, amphistomids) or upon the shells of snails (notocotylids); others such as those of *Triganodistomum mutabile* (Cort), after escaping from the snail, fall to the bottom where they are eaten by *Chaetogaster limnaei* v. Baer, an oligochaete commensal of snails, or at times by planarians. In both cases, encysted metacercariae are found in the body cavity of these hosts that are subsequently eaten by fishes, the final hosts. The cercariae of *Phyllodistomum solidum* Rankin are swallowed either by salamander larvae or by larvae of damsel flies (*Ischnura*), in both of which they encyst and become metacercariae (Groves). The very peculiar cercariae belonging to the genus *Halipegus* are eaten by cope-

pods and escape through the gut into the body cavity of the latter where they become metacercariae without encysting. The adults are found in the mouth and Eustachian tubes of frogs (Rankin).

In all the other known life cycles, the cercariae penetrate actively into the tissues of the second intermediate host and encyst (Fig. 149).

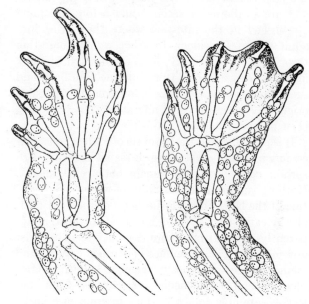

FIG. 149. Metacercariae of *Leptophallus nigrovenosus* (Bellingh.) encysted in the feet of a frog (Brumpt).

In most trematodes, the transformation of a cercaria into a metacercaria occurs rather rapidly. In strigeids, however, the life history is prolonged, for here the cercaria undergoes complete metamorphosis before becoming an infestive larva. Moreover, the latter, although biologically homologous to a metacercaria, is anatomically very different from a typical metacercaria.

In a few instances, as in *Alaria* for example, the life cycle requires a third intermediate host. In this genus, that occurs in carnivores, the cercariae penetrate into the second intermediate host, tadpoles or frogs and, losing their tails, grow into an intermediate larval stage known as a mesocercaria that is not encysted in the host's tissues. When tadpoles containing mesocercariae are eaten by rodents, the third intermediate host, they penetrate the intestinal wall and become metacercariae in the peritoneal cavity of the rodent.

A third intermediate host, however, is not absolutely necessary for the successful completion of the life cycle, because if a suitable mammalian host eats frogs containing mesocercariae, the latter will escape through the gut wall into the abdominal cavity, and from here, piercing the diaphragm, enter the lungs. Working their way from the alveoli into the bronchi, the flukes finally reach the trachea, then the mouth, and are swallowed a second time before becoming established in the intestine where they grow into adult worms (Cuckler). In other words, migration through the body cavity, lungs, and trachea of the final host can replace a third intermediate host, and such migration sheds a new light on the possible origin of certain types of migration that have also been observed in other parasites.

It is probable that the life cycle of *Pharyngostomum cordatum* (Dies.) revolves on the same lines although certain parts of it still remain obscure (Wallace). Nothing is known, for instance, of a possible migration of the larva through the body of the final host, also a carnivore. A third intermediate host is apparently optional but there does not seem to exist any morphological difference between the meso- and metacercariae. Curiously enough, both warm-blooded and cold-blooded vertebrates (rats and snakes) are able to act as third intermediate hosts. The presence of a paratenic host has been envisaged but, so far, is not substantiated by experimental results. From a taxonomic standpoint, it is interesting to discover that the genus *Pharyngostomum* is closely related to *Alaria* and that these are the only known strigeids whose life history requires three intermediate hosts, the last one of these being optional.

Although most trematodes become adult in the intestine of the final host, some migrate to the bladder, others to the nasal sinuses. Lung parasites, such as *Paragonimus*, reach this organ when the metacercaria escapes through the gut wall into the abdominal cavity and from there, through the diaphragm, directly into the lungs. Flukes that live in the liver gain access to the latter organ either directly, from the gut through the bile duct, or indirectly, via either the blood stream or the abdominal cavity.

In several instances, the life cycle may be shortened by the metacercaria becoming progenetic, i.e., producing viable eggs while still encysted within the second intermediate host, thus rendering a final host superfluous (for a recent summary see Kuang). In the case of *Ratzia parva* Stoss. the final host is entirely unnecessary and has never been found to occur naturally. The metacercaria, encysted in the skin of a toad, *Discoglossus pictus* Otth, becomes normally progenetic and produces viable eggs (Joyeux & Baer).

Life history studies of digenetic trematodes, as outlined above, show that variations occur chiefly in the mode of penetration of the cercariae into the second intermediate host. Moreover, the life cycle may be telescoped in two different parts, either at the beginning or at the end. When this happens in the beginning, a free-living stage is suppressed and metacercariae encysted in the sporocyst are swallowed, together with the latter, by the final host. It is telescoped in the end when metacercariae become progenetic and, consequently, the second intermediate host becomes either an optional or a permanent final host. From a theoretical standpoint, it would be interesting to postulate a combined effect of both these factors on the life cycle, so that progenetic metacercariae would arise within the sporocyst and, consequently, a direct life cycle would be the result which would require only a single host! Unfortunately, such an hypothesis is untenable as long as no progenetic metacercaria has been described from molluscs. All the cases so far reported occur in arthropods and mostly in crustaceans.

Another interesting fact about the life history of digenetic trematodes is the complete absence of paratenic hosts. Not only do these never occur normally but they have not even been obtained experimentally. This is doubtless due to the metacercaria being encysted and becoming adult within a short time after the cyst is digested. This explains the ecological nature of host relationships and also speaks in favor of the theory mentioned previously (see page 116) that development and maturity of the gonads precludes the existence of a paratenic host.

Although knowledge of trematode life histories is as yet incomplete, numerous fragmentary cycles have been described and it is possible to discern to what extent similar ecological conditions are necessary for animals harboring the same or related species of trematodes. A few of these ecological relationships have been grouped in Table 3.

Ecological relations between the definitive hosts and the final intermediate hosts appear clearly when adult trematodes are grouped according to their hosts. However, in this case, the problem of host specificity is much more complicated than it might appear at first sight. Although essentially a problem of ecology, it should be remembered that in this case ecological factors are exerting their influence at two different levels, on two distinct phases of the life history, i.e., both at the larval and at the adult levels. Host specificity at the larval level implies that a miracidium will not penetrate or the egg hatch indiscriminately in any molluscan host, and that the latter may be an unfavorable host that will retard and even inhibit development of either sporocysts or rediae. Such an assumption is borne out both by experimental and by statistical investigations. There very definitely exists a host specificity for larval trematodes, some of which seem to be extremely narrow in the choice of their host, a choice that is not exclusively due to ecological factors but also to intrinsic physiological properties of the miracidium. For instance, in *Opisthorchis felineus* (Riv.) the miracidium has been shown to develop in a fresh-water prosobranch, *Bithynia leachi* Shepp., but fails however to develop in the closely related species *B. tentaculata* (L.) that occurs simultaneously in the same biotope and that is also much more widely distributed in Europe than the former species. In this country, the liver fluke (*Fasciola hepatica* L.) occurs normally in the South in *Stagnicola bulimoides tachella* (Hald.), while in Utah, it is found in *Fossaria modicella* Say. In Europe, the same parasite develops in *Limnaea* (*Galba*) *truncatula* (Müll.) but not in *L. peregra* (Müll.) although the latter occurs commonly in the same biotope as the former. Of the human blood flukes, *Schistosoma mansoni* Sambon can infest a considerable number of species of tropical and subtropical snails belonging to the planorbids, while *S. japonicum* Kats., whose distribution is more northerly, is found exclusively in oncomelanid snails. Cross-infestations of the intermediate host do not even occur. experimentally

Identical conclusions may be drawn from statistical data obtained by various investigators who have studied the cercarial fauna of snails. There is valid evidence that a certain degree of parasitization by a given trematode species may cause the snail host to elaborate some unidentified substance that inhibits penetration by subsequent miracidia of the same species of trematode already harbored by the snail. On the other hand, the influence exerted on miracidia of other species does not appear to be so marked (Cort *et al.*).

Except in cases where the cercariae penetrate directly into the definitive host, through the skin as in *Schistosoma*, for example, ecological segregation is also effective at the metacercarial stage of the life cycle. Cercariae do not penetrate indiscriminately into any intermediate host. These minute larvae are provided with so-called penetration glands, stylets, and spines that become effective under certain conditions, in the presence of favorable hosts, i.e., those whose tissues can be successfully attacked and penetrated by the cercaria. Here also, it is found that certain host tissues inhibit further development and that the cercariae die without being able to complete their life cycle. Consequently, at this stage also of the latter, natural selection, through elimination of

TABLE 3. Host relations in Digenetic Trematodes.

TREMATODES	2ND INTERMEDIATE HOST	FINAL HOST
Hemiurids	copepods	fishes, amphibians
Plagiorchids	aquatic arthropods or having aquatic larvae	amphibians, reptiles, birds, mammals
Echinostomids	snails, fishes	birds, mammals
Opistorchiids	fishes	birds, mammals
Heterophyids	crustaceans, fishes	birds, mammals
Strigeids	fishes, amphibians, reptiles, mammals	aquatic reptiles, birds, mammals
Fasciolids	metacercariae encysted on plants	herbivorous and omnivorous mammals
Schistosomatids	none (cercariae free in water)	aquatic birds and mammals

the unsuccessful attempts of the metacercariae and cercariae to develop in unfavorable hosts, will result in these larvae being segregated in certain hosts only.

It is therefore easy to understand that the definitive hosts of trematodes will be those that frequent either normally or accidentally any of the numerous ecological associations in which the above mentioned selective influences have exerted their effects, and that feed on the various elements susceptible of bearing metacercarial cysts.

As a rule all adult trematodes are hermaphroditic although separation of the sexes with more or less marked sexual dimorphism occurs occasionally That the bisexual stage has been acquired secondarily is supported by a series of investigations carried out on schistosomatids. By infesting snails with a single miracidium, it is possible to obtain unisexual cercariae that penetrate into mice and become adult worms. On such an experimental basis, it has been possible to obtain mixed infestations of mice with male trematodes of one species copulating with females of another (Vogel, 1941). The eggs produced from a series of such crosses between the three common species of human blood flukes are invariably of the maternal type, as is also the case for the miracidia, the latter being attracted only to snails of species in which the female trematode develops normally. Cytological evidence, however, shows that no true hybrids are formed and that all the eggs are produced parthenogenetically. Very similar results have also been obtained with intergeneric crosses between *Schistosoma mansoni* and *Schistosomatium douthitti*. In this case, also, the eggs belong to the maternal type and are produced parthenogenetically (Short).

Moreover, when various species of definitive hosts are infested experimentally only with male cercariae, a considerable proportion of adult worms is produced that shows an ovary, yolk glands, and very rarely, a short uterus. The percentage of such imperfect hermaphrodites is high in guinea pigs and hamsters (43 per cent and 40 per cent), but very low in mice and monkeys (1.2 per cent and none). To avoid the possibility of there being genetical races, both guinea pigs and mice were infested with cercariae from the same snail that had been previously infested with a single miracidium. Consequently, the cercariae were genetically identical. The results showed that half of the worms recovered from guinea pigs were hermaphrodites and that true males only occurred in the mice (Vogel). No such results, however, were obtained when the above experiments were repeated with *S. haematobium* and *S. japonicum*.

Finally, experimental evidence shows that infestations with females only of *S. douthitti* yield viable eggs and that the latter are able to develop into cercariae in suitable hosts. Three of these snails yielded only male cercariae and one, only females (Short).

Such experiments clearly indicate that the bisexual state in certain schistosomatids is not very stable and that under certain conditions, imperfect hermaphrodites occur. The necessary conditions, moreover, appear to be related to the nature of the host and, consequently, to physiological conditions. The available evidence is insufficient to allow any formal conclusions.

There seems to be no possible doubt whatever of the digenetic trematodes having originated in fresh water, as is witnessed today by their developing invariably in gastropods and lamellibranchs. Moreover, the majority of the species are still bound by their life cycle to water and, consequently, the adult worms, to either wholly or partly aquatic vertebrates ecologically. Successful adaptation to land vertebrates became possible when metacercariae encysted in aquatic larvae of airborne insects and thus became available to hosts such as bats or birds. Encystation on plants has also distinctly favored an invasion by trematodes of land vertebrates, especially mammals. The final passage into hosts that are ecologically independent of water became possible with the adaptation of the first larval stages to amphibious or terrestrial snails. In the latter, the structure of the cercaria has also become modified, especially as to the tail which is usually rudimentary and sometimes even has disappeared. Curiously enough, the passage from aquatic to terrestrial snails, as far as is known, appears to have occurred independently in families that are in no way related to one another as the *Brachylaemidae*, *Dicrocoelidae*, and *Eucotylidae*, most of the species of which are parasitic in birds and, to a lesser degree, in mammals. Moreover, the first-mentioned family is situated, taxonomically, in a group of which all the other members are aquatic and possess fork-tailed cercariae, thus showing that this latter character is perhaps more adaptive than phylogenetic.

The passage from fresh-water snails to marine species has certainly occurred on several occasions, and some "memory" of this appears to have been retained by certain species of marine cercariae that are able to withstand a progressive dilution of sea water (Stunkard & Shaw). Their natural euryhalinity has enabled them in the past to become adapted to sea water. Moreover, the complete absence of sporocysts, rediae, and cercariae from cephalopods would indicate that digenetic trematodes have arisen in fresh water and that they were already well established in gastropods and lamellibranchs a considerable time before their introduction into the marine fauna. This probably occurred at a geological period prior to the appearance of the present-day cephalopods, toward mid-Mesozoic times, whereas fresh-water gastropods and lamellibranchs had already been established several million years previously as witnessed by their presence in Carboniferous deposits.

REFERENCES

CORT, W. W. 1944. The germ cell cycle in the digenetic trematodes. *Quart. Rev. Biol.*, 19:275–84.

CORT, W. W., BRACKETT, S., OLIVIER, L., & NOLF, R. 1945. Influence of larval trematode infections in snails on their second intermediate host relations to the strigeid trematode *Cotylurus flabelliformis* (Faust, 1917). *J. Parasit.*, 31:61–78.

CUCKLER, A. C. 1940. Studies on the migration and development of *Alaria* spp. (Trematoda: Strigeata) in the definitive host. *J. Parasit. Supp.*, 26:36.

*DAWES, BEN. 1946. The trematoda. xvi + 644 pp., 80 figs., Cambridge.

DENTON, F. J. 1945. Studies on the life history of *Brachylecithum americanum* n. sp., a liver fluke of passerine birds. *J. Parasit.*, 31:131–41, 10 figs.

DICKERMAN, E. E. 1945. Studies on the trematode family Azygiidae II. Parthenitae and cercariae of *Proterometra macrostoma* (Faust). *Trans. Am. Micros. Soc.*, 64:138–44, 6 figs.

GROVES, R. E. 1945. An ecological study of *Phyllodistomum solidum* Rankin, 1937. (Trematoda: Gorgoderiidae) *Trans. Am. Micros. Soc.*, 64:112–32, 35 figs.

JOYEUX, CH., DuNOYER, R., & BAER, J. G. 1930. L'activité génitale chez les métacercaires progénétiques des trématodes. *Rap. 1er Congr. internat. Microbiol. Paris*, 3 pp.

KRUIDENIER, F. J. 1947. Mucin in developing digenetic Trematodes. *J. Parasit. Supp.*, 33:36

KUANG, WU. 1938. Progenesis of *Phyllodistomum lesteri* n. sp. (Trematoda: Gorgoderidae) in fresh water shrimps. *Parasitology*, 30:4–19, 3 pls.

* All other references mentioned in the text and not cited here may be found in this book.

LEIGH, W. H., & VAN CLEAVE, H. J. 1945. Metamorphosis of the frog host as a factor in cercarial penetration by *Glyphthelmins quieta. J. Parasit.*, 31:205–9, 6 figs.

LEVINE, M. D., GARZOLI, R. F., KUNTZ, R. E., & KILLOUGH, J. H. 1948. On the demonstration of hyaluronidase in cercariae of *Schistosoma mansoni. J. Parasit.* 34:158–61, 2 figs.

PALOMBI, A. 1942. Il ciclo biologico di *Ptychogonimus megastoma* (Rud.). Osservazione sulla morfologia e fisiologia delle forme larvali e considerazioni filogenetiche. *Riv. Parassit.*, 6:117–72, 2 pls.

RANKIN, J. S. 1944. A revision of the Trematode genus *Glyphthelmins* Stafford, 1905, with an account of the life cycle of *G. quieta* (Stafford, 1900) Stafford, 1905. *Trans. Am. Micros. Soc.*, 63: 30–43, 19 figs.

———. 1944a. A revision of the Trematode genus *Halipegus* Looss, 1899, with an account of the life history of *H. amherstensis* n. sp. *Ibid.*, 63:149–64, 12 figs.

ROTHSCHILD, M. 1942. A seven year old infection of *Cryptocotyle lingua* (Creplin) in the winkle *Littorina littorea* L. *J. Parasit.*, 28:350.

SHORT, R. B. 1947. Unisexual infections with *Schistosomatium douthitti* (Trematoda). *J. Parasit. Supp.*, 33:9.

———. 1948. Intergeneric crosses among Schistosomes (Trematoda: Schistosomatidae). *Ibid.*, 34:30.

———. 1948a. Infective uniparental miracidia of *Schistosomatium douthitti* (Trematoda: Schistosomatidae). *Ibid.*, 34:30.

STUNKARD, H. W., & SHAW, C. R. 1931. The effect of dilution of sea water on the activity and longevity of certain marine cercariae with descriptions of two new species. *Biol. Bull.*, 61:242–71.

VOGEL, H. 1941. Ueber den Einfluss des Geschlechtspartners auf Wachstum und Entwicklung bei *Bilharzia mansoni* und bei Kreuzpaarungen zwischen verschiedenen Bilharzia-Arten. *Centralbl. Bakt. Parasit. Orig.*, 148:78–96, 4 figs.

———. 1947. Hermaphrodites of *Schistosoma mansoni. Ann. Trop. Med. Parasit.*, 41:266–77, 6 figs.

CHAPTER ELEVEN

Cestodaria

Formerly much confusion was created by the establishment of two ontogenetically erroneous groups, the so-called polyzoic and monozoic cestodes. The former includes all tapeworms with a segmented strobila and, consequently, with as many complete hermaphroditic reproductive organs as segments, while the latter includes all forms that are not segmented but are provided with a single set of reproductive organs. Subsequent investigations of both the morphology and life history of the so-called monozoic cestodes has shown that the latter, as conceived by earlier authors, was a heterogeneous group of species, most of which were related to pseudophyllidean tapeworms. Moreover, the study of their life histories has revealed them to be progenetic larvae which accounts also for their "monozoic" anatomy. Other so-called monozoic cestodes have been found to be detached segments of tetraphyllidean cestodes that remain in the gut of the host and continue to lead an independent life. Finally, included in this artificial category were the cestodarians.

The latter have been considered at one time as being intermediate forms between trematodes and cestodes, yet even if there appears to be a very vague, superficial resemblance, their internal anatomy and life history dispel the illusion (Fuhrmann). Most authors have considered cestodarians as primitive tapeworms and consequently regarded them as cestodes. But even if cestodarians and cestodes demonstrate fundamental affinities, that would indicate their having arisen from a common stock. The latter must be extremely distant, since both groups have evolved along diverging lines.

The structure of the excretory and reproductive systems, the absence of a cirrus pouch, together with the anatomy of the larva formed within the egg indicate characters that are distinct from all that is known for cestodes. This is especially clear in the structure of the larva, a so-called *lycophora* with *five pairs* of small hooks, a distinct nervous center, and a mass of glandular cells opening at the anterior end of the larva (Fig. 150).

Cestodarians are not primitive cestodes but an extremely ancient group of parasites that may have been much more widespread in former times, although restricted today to only a few genera and a small number of species.

From both a morphological and a biological standpoint, it is possible to divide cestodarians into two distinct groups, or orders, the *Amphilinidea* and the *Gyrocotylidea*, all the genera of which, except one, occur exclusively in fishes. (For a detailed anatomy of these parasites see Fuhrmann and Lynch).

Amphilinids are found only within the body cavity of their hosts and never in the gut. Eggs, containing a *lycophora*, pass out of the host through the abdominal pores if the host is a ganoid while, in teleosts, this is not possible. There exists some evidence, however, that in the latter hosts the parasites are able to bore their way out of the cavity through the body wall. Individuals of *Gephyrolina paragonopora* (Woodl.) have been found protruding from the body, near the base of the pectoral fins of an Indian siluroid. Since several holes also occurred in this region, these have been interpreted as having been caused by escaping worms. One might even be inclined to interpret such facts as indicating that the adult worms are free-living or, at least, that they escape from their host when their uterus is filled with eggs and that the latter are liberated when the worm disintegrates.

Austramphilina elongata Johnst. has been found only twice, in the body cavity of a turtle, and a few of these specimens were also discovered having pierced the wall of the lungs. This might be the only way in which the eggs, and perhaps the worms also, could be expelled from the host.

The life history of only a single species is known so far; this is that of *Amphilina foliacea* (Rud.), a parasite of sturgeons from European waters. Although the eggs contain a ciliated *lycophora*, they

136

are not operculated nor do they hatch spontaneously. These eggs are much longer than their diameter and possess a very thin, membranous shell bearing a tiny stalk at one pole. Curiously enough, the larva is always so situated inside the shell that its long axis is parallel to the egg's equator. The egg increases as much as three times in length from the moment it leaves the ootype until it reaches the distal end of the uterus. The tiny stalk is apparently a very fine capillary tube that remains open and through which water and vital stains can easily penetrate. On the other hand, a mucous substance, originating doubtless in the glands found in the *lycophora*, is extruded through this capillary tube and spreads over the corresponding pole of the eggs to which it adheres, swelling considerably on coming into contact with water. It is possible that the presence of this mass of mucoid prevents the egg from falling to the bottom, keeping it afloat and accessible to intermediate hosts. The latter are found to be fresh water amphipods belonging to the genera *Gammarus* and *Dikerogammarus*. Other amphipods of the genera *Corophium* and *Metamysis* may also swallow the eggs but the latter fail to develop in these hosts. The egg shell is ruptured by the mandibles of the amphipod and the *lycophora* is swallowed. Although the latter is ciliated, it escapes from the intestine of the intermediate host into the body cavity of the latter and loses its ciliated coating. The larva becomes gradually transformed into a very small organism that resembles the adult. The larval hooks remain at the posterior end and here there also appears a small bud, containing numerous cells, that gradually increases in size before being separated from the larva, after which it degenerates (Janicki). Infestation of the definitive host occurs through eating infested gammarids.

The morphological peculiarities of amphilinids, coupled with their living in the body cavity of their host and having only a single intermediate host, have been interpreted by most authors as indicating neotenic plerocercoid larvae.

It has even been suggested that neoteny is due to the fact that amphilinids formerly possessed a definitive host, in the gut of which they became adult, and that this host has since become extinct. Consequently, neoteny of the plerocercoid larva would have accompanied the disappearance of the final host. On the other hand, as these parasites are certainly very ancient, some of the larger Mesozoic reptiles, capable of eating sturgeons, must have been the original definitive hosts (Janicki). A theory such as this, although interesting in itself, is however untenable. Neoteny is frequently found to occur among parasites (see page 212) where it is nearly always caused by an excess of food, and no single instance can be found in which it might be due to the final host's having disappeared. This theory is far too teleological; it is unsubstantiated by either experimental or statistical evidence. It seems highly improbable to the writer that when, in a life cycle, the final host drops out, the larvae compensate this loss by becoming adult! If such were the case, it is more than likely that the parasite also would become extinct.

Although gyrocotylids do not appear to bear any resemblance to amphilinids, they are certainly related to them, both possessing decacanth *lycophorae*. In gyrocotylids, the posterior end of the body is a fleshy, funnel-shaped organ, the free border of which is in folds, forming the so-called "rosette" (Fig. 151)

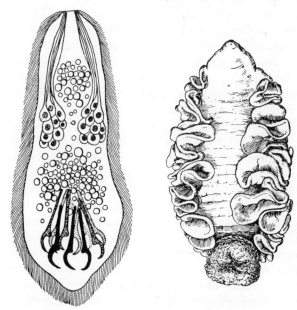

FIG. 150   FIG. 151

FIG. 150. *Lycophora* larva of *Gyrocotyle urna* (Gr. & Wag.) showing the two masses of glands and the ten larval hooks (Ruskowski).

FIG. 151. *Gyrocotyle urna* (Gr. & Wag.) adult worm (Fuhrmann).

The narrow end of the funnel leads into a duct that opens on the dorsal surface of the worm. It is short in *Gyrocotyle* but very long in *Gyrocotyloides*, the latter also having a smaller and less powerfully developed rosette-organ. The function of this duct is unknown. At the opposite end of the body is located a large sucker that is particularly well developed in *Gyrocotyle*. In this genus, the lateral edges of the body are frilled and also bear large spines, but both the frills and spines are absent in *Gyrocotyloides*.

Gyrocotylids have been known to occur, so far, only in the gut of chimaerids, a group of archaic fishes somewhat distantly related to elasmobranchs, which are found either in the polar seas or in the ocean depths. The eggs, when laid, contain a mass of cells and are thick-shelled, but operculated. In *Gyrocotyle rugosa* Dies., however, they contain a completely formed *lycophora* while still within the uterus. When eggs are kept in sea water, they become agglomerated to one another by a mucoid substance that is presumably extruded through the opercule and produced by cells similar to those described in amphilinids. On contact with sea water, this substance swells considerably (Ruskowski). When eggs are incubated, the *lychophorae* are formed gradually in about three weeks (temperature not stated). Contrary to the eggs of amphilinids, those of gyrocotylids hatch spontaneously, the larva swimming freely by means of its ciliated coating. It possesses two large ducts opening at the anterior end and apparently arising from a mass of glandular cells located at the posterior end of the larva (Lynch). Since the larvae die after a short time in sea water, it is probable that they must be swallowed by an intermediate host, although the latter is as yet unknown. Postlarval juveniles, recovered from the gut of chimaerids, differ from lycophorae by the presence of an anterior sucker and a posterior rosette-organ, as also by the spines being apparent. Such larvae, curiously enough, have also been found on many occasions in the body parenchyma of adult worms. In certain instances they occupied the distal end of the uterus and have been thought to develop *in situ* (Lynch). However, until further investigations are forthcoming, nothing can be said of the life history of gyrocotylids, although the fact that postlarval juveniles do occur in the parenchyma of adult worms would indicate that these cestodarians, like many species of pseudophyllidean cestodes, are capable of penetrating into a considerable number of paratenic hosts. It is possible that here also, as in certain acanthocephalans

(see page 115), ingestion of intermediate hosts containing immature larval forms would cause the latter to re-encapsulate. Such forms have never been recorded from the walls of the spiral valve of chimaerids, but their very small size would render them hard to see unless searched for systematically.

The location of amphilinids within the body cavity of their hosts, all of which occur in fresh water, could be interpreted as evidence of a primitive condition or as having arisen secondarily. The latter interpretation is tacitly assumed if they are to be considered as neotenic plerocercoids. Yet in spite of the very teleological assumption of their having been originally parasites of ichthyosaurs, they certainly do form a group of worms that first appeared a very long time ago. This is also borne out by their evident relationship to gyrocotylids, gut parasites of archaic fishes. Such considerations as their peculiar anatomical and larval structures lead the writer to consider cestodarians as the remains of a once flourishing group of parasites that must have originated in fresh-water hosts, as did the present-day amphilinids, and later passed into the sea with the primitive elasmobranchs, of which the chimaerids are today among the sole survivors. This would place their origin in the early Mesozoic and possibly even in the Paleozoic. It is possible, as mentioned above, that the primitive amphilinids were parasitic only in the larval stage and that the adult worms were free-living.

REFERENCES

FUHRMANN, O. 1930. Erste Unterklasse der Cestoidea. Cestodaria Monticelli. *Handb. Zool.*, 2:144–80, figs. 178–210.

JANICKI, C. VON. 1930. Ueber die jungsten Zustände von *Amphilina foliacea* in der Fischleibeshöhle, sowie Generelles zur Auffassung des genus *Amphilina* G. Wagen. *Zool. Anz.*, 90:190–205, 4 figs.

JOHNSTON, T. H. 1931. An amphilinid cestode from an Australian tortoise. *Austr. J. Exper. Biol. & Med.*, 8:1–7, 9 figs.

LYNCH, J. E. 1945. Redescription of the species of *Gyrocotyle* from the ratfish *Hydrolagus collei* (Lay & Bennet), with notes on the morphology and taxonomy of the genus. *J. Parasit.*, 31:418–46, 38 figs.

RUSKOWSKI, J. S. 1931. Etudes sur le cycle évolutif et la structure des Cestodes de mer. IIme partie. Sur les larves de Gyrocotyle urna (Gr. & Wagen.). *Bull. Acad. Polon. Sc. Litt. Ser. B*, 2:629–41, 2 figs., pl. 41.

CHAPTER TWELVE

Cestoda

Tapeworms are by far the most highly specialized parasites known and although their origin from some distant platyhelminth stock is obvious, all traces of any direct affinities have disappeared.

Several distinct groups can be recognized among cestodes, yet they all share in common the complete absence of a digestive system at all stages of their life history.

Since all adult cestodes are intestinal parasites, they absorb their nourishment from the intestinal contents of their host, and such conditions necessarily imply an intimate association with the latter. Consequently, it is not astonishing that tapeworms show a much more marked degree of host specificity than do most other parasites.

A cestode, barring a few exceptions to be referred to later, is provided with a scolex or attachment organ and a segmented body, each segment containing a complete hermaphroditic reproductive apparatus. The segments originate in a zone situated immediately behind the scolex and increase in size, especially in width and in length, as they are pushed farther from the proliferating zone by the continual growth of new segments. At a variable distance from the scolex the segments contain adult reproductive organs and are frequently self-impregnated. Consequently, the end segments nearly always contain a gravid uterus distended with eggs. Since new segments are formed continuously and also gravid segments are shed unceasingly, the total length of a given mature strobila remains fairly constant within certain limits.

From experimental data it is possible to evaluate the rate of growth of the broad fish tapeworm, *Diphyllobothrium latum* (L.), that usually reaches a length of eight to ten meters in man. The worm grows about two centimeters per day, and as its longevity has been found to exceed ten years, within that span it will have produced approximately seven kilometers of segments containing something like two billion eggs.

Reduplication of the sexual organs is found in several genera and might be considered as being an advantageous adaptation for the species, since the chances for impregnation and also, to a certain extent, egg production are both increased. The origin of such reduplications remains obscure, yet in nearly all cases it is possible to discover the original genus from which reduplication of the organs has arisen (Fig. 152). This is all the more interesting, as in almost every instance, both the normal and the reduplicated genera occur within the same host or group of hosts, an indication that whatever the origin or the mode of reduplication, it has in no way affected the degree of host specificity of the parasite.

In Table 4 are listed some of the normal genera from which it is possible to derive double-pored forms, together with their hosts.

The origin of other double-pored genera such as *Moniezia* and *Dipylidium* cannot be discovered from data available at present. They both occur in mammals and the normal corresponding genera might either have originated in birds or have been lost in present-day mammals. On the other hand, complete reduplication appears to be much more frequent in certain groups than in others. More than seven cases occur in anoplocephalans, for instance. In several other genera, it is found that reduplication is only partial and affects independently the male and the female organs. In *Diploposthe*, for example, only the male organs are reduplicated, the female organs remaining normal although possessing two vaginae. It goes, of course, without saying that in all cases where the genital organs are reduplicated, this only affects these organs and no other structure within the strobila is modified. This is especially true for the scolex.

A recent cytological study of the germ cells in a small number of species of *Hymenolepis* appears to indicate the existence of a certain uniformity throughout this family (Jones), although that author does not hesitate to create subspecies based on chromo- difficulty, morphologically. Moreover, a great deal more investigation will be necessary before argu-

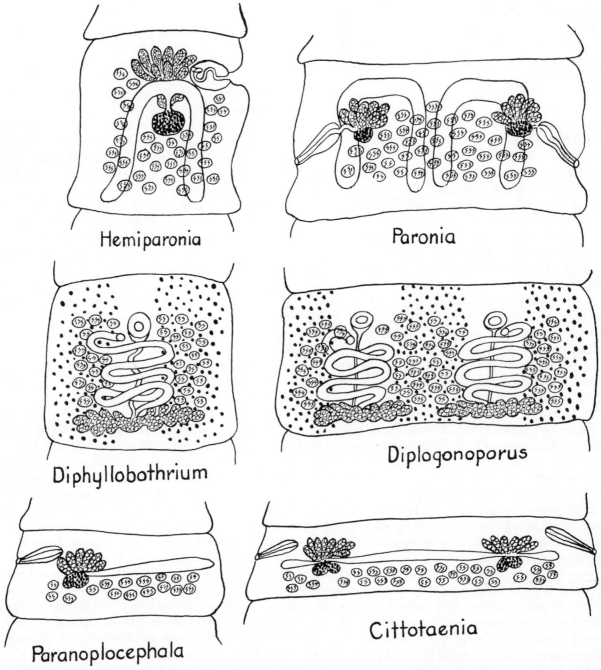

Hemiparonia

Paronia

Diphyllobothrium

Diplogonoporus

Paranoplocephala

Cittotaenia

Fig. 152. Diagram of sexual organs of cestodes, showing reduplication.

some size, a procedure that is hardly to be recommended in a genus that contains more than three hundred species, many of which are recognized with

ments based on such data as the above can be useful to taxonomists. Future research may even show that in such groups as these the generic characters used today will be found to fall within the cytological limits of a species. This, of course, would not modify the present species concept based on purely morphological characters, nor the taxonomic arrangements adopted so far. It would be interesting to investigate from a cytological standpoint such monstrosities as the "genus" *Jardugia* that possess a scolex of *Hymenolepis*, young segments that belong to the subgenus *Drepanidotaenia*, adult segments to the genus *Diploposthe*, and gravid segments to the genus *Diplogynia*. In other words a single worm combines characters of at least three presumably distinct genera, visible in separate segments. Even if such cases as these vindicate the opinion of the taxonomist who placed them all in the same family, they do not explain to what genus a second generation of parasites derived from individual eggs of such "generic" segments would belong. It is true that this is an exceptional example; nonetheless it is of more than passing interest on account of the problems that it creates.

In most cestodes, hermaphroditism is of the protandrous type and, consequently, the male organs develop before the female organs. In several instances, however (*Gyrocoelia, Shipleyia*), development of the female organs is retarded to the extent that the whole anterior part of the strobila is male and the posterior part, female. Occasionally, the reverse is also found (*Proterogynotaenia*) and the anterior part of the strobila is female, whereas the posterior part is male but contains also a gravid uterus. Complete separation of the sexes occurs in *Dioecocestus* where there also exists a marked sexual dimorphism, since male strobilae contain reduplicated organs although female strobilae have normal organs. Intersexes have been reported in a few particularly favorable instances (Clerc).

The structure of the scolex does not furnish any evidence of what might be considered an evolutionary process related to parasitism. On the contrary, scolex structures appear to indicate the presence of at least six distinct directions along which the parasites have developed. Each of these, moreover, corresponds to a characteristic arrangement of the reproductive organs and more especially of the vitelline glands, and also to definite groups of hosts. In other words, it is possible to distinguish several natural groups based on both morphological and physiological grounds.

In pseudophyllids, the scolex bears two muscular grooves, the so-called pseudobothridia, that enable it to become attached to the mucosa. From this simple type of scolex (*Diphyllobothrium*) is derived,

through secondary fusion of the edges of each groove, the genus *Bothridium* and probably, as an intermediate step, the genus *Duthiersia*, both of the latter genera occurring in monitor lizards. Occasionally, the scolex in pseudophyllids may bear hooks on its apex (*Triaenophorus*).

Tetrarhynchids and also diphyllids, both of which are doubtless derived from pseudophyllids, possess a very peculiar type of scolex borne upon a stalk-like portion that is never segmented. In diphyllids, both the apex of the scolex and the stalk bear numerous large spines (Fig. 153G). In tetrarhynchids besides two or four leaflike pseudobothridia, the scolex bears four retractile proboscides that are

TABLE 4. The Parallel between Normal and Reduplicated Organs in Cestodes.

NORMAL GENUS	REDUPLICATED GENUS	HOST
Sphyriocephala	*Hepatoxylon*	Sharks
Oochoristica	*Pancerina*	Reptiles
Davainea	*Cotugnia*	Birds
Hymenolepis	*Diplogynia*	Anserine birds
Ligula	*Digramma*	Grebes
Diphyllobothrium	*Diplogonoporus*	Fish-eating mammals
Hemiparonia	*Paronia*	Psittaciform birds
Andrya	*Diandrya*	Rodents
Monoecocestus		
Paranoplocephala	*Cittotaenia*[a]	Rodents
Progamotaenia	*Hepatotaenia*	Marsupials

[a] It is possible that this genus has arisen from two distinct normal genera, since certain species possess a reticulate uterus (*Monoecocestus*) and others a tubular uterus (*Paranoplocephala*).

armed with hooks and spines and that can be withdrawn into the stalk region of the scolex by individual muscles. The latter are attached each within a muscular bulb that is located at the base of the stalk (Fig. 153F).

Using scolex characters, at least two distinct groups of tetraphyllids may be recognized, namely those bearing suckers and those bearing bothridia. In the latter case, the scolex may assume the most extravagant aspect since each bothridium can be carried on a contractile stalk, and be itself divided into smaller haptorial organs that may also be combined with either hooks or spines (Fig. 153). It is interesting to draw attention to the fact that this group is absolutely characteristic for elasmobranchs and that it does not occur in any other group of fishes. This is also the case for diphyllids and tetrarhynchids.

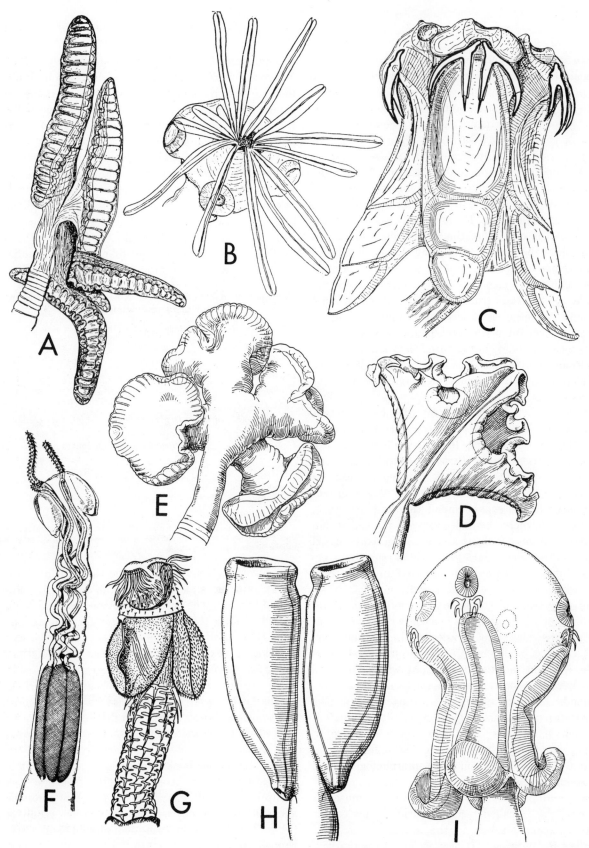

FIG. 153 (see legend opposite page).

The scolex bears four suckers, with sometimes a fifth one at the apex in tetraphyllids from freshwater teleosts, amphibians, and reptiles. This condition probably represents the passage from aquatic to terrestrial hosts.

From an ontogenetical standpoint, the pseudophyllid-tetraphyllid group differs from the tetraphyllid-cyclophyllid group of tapeworms by the nature of the egg membranes. In the former, the egg is usually operculated as in trematodes and contains a larva that is frequently ciliated, whereas in the latter case the outer shell is always very thin and an inner shell, sometimes named the embryophore, protects the larva.

In the first of the above two groups, the egg does not usually contain a larva when it is expelled from the gravid uterus, but must undergo a period of incubation in the water. In the second group mentioned the eggs always contain a larva when they are expelled either from the uterus or when the gravid segments are set free from the strobila.

From an embryological standpoint, the ciliated coat observed around the larvae of the first group which is later shed is homologous for the embryophore. On the other hand, the completely formed larva is identical in all groups of cestodes. It bears three pairs of small hooklets and is therefore often known as the hexacanth larva or the onchosphere. This larva contains several different types of cells, some of which have been found to be glandular and no doubt are used when the larva penetrates into the body cavity or the tissues of the intermediate host (Reid). Such glandular cells, originally described in cyclophyllids, also occur, although they have not been recognized as such, in pseudophyllids (Michajlow: Vogel).

Postembryonic development in tapeworms proceeds along almost identical lines in all of the groups considered above, although in pseudophyllids and tetrarhynchids only, there occurs a free larval stage, a ciliated onchosphere known as a *coracidium*. The latter usually hatches spontaneously and swims about in the water until it is swallowed by an intermediate host (Fig. 154). In all tapeworms other than those mentioned, the onchosphere remains within the egg which is ingested by an intermediate host.

FIG. 153. Various types of scolices. A. *Rhinebothrium*. B. *Parataenia*. C. *Acanthobothrium*. D. *Duthiersia*. E. *Phyllobothrium*. F. *Tetrarhynchobothrium*. G. *Echinobothrium*. H. *Bothridium*. I. *Balanobothrium*.

Barring a very small number of exceptions that occur among cyclophyllids, an onchosphere is only able to undergo metamorphosis into the infestive larval stage in the body cavity or the tissues of an intermediate host. Many different types of tapeworm larvae have been recognized, yet their ontogeny is practically identical and can be summarized as follows (Fig. 155). Within the intermediate host, the onchosphere increases in size and becomes a very mobile organism, at one end of which are found the

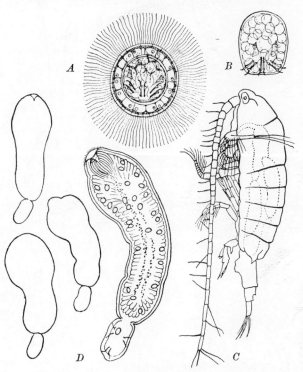

FIG. 154. *Diphyllobothrium latum* (L.). A. Coracidium. B. Onchosphere from the gut of the copepod, having shed its ciliary envelope. C. *Diaptomus* containing procercoids. D. Procercoids in various stages of contraction (Delachaux).

embryonic hooklets. This posterior end is sometimes constricted and separated from the rest of the body, the hooklets ultimately being shed. At this stage the larva is known as the procercoid, and in many cases (pseudophyllids, tetrarhynchids) ceases to develop any further although remaining active in the body cavity of the intermediate host. In all the other groups of tapeworms, at least for as much as is known at present, development proceeds beyond the procercoid stage, the latter representing an intermediate phase of the postlarval development only. The anterior end of the larva begins to differentiate

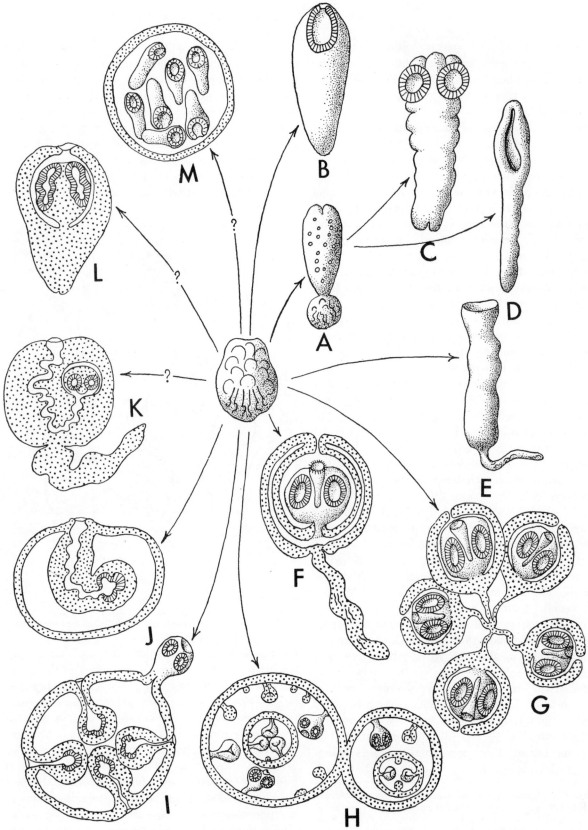

FIG. 155 (*see legend on opposite page*).

gradually, and a scolex, complete with suckers and hooks when these are present, is formed. In the mature, infestive larva these structures are always identical to those of the adult worm.[1]

In numerous cases, the scolex is subsequently retracted within the anterior end of the larva that surrounds it completely, forming protective membranes that enable the scolex to resist successfully the reaction that its presence causes within the intermediate host. According to whether the excretory pore is located at the posterior end of the larva or at the base of the scolex, the latter being either invaginated or simply retracted, it is possible to recognize two principal types of larvae. In the first case, the larvae are known as plerocercoids or plerocercus larvae (Fig. 155K, L) and in the second case, as cysticercoids or cysticercous larvae (Fig. 155F, J). In cysticercoids, the "tail" of the larva often still bears the embryonic hooklets; this type of larva usually occurs in invertebrates only. The cysticercous larvae, on the other hand, present a very different structure because the larval tissues that surround the scolex form a vesicle containing a transudate from the host's tissues. These larvae are always found in vertebrates and almost exclusively in mammals.

Polyembryony is infrequent among cestodes, yet it occurs sometimes in both the cysticercous type (*Multiceps*) (Fig. 156) and in the cysticercoid type (*Staphylocystis*) (Fig. 155G), each larva possessing numerous scolices. On the other hand, larval multiplication by budding is exceptional and has been reported so far in *Echinococcus* and in several species of *Taenia*, both genera incidentally being harbored by carnivores. In *Echinococcus*, the so-called hydatid cyst, budding is mostly endogenous, arising from a germinal layer that lines the cyst wall. Daughter vesicles, also containing scolices, may be produced

[1] So far, the only exception to this rule occurs in the merocercoid larva of *Catenotaenia* that possess a single, large terminal sucker with which it attaches itself to the intestinal mucosa of the final host (mouse). As soon as the larva has become attached, four suckers are gradually formed and the terminal larval sucker is resorbed and finally disappears without leaving a trace (Joyeux & Baer).

FIG. 155. Larval types in cestodes. A. Procercoid. B. Merocercoid. C. Plerocercoid of a tetraphyllidean species. D. Plerocercoid of a pseudophyllidean species. E. Neotenic procercoid (*Archigetes*). F. Cysticercoid. G. *Staphylocystis*. H. *Echinococcus*. I. *Multiceps*. J. Cysticercus. K. Plerocercus (*Tetrathyridium*). L. Plerocercus of tetraphyllidean type. M. *Merocercus* (budding plerocercoid?) (Baer).

within the original cyst, and the latter increase considerably in size, reaching as much as 15 to 25 cm. in diameter. Such daughter vesicles are produced from a single scolex that for an unrecognized reason dedifferentiates, losing its characteristic structure and its hooks to become a small vesicle, the internal membrane of which begins to germinate new scolices. In the *Taenia*-larvae, as for instance *T. crassiceps*, budding is always exogenous, the daughter buds becoming detached before the scolex is formed and continuing their ontogeny independently. Curiously enough, both of the above-mentioned larval types may be inoculated into the body cavity of experi-

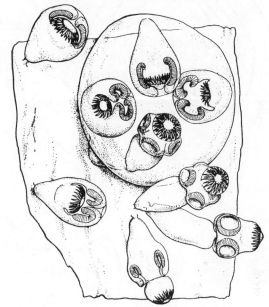

FIG. 156. *Echinococcus echinococcus* (Goeze), showing mode of budding of the scolices (Fuhrmann).

mental hosts and continue to produce more scolices (Studer & Baer). What might be either a case of polyembryony or of budding, although the former is more probable, has been reported for a plerocercoid larva found in a tropical species of oyster. Unfortunately this discovery has never been repeated so that nothing very definite is known about this peculiar larva (Fig. 155M).

As mentioned previously, in both pseudophyllids and tetrarhynchids, larval development requires two intermediate hosts whereas one only is sufficient for all the other cestodes.

As soon as infestive larval tapeworms are eaten by suitable definitive hosts, the scolex attaches itself to the intestinal mucosa and all the larval append-ages are shed. This even occurs in larvae such as *Taenia taeniaeformis* that possess a "strobila" some-times as long as 30 cm. or more, but that is just a larval structure. In plerocercoid larvae also, the

or simplified secondarily according to whether a paratenic host is introduced or whether the life cycle is telescoped. In the latter case, two onto-genetically distinct processes are found; the larva becomes progenetic in the one, and in the other

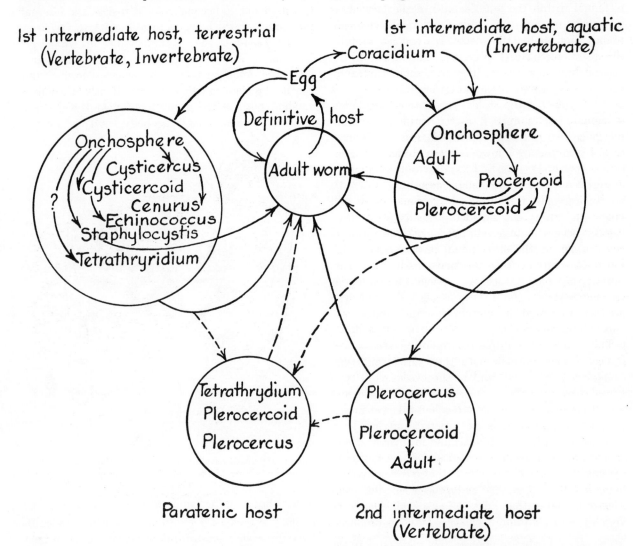

FIG. 157. Diagram of the principal life cycles of cestodes.

posterior extremity of the body is resorbed or de-stroyed by the digestive juices present in the intes-tine of the final host (Joyeux & Baer).

From the foregoing, it is clear that there exist at least two fundamental types of cestode life cycles requiring one or two intermediate hosts respectively. Moreover, it is known from experimental evidence that the original type of life cycle may be complicated

the intermediate host also becomes the final host (Fig. 157).

Consequently, tapeworm life histories are much more varied than might be supposed at first sight, since different combinations of the above mecha-nisms are able to exert their influence upon the life cycle. By leaving out all taxonomic considerations, it is possible to distinguish five different types of life histories based on the principle represented in Figure 159.

For reasons to be stated later, the writer considers the most primitive type of life cycle is that requiring two intermediate hosts.

I. *Two intermediate hosts; paratenic host optional.*

This is the life cycle as found in *Diphyllobothrium latum* (L.) where the first intermediate host, within which is formed the procercoid, is a copepod and the second intermediate host, a fish, carries the plerocercoid in its muscles. If, however, such an infested fish be eaten by another larger fish, the latter will become a paratenic host, the plerocercoids re-encapsulating in the immediate vicinity of the gut. Several hundred plerocercoid larvae may thus accumulate in the peri-intestinal fat of a pike that has fed on infested fishes. A large pike may contain a thousand and even more of these plerocercoids and constitute an important reservoir for carnivorous final hosts. However, since man does not normally eat the intestines and peri-intestinal fat of pike, the larvae accumulated by the latter would be withdrawn from the human cycle. This example clearly illustrates the way in which a paratenic host may either facilitate infestation of the final host or, on the contrary, interrupt the cycle by forcing it out on a tangent.

This type of life cycle is apparently found in all pseudophyllidean tapeworms excepting the caryophyllaeids and will no doubt also be found to occur, according to some unpublished data, in tetrarhynchids. However, further investigations will be necessary before this can be definitely established.

II. *One intermediate host; paratenic host optional.*

This is the typical tetraphyllidean type of life cycle, at least for as much as it has been investigated in both reptiles and fresh-water teleosts. Here the procercoid larva that is formed within the intermediate host, usually an aquatic crustacean, continues its development to the plerocercoid stage so that when it is fed to a suitable definitive host, it will grow into an adult worm. It appears, however, for ecological reasons that a paratenic host has almost become indispensable, since the final hosts do not normally feed on plankton, but on small fishes which do so. From experimental evidence, it is possible to assume that theoretically a paratenic host is optional but that practically it has become indispensable.

Many plerocercoid and plerocercous larvae of elasmobranch-tetraphyllids have been reported from a great variety of marine vertebrates and invertebrates, many of which are never eaten by sharks or skates. Such statistical data would indicate that these are paratenic hosts that have become infested by eating the first intermediate host, the latter being probably a crustacean although there is not enough experimental evidence as yet to prove it.

III. *One intermediate host; no paratenic host.*

This is the typical life cycle of a cyclophyllidean tapeworm, the intermediate host containing either a cysticercous or a cysticercoid type of larva according

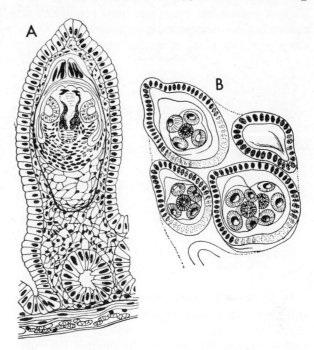

Fig. 158. *Hymenolepis nana fraterna* (Stiles). A. Section of an intestinal villus containing a cysticercoid. B. Whole mount of villi with cysticercoids (Delachaux).

to whether the host is a vertebrate or an invertebrate. All experimental data furnished so far indicate that no tapeworm larva of the above types is able to re-encapsulate in a paratenic host and, consequently, the latter never occurs in their life history.

IV. *Intermediate host optional.*

The rat tapeworm, *Hymenolepis nana fraterna* (Stiles), normally does not require an intermediate host (see V). The latter, an insect, has however been reported from tropical America and can also be infested, although not always successfully, in the laboratory. This is, so far, the only case of its kind that is known and it is particularly interesting to observe that the cysticercoid larva thus formed within the insect, differs from the normal type described below, thus showing that larval adnexae have no bearing on the structure of the adult worm.

V. *No intermediate or paratenic hosts; development direct.*

This completely telescoped type of life cycle occurs normally in the rat tapeworm mentioned above and also in *H. n. nana* (v. Sieb.) from man as well as in *Hymenolepis erinacei* (Gmel.) from hedgehogs (Fig. 158). A similar life cycle has been postulated although never demonstrated experimentally for *Baerietta jägerskiöldi* (Jan.) (Joyeux).

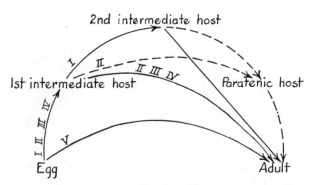

Fig. 159. Diagram to show how the gradual shortening of the life cycle of cestodes occurs.

In *H. nana* the cysticercoid is formed within the intestinal villosities of the upper jejunum in the very short time of seventy-two hours. As soon as the scolex appears, the larva breaks through the villus and falls into the lumen of the gut where it attaches itself to the mucosa and becomes adult.

It has been assumed that the eggs produced by this cestode could develop *in situ* without leaving the host. But, so far, no experimental evidence has been furnished in support of this belief. On the other hand, laboratory investigations tend to show that such a form of development is not possible under normal circumstances.

If a mouse harboring cysticercoids in its gut is eaten by another mouse or by a rat, the cysticercoids will grow into adult tapeworms in the latter. This would also indicate that, primarily, the life cycle contained an intermediate host belonging to the same group as the final host, so that transmission of

the parasites would have been possible on account of the cannibalistic habits in rodent colonies.

Among pseudophyllidean tapeworms, caryophyllaeids appear to possess an exceptional type of life cycle since they require only a single intermediate host.

In *Caryophyllaeus* and related genera, the eggs are swallowed by an aquatic oligochaete and the onchosphere, escaping into the latter's body cavity, grows into a procercoid. When fresh-water teleosts eat such infested oligochaetes, the procercoids escape and become adult in the gut of the fish. Moreover, adult caryophyllaeids differ from all other pseudophyllids, and also from all other cestodes, by the absence of segments. The entire strobila consists of a single segment that consequently contains only a single reproductive apparatus of the usual pseudophyllidean type.

Before the life history of this family had been discovered and compared with that of *Diphyllobothrium*, the genera were considered as monozoic tapeworms closely related to cestodarians, whereas they are now interpreted as neotenic plerocercoids, although they may also be envisaged as primitive tapeworms (see page 150).

Another member of this family, *Archigetes*, is the only known tapeworm that occurs as adult in an invertebrate. It is found in the body cavity of aquatic oligochaetes. Its life history is direct, without any intermediate host. The eggs are liberated when the host dies and are swallowed subsequently by another host. The onchosphere grows into a procercoid and the latter is found to possess functional genitalia. In other words, *Archigetes* is a neotenic procercoid. This explains how a pseudophyllidean life history has become independent of an intermediate host[2] (Fig. 159).

Host specificity among tapeworms is extremely marked, each group of vertebrates possessing its own particular genera and species (see page 167). There exists also very definite evidence that the hosts and their cestodes have evolved on parallel lines, and consequently that the most primitive hosts also

[2] Evidence based on an insufficiently controlled experiment has led Szidat to consider *Archigetes* as the progenetic larva of a genus described from this country in fishes. However, since both his morphological and taxonomic conclusions are liable to create considerable confusion and, besides, are in contradiction with the laws of nomenclature, they should be discarded.

harbor the most primitive cestodes. A corollary of this is that the distribution of tapeworms within their hosts cannot be referred to ecological causes, but to the zoological affinities of the hosts among themselves (Baer).

The most archaic hosts are without any doubt the fishes, and it is here also that the most primitive tapeworms are found.

The actual elasmobranchs are descended from fresh-water stock that has itself since disappeared, but from which has also arisen a fish that has remained in fresh water and apparently that has not evolved along specialized lines. The bowfin, *Amia calva* (L.), is probably the most archaic host known today and its ancestors have witnessed the passage into the sea of the extinct forerunners of present-day elasmobranchs. Consequently, the tapeworm of the bowfin should have every chance of being the most primitive of cestodes.

The genus *Haplobothrium* is the only cestode that has been described from this host for which it is absolutely specific, and its systematic status remains to this day a much discussed problem among taxonomists. The scolex, bearing four retractile proboscides armed with spines at their base but no pseudobothridia, denotes evident affinities with tetrarhynchids. The internal anatomy, on the other hand, shows distinct pseudophyllidean relationships. Curiously enough, the strobila becomes secondarily segmented, breaking off into smaller pieces, the anterior end of each one becoming differentiated into a secondary pseudophyllidean scolex! Moreover, from the incomplete evidence that has been gathered so far, it is found that the life cycle of *Haplobothrium* requires at least two intermediate hosts, a copepod and a fish, and that the infestive larva is of the plerocercous type (Essex; Meinkoth) (Fig. 160).

From the above morphological characters of *Haplobothrium* it is possible to derive on the one hand the pseudophyllids, and on the other, both tetraphyllids and diphyllids.

Among pseudophyllids, bothriocephalids and related families may be distinguished from diphyllobothriids by their hosts, the former occurring in teleosts and the latter in mammals and birds. Moreover, the majority of teleosts that harbor bothriocephalids belong to marine genera and species, only a small number being found in fresh water. Diphyllobothriids have obviously arisen from the bothriocephalid stock and have become established in mam-

mals and birds, a passage that was easy since the larvae occur in fish that are eaten by these hosts.

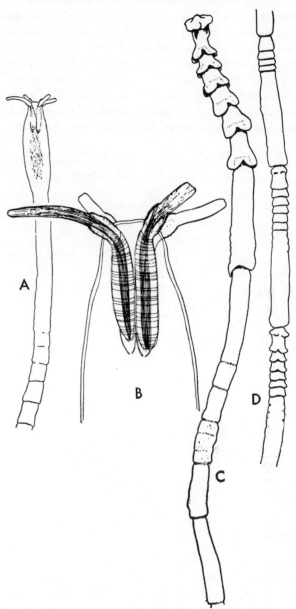

FIG. 160. *Haplobothrium globuliforme* Cooper. A. Scolex. B. Scolex greatly enlarged showing the four retractile tentacles. C. Portion of a strobila showing a pseudoscolex that resembles the scolex of pseudophyllidean species. D. Strobila dividing secondarily into identical pieces (Fuhrmann).

Tetrarhynchids and diphyllids occur exclusively in elasmobranchs, where the former have split up into several distinct genera that have arisen from a common stock nearly related to *Haplobothrium*.

As elasmobranchs form an isolated group of fishes, so also have their parasites become highly specialized.

Among the tetraphyllidean cestodes from elasmobranchs, the family *Disculicipitidae* is of particular interest since it is related to pseudophyllids by the structure of its reproductive glands, especially the vitellaria, and at the same time to tetraphyllids by its scolex although it has lost all trace of suckers. This family should probably be located close to the tetraphyllidean stem that diverges on the one side toward the extravagant species occurring in elasmo-

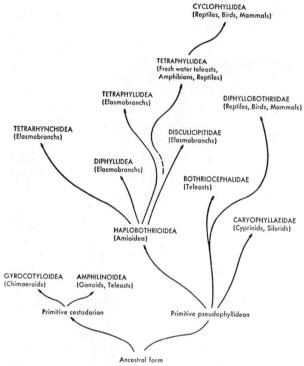

FIG. 161. Phylogenetic tree of cestodarian and cestode worms as deduced from their host relationships.

branchs, and on the other, toward the more conservative type of scolex with four suckers that is found in all the species from fresh-water teleosts, amphibians, and reptiles. From the latter line, it is also possible to derive the entire cyclophyllidean group that occurs only in higher vertebrates. The writer is persuaded that an evolutionary tree of the cestodes, planted and pruned according to the above suggestions, is in keeping with the facts and also explains the reason for two types of life histories in teleost parasites, namely those that have been derived from pseudophyllidean and those derived from tetraphyllidean ancestors (Fig. 161).

The evidence of a parallel evolution of cestodes and their hosts is very strong and has frequently been used to support certain taxonomic arrangements (Baer). This is the first time that it is applied to the interpretation of the life cycles.

The origin of parasite life cycles has often been postulated, yet mostly without satisfactory results owing to the authors' basing their conclusions on nonspecific or only slightly specific parasites.

The common theory, most often found in textbooks, assumes that all parasites originally were harbored by invertebrates in which they completed their life histories. Subsequently, when these hosts were eaten by vertebrates the parasites became adapted to their new surroundings while retaining their mode of ingress into the host.

This theory has again been formulated recently (Stunkard) for platyhelminths, although the arguments put forward are not based upon facts but upon ideas. Moreover, trematodes being essentially ecologically specific and apparently also recent parasites, they are not a favorable subject upon which to base such a theory.

For tapeworms, there is no justification whatever for assuming that they were originally parasites of invertebrates that might be, today, the intermediate hosts. The example of *Archigetes*, the only adult cestode reported from invertebrates, is always cited as furnishing proof of the above-mentioned theory. This genus may, however, be interpreted in two ways: from its direct mode of development and its location within the body cavity of an aquatic oligochaete, it could be assumed to be a neotenic procercoid; on the other hand, it could be looked upon as an ancestral form of tapeworm. Physiological arguments based on experimental investigations oppose this latter interpretation. If, as assumed, ancestral cestodes lived within the body cavity of their hosts, there should be no reason for their ever having become successfully adapted to parasitism, since one of the most essential conditions for this would be that the eggs be expelled into the surrounding medium. This, however, is not the case. On the other hand, the argument that supposes *Archigetes* to have been at one time a larva that had to be eaten by another host, and that became subsequently adult to "compensate" the loss of the final host through extinction, is highly teleological and also contrary to what is known today of the possible causes for neoteny.

Cestodarians are certainly more closely related to an ancestral stock than are cestodes. Detailed accounts of all of their life histories are not known except in amphilinids, a group that might perhaps furnish a clue to the possible origin of life cycles. *Amphilina* lives within the body cavity of sturgeons and can escape from the latter through the abdominal pores. In teleosts that do not possess abdominal pores, the cestodarians have been found to escape by piercing the body wall of their host (see page 136). Such data appear to indicate that adult amphilinids may be free-living organisms and that the larvae only are parasitic as is the case in *Fecampia*, a nonrelated turbellarian (see page 35).

In the absence of any evidence as to neotenic larvae from invertebrates representing the original, ancestral form of the parasites, it is necessary to consider another alternative, namely that from the beginning ancestral tapeworms were parasitic in fishes.

It is possible to imagine a turbellarian-like ancestor that was in some way preadapted to resisting the possible defense reactions of fishes by possessing a mucoid secretion on the surface of its body as is sometimes found in turbellarians. On the other hand, there is no possible doubt that the entire ancestral group has always been hermaphroditic. Consequently when such an organism was accidentally swallowed by a fish, two alternatives might arise. In the first case, the adult worm might pass unscathed through the gut and no parasitism would result. In the second case, however, supposing the worm were not adult and that consequently the reproductive organs were not functional, the worm might attempt to escape from an unfavorable medium by piercing the gut wall and falling into the body cavity. The conditions here would enable it to become adult and to produce eggs that would be eliminated by the abdominal pores. Excess nourishment within the body cavity of the fish would increase the rate of egg output of the worm and consequently affect inversely the rate of incubation of the eggs. The latter now, on being expelled, would no longer contain a larva but only a cellular mass requiring a period of incubation. Eggs lying on the bottom during this period could easily be eaten by some invertebrate scavenger, an oligochaete or a crustacean. Such a possibility becomes greater, as incubation of the eggs would require a longer time. If the egg eaten by the scavenger contains a larva about to hatch, the latter may attempt

to escape from the gut into the body cavity of the invertebrate. Should this be the case, it is possible to imagine that the presence of this larva would evoke some kind of immunity reaction in the host organism, that would inhibit or retard all further development. If such an invertebrate were eaten by a fish, the immature flatworm would once more pass into its body cavity and the first life cycle would thus be completed just as it is found today in amphilinids.

It is possible, however, to postulate that the fish feeding on an invertebrate harboring such larval worms would not possess abdominal pores and would also react to the presence of the larva by secreting antibodies inhibiting larval maturation. This would of course mean that the life cycle had been interrupted and the attempt at parasitism was unsuccessful. On the other hand, the fish harboring this immature worm might very well become the prey of another larger fish, and maturation of the worm might consequently be possible in this host, but this time in the gut, from where the maturing reproductive organs would prevent the larva from passing once more into the body cavity (see page 115). This would also correspond to the life cycle of pseudophyllids that should be considered as being the most primitive tapeworms.

Another possibility that should be envisaged is that the larva eaten with the invertebrate is able to remain within the gut of the fish and to become adult, thus creating a simple life cycle as occurs today in caryophyllaeids.

It is interesting to remark, in support of this theory, that all of the postulated successful attempts mentioned above occur today, and that what should be considered as the most primitive type of life cycle (amphilinids) has been retained by the most archaic parasites, the cestodarians. Moreover, the next most primitive cycle is that of the caryophyllaeids, a group considered formerly as being netotenic plerocercoids, occurring exclusively in siluroids and cyprinids, two groups of fishes that have originated from a common stock and that are today considered as being the most primitive teleosts.

Life cycles requiring two intermediate hosts are found in pseudophyllids, diphyllids, and probably also in tetrarhynchids and tetraphyllids from elasmobranchs. The ancestral tapeworm of this group is today represented by a parasite of the bowfin, that is itself a living fossil whose Mesozoic ancestors were related to the ancestral elasmobranchs. From data available from the study of host specificity, avian and mammalian tapeworms have no doubt originated at the beginning of the Tertiary and it is, consequently, during the few million years that separated the Triassic from the Eocene, that life cycles with a single host were evolved as an adaptation to a terrestrial mode of life (Fig. 162).

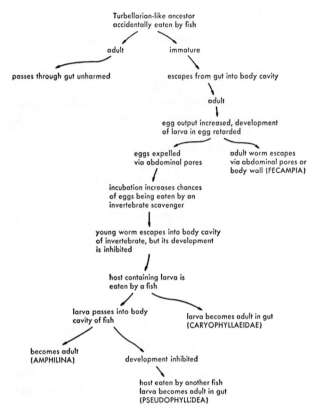

Fig. 162. Diagram of the hypothetical origin of parasitism in tapeworms.

Tapeworm life cycles, as they occur today, are the final outcome of the successful attempts only, and subsequent selective influences have caused them to appear in the light of teleological adaptations.

REFERENCES

Baer, J. G. 1933. L'adaptation des helminthes a leurs hôtes. *Bull. Soc. Neuch. Sc. Nat.*, 58:57–76.

———. 1946. Les Helminthes parasites des Vertébrés. Relations phylogénétiques entre leur évolution et celle de leurs hôtes. Conséquences biologiques et médicales. *Ann. Franche-Comté et de l'Université de Besançon*, 15 pp.

*Fuhrmann, O. 1928. Cestoda. *Handb. der Zool.* (2), 2:181–416, figs. 211–435.

———. 1932. Les Ténias des Oiseaux. *Mém. Univ. Neuchâtel*, vol. 8, 383 pp., 147 figs.

Jones, A. W. 1945. Studies in cestode cytology. *J. Parasit.*, 31:213–35, 21 figs.

Joyeux, Ch., & Baer, J. G. 1936. Cestodes. *Faune de France*, vol. 30, 613 pp., 569 figs.

———. 1936. Les hôtes d'attente dans le cycle évolutif des helminthes. *Biologie médicale*, 24:1–25, 6 figs.

———. 1945. Morphologie, évolution et position systématique de *Catenotaenia pusilla* (Goeze, 1782), cestode parasite de Rongeurs. *Rev. suisse Zool.*, 52:13–51, 29 figs.

Meinkoth, N. A. 1947. Notes on the life cycle and taxonomic position of *Haplobothrium globuliforme* Cooper, a tapeworm of *Amia calva* L. *Trans. Am. Micros. Soc.*, 66:256–61, 1 pl.

Michajlow, W. 1933. Les stades larvaires de *Triaenophorus nodulosus* (Pall). I. Le coracidium. *Ann. Parasit.*, 11:349–58, 6 figs.

Reid, W. M. 1948. Penetration glands in cyclophyllidean onchospheres. *Trans. Am. Micros. Soc.*, 67:177–82, 2 pls.

Studer, M., & Baer, J. G. 1949. Une larve de cestode bourgeonnante. *Bull. Soc. Neuch. Sc. Nat.*, 72:225.

Stunkard, H. W. 1946. Interrelationships and taxonomy of the digenetic trematodes. *Biol. Rev.*, 21:148–58.

Szidat, L. 1937. Archigetes R. Leuckart, 1878, die progenetische Larve einer für Europa neuen Caryphyllaeiden-Gattung Biacetabulum Hunter, 1927. *Zool. Anz.*, 119:166–72, 1 fig.

Vogel, H. 1929. Studien zur Entwicklung von *Diphyllobothrium*. I. Die Wimperlarve von *Diphyllobothrium latum*. *Zeitschr. f. Parasitenk.*, 2:213–22, 6 figs.

* A complete bibliography to date will be found in this work.

PART THREE

Host-parasite relationships

In the preceding chapters, adaptation to parasitism of each of the different groups has been examined in a somewhat analytical manner. From a purely dogmatical standpoint such an arrangement of the materials is justified, since it stresses the morphological aspect of the problem and also makes it possible to recognize the physiological significance of the life histories.

The study of host-parasite relationship stresses both the nature and the intimacy of the association between the parasite and the host, as also the reactions of the former to the latter, irrespective of the species to which the parasite belongs.

Such investigations also reveal some of the more fundamental aspects of parasitology and clearly show that parasites are subject to the same laws as free-living organisms but that their biotopes are more specialized.

CHAPTER THIRTEEN

Host specificity

Host specificity does not necessarily imply that a parasite always occurs in or on one and the same species of host, because it may occur also in or on hosts that are more or less directly related to one another either phylogenetically or ecologically.

Although host specificity is primarily a problem of physiology, the greatest part of the available data is derived from statistical reports on the distribution of the parasites within or upon their hosts.

To be of any value, such data must be obtained by careful investigations into the taxonomy of parasites, omitting any results derived from the study of captive or domestic animals as these may in certain cases be contaminated accidentally. Far too much hastily compiled information has been published that tends to confuse the more fundamental aspects of this problem.

Host specificity should be regarded as essentially one of the more specialized aspects of animal ecology, an association in which the host is to the parasite what the biotope is to the free-living organism. Parasites are isolated upon or within their hosts and in certain cases their entire life cycle is spent without leaving the host. Consequently, from an ecological stand-point, the host may be considered as comparable to an island and the parasites as an insular fauna.

It is a well known fact that animals unable to leave an island tend to form subspecies that become distinctive for each island. This is primarily due to the fact that genetic stabilization of the populations occurs and that variation remains within definite limits.

The ecological study of insular faunae makes it also possible to discover at what period the islands became inhabited or, speaking in terms of parasitol-ogy, to deduce eventual relationships between the hosts from the study of their parasites.

To bring out the ecological nature of host-parasite relationships it will be necessary to examine the statistical data available independently of the groups to which the parasites belong, and only in the light of their host adaptations.

In parasites that possess complicated life histories involving several intermediate hosts, ecological segregation may occur at each of the larval stages and consequently the final interpretation will have to take into consideration all of the data.

As stated above, the basis for all statistical studies is careful taxonomic investigation of large collections from a great variety of hosts. Unfortunately, this has not been done in all of the groups and many of them cannot be used as statistical evidence of host-parasite relationship.

From an ecological standpoint, one must consider separately the ectoparasites and the endoparasites, although it is obvious that in several instances cases will be found that are on the borderline between these two categories. These are, however, relatively few and do not modify to any extent the general conclusions.

1. ECTOPARASITES

All ectoparasites can be conveniently grouped into three categories according to whether the larval stages or the adults are parasitic or whether all the stages include parasites.

a. *Larval stages parasitic; adults free-living.*

This type of parasitism, sometimes known as protelian parasitism, apparently occurs only in unionids in which the glochidial stage attaches itself either to the skin or to the gills of fishes (see page 20).

Experimentally, glochidia can be induced to fix themselves to many different living supports, so much so that the closing of the glochidial valves seems to be caused by reflex action that may be set off by several substances as, for instance, mucous dissolved in water. It is also possible that there exist certain mechanical stimuli such as might be caused by currents arising in the water.

155

From data available, it is clear that specific glochidia occur on fishes that inhabit the same biotope as the adult clams, and that both the speed of the fish and the levels at which it swims influence the fixation of the larval clams. Consequently, ecological segregation appears to be the principal cause of this form of ectoparasitism. It should, however, be borne in mind that results obtained experimentally are not always comparable with conditions as found in the field. Usually, experimental infestation of aquarium fishes with glochidia are far more intense than in nature, since the fishes cannot escape from the parasites. On the other hand, from experimental evidence it appears that the fish reacts to the presence of the parasites in such a way that subsequent infestations become lighter and finally that no more infestation occurs. This would indicate that the fish can acquire some kind of immunity toward successive infestations by the same parasites. A tissue reaction has been found in the host and has been studied by various authors, although its nature has not yet been discovered (Reuling). Since this reaction is correlative with the intensity of the infestation, it is probable that it hardly ever occurs naturally since most hosts are able to escape from massive infestations such as would occur in the laboratory.

b. *Adults parasitic; larval stages free-living.*

The nature of the relationship between parasitic prosobranchs and their hosts has not been sufficiently investigated to support any evidence of host specificity. Moreover, the data available as to the rate of infestation are far too scanty to be of any statistical value. It should be noted, however, that in all cases where parasitic prosobranchs have been reported, the hosts are always echinoderms and no species of parasitic snail is known from any other group of hosts. Since both gastropods and echinoderms are exceedingly old forms of animal life, it seems likely that the association that has sprung up between them must have arisen sometime in the late Paleozoic or in early Mesozoic times.

Most of the parasitic copepods can be included under this heading, although in several cases their free-living larval existence is shortened through metamorphosis occurring while the young is still within the egg membranes.

In many cases there exists a very distinct host specificity visible in that certain genera and species always occur upon the same hosts. Many genera are specific for ascidians, others for annelids. Fishes belonging to the same family harbor identical genera of copepods that are sometimes different from those harbored by other fish families. Unfortunately, here also, statistical evidence is insufficient to warrant definite results. Parasitic copepods are obviously ecologically segregated upon their hosts; and the more specialized modes of feeding, with the morphological adaptations that appear subsequently, have certainly caused the association to become very intimate. This is particularly well marked in blood feeders of which each genus and often even each species is adapted to a definite species of host.

The majority of fleas have free-living larvae that occur either in the nests or in the dens of their hosts where they feed on organic detritus. Consequently, the relationship of the parasite and the host acquires a definite degree of permanence. On the other hand, as everybody knows, fleas are apt to abandon one host to pass onto another. Such exchanges occur even when both of the hosts are living. The ecological isolating factor, however, still occurs and in certain cases this has given rise to new species of parasites.

Fleas occur exclusively on mammals and on birds, the mammalian species being the more primitive. *Palaeopsylla*, a genus found on present-day shrews and moles, occurred in the Oligocene where it has been reported from Baltic amber.

Ecological segregation of adult fleas upon their hosts is very clearly marked when the hosts themselves occupy a specialized biotope. For instance, ischnopsyllines have been reported only from bats, and coptophyllines from jerboas, a group of Old World jumping mice. Such instances of isolation upon hosts living in colonies from specialized biotopes may even lead to supporting evidence of phylogenetical relationship between hosts.

European ground squirrels harbor a series of genera and species that are included in the citellophyllinines. One species of ground squirrel, *Citellus fulvus* (Licht.), from Southern Russia occasionally harbors only fleas belonging to the oropsyllines, a group that occurs exclusively on American ground squirrels and prairie dogs. Since both prairie dogs and ground squirrels are known to have arisen from common ancestors, it can be assumed that the latter already harbored fleas. This situation must have existed before Eurasia became separated from America, or in other words, during the Miocene. It is also possible to assume that the species of fleas from the Russian ground squirrel has retained ancestral characters that it derived from the common ancestor of both the ground squirrels and the prairie dogs.

Another such instance has been reported from the Turkestan hare, *Lepus tolai* Pall. which harbors a single species of flea, *Hoplopsyllus glacialis* (Tach.) that also occurs upon the Polar hare, *L. timidus glacialis* Peters from both Greenland and Canada. Yet this species of flea has never been found upon the European and Siberian hare, *Lepus timidus* L. Consequently, *L. tolai*, the Turkestan hare, is assumed to have arisen from the Arctic hare and to have a Polar origin (Wagner).

Bird fleas have very obviously been derived from mammal fleas, and in several cases it is even possible to trace back the original species from which the avian flea has originated (Rothschild). It is also found that bird fleas have arisen at different times from distinct lines of mammal fleas. The genus *Ceratophyllus*, for example, is clearly derived from parasites of tree-climbing rodents such as squirrels, and such fleas would have been to a certain extent preadapted to a dry environment. Moreover, the larvae would apparently find in the birds' nests, conditions similar to those occurring in squirrels' nests.

In some unexplained fashion, *Orneascus*, a genus of bird fleas closely related to *Citellophyllus* mentioned above, has succeeded in establishing itself on martins. It has been reported from these birds in Scotland, the Swiss Alps, and Kashmir. It is difficult to understand how the transfer from ground squirrels to martins has occurred but it must obviously have taken place somewhere in the Palearctic region. Since ground squirrels are particularly abundant in the higher regions of Asia, one might assume that the Kashmir martins first acquired this flea, and then passed it on to the Scottish and Alpine martins when they all wintered together in southern Africa.

Other examples of speciation being favored by isolation occur within the genus *Xenopsylla* that is characteristic for African rats and mice, and of which a single species has become isolated on shearwaters from the Canary Isles and Pityuse Isle. In the southern Atlantic on Kerguelen Isles and Antipodes Isles the diving petrel, a gull, and a burrow-nesting parakeet have acquired a species of flea belonging to a group of primitive marsupial fleas that are dominant in the Australian region. In this case, the ecological factor is particularly evident.

A rabbit flea has succeeded in establishing itself at least twice on burrow-nesting birds, once on puffins and shearwaters from the west coast of Britain and again on an auklet from Coronados Isles in the Gulf of California. Although rabbits and shearwaters nest in the same burrows, it is not possible to derive the shearwater flea directly from the rabbit flea as occurring on British rabbits. It must have had in the distant past a common ancestor with fleas from American rabbits and those that occur on the Arctic hare.

The effects of isolation are clearly seen in the case of the British rabbit flea that frequently occurs upon sheldrakes, *Tadorna tadorna* (L.), a species that nests within rabbit burrows but that occurs exclusively on the mainland and not on the off shore islands. Consequently, the isolating factor cannot exert its effect upon the straggling rabbit fleas.

The introduction into this country of the common European house sparrow also introduced the European fowl flea. This species has since spread to several different hosts, both wild and domesticated.

Although no species of flea from this country has been introduced in like manner into Europe, it has been discovered that a South American flea, known as the parrot sticktight flea, is frequently collected from a variety of captive birds in the London zoological gardens, and that it has also been found on tame pigeons. This flea is related to the jigger that burrows into the horny skin of the feet of both South American and African natives, and in spite of its specialized mode of attachment, is capable of attacking a large number of different bird hosts that are in no way related to one another.

Stragglers have been found to pass from birds to carnivorous mammals or from small mammals to birds of prey, yet no satisfactory evidence has been produced as to the possible longevity of such species upon their new hosts.

There exists some very clear evidence that at least once a bird flea has passed back onto a mammal. This is a species belonging to the genus *Ceratophyllus* that occurs on both stoats and martins from the Palearctic region. This return to a mammal must have occurred fairly early in its history as a bird flea, before or during the last Ice Age, judging from the boreal-alpine distribution of the hosts. Moreover, the fact that a number of bird fleas have the same distribution proves that they had already changed onto avian hosts before the glaciation in Europe, that is to say, at least twenty thousand years ago (Rothschild). Consequently this also shows how much more recent bird fleas are than mammal fleas which date back to the Miocene, more than twenty-five million years ago.

c. *Both larvae and adults parasitic.*

In this category are included ectoparasites, some of which, as monogenetic trematodes and isopods, possess a very short free-living larval stage.

Ectoparasitic annelids should also be included here although there does not appear to be very much information available as to their relationship with their hosts. It has been stated previously (see page 38) that *Ichthyotomus* may be transferred experimentally from the eel to other species of fishes, and that its close association with the former in nature appears to be due solely to ecological factors.

For myzostomids also, the available data are meager. One fact however is clear, that these parasites occur only on echinoderms and more especially on asteroids and on ophiuroids. The presence of the same species of myzostomid on hosts that are today very widely separated geographically would indicate that parasitism had originated at an early period of their history.

One would expect that monogenetic trematodes that do not possess a complicated life cycle, and that usually attach their eggs to the surface of the host, would realize almost perfect conditions for isolation, and consequently that host specificity would be very marked. This actually appears to be the case as already indicated previously (see page 124) and many genera occur upon certain hosts only and not upon others.

In particular conditions, such as occur in an aquarium, for instance, host specificity may be less marked, owing to the possibilities of the fishes exchanging their parasites when in a restricted environment. Even here it is found that not all the fishes are equally susceptible of becoming parasitized by the same species, and that certain species even appear to possess a natural resistance that renders them immune to infestation, whereas others acquire a certain degree of resistance after having been parasitized (Nigrelli & Breder). These observations also indicate that there must also exist some sort of physiological mechanism that is stimulated in the host by the parasite. It has been tentatively ascribed to changes that occur in the mucous secreted by the skin of the fish (Nigrelli).

The genus *Dactylogyrus* is characteristic for fresh-water teleosts, particularly for cyprinids from which numerous species have been reported. Host specificity here appears to be very marked, each species of infested fish harboring at least one distinctive species of parasite. Curiously enough, fishes that harbor the same species of *Dactylogyrus* are those that form hybrids among themselves and, consequently, the physiological mechanism postulated above seems to bear, in this case, a phylogenetic origin. The converse is also true in that fishes bearing distinctive species of parasites are unable to form hybrids between themselves (Bychowsky)

Several groups of parasitic arthropods in which the larval stages also occur, either upon the same or on different hosts, are known, although in most cases the statistical data available are as yet insufficient.

Parasitic isopods (see page 69) were formerly considered as being absolutely host specific, so that each species of host was assumed to harbor a distinctive species of parasite. Further investigations, however, show that here also the host-parasite relationship is not as highly specialized as was formerly assumed. In parasitic isopods host-parasite relationship is distinctly ecological and, moreover, is found to occur both at the larval and at the adult levels. The larval forms occur on planktonic copepods that are themselves subject to the movements of the tides and to the seasonal currents. Consequently, infestations occur on appropriate hosts that appear in cyclic fashion within a given biotope (Reverberi & Pitotti). Further research into the host-parasite relationship of parasitic isopods is necessary before any definite conclusions can be reached about this group of parasites.

Host specificity among mites is essentially of an ecological type and here, as in other cases, isolation of the parasites upon their hosts or within natural cavities, such as the nasal passages or the lungs or even in the shafts of feathers, have exerted a selective effect upon the species. There is also a tendency toward forming physiologically adapted species that belong to a given species but that occur on very different hosts. This is the case for itch mites of the genus *Acarus*, for instance, that can be transferred only with difficulty and that do not remain permanently upon such "foster hosts."

Isolation of mites upon groups such as lizards or bats that occupy very specialized biotopes has led to an abundant speciation as well as to morphologically specialized types. Moreover, ecological evidence as to the distribution of the hosts points to parasitism having arisen a very long time ago (see page 77). This is also evidenced by the fact that the feather mites, *Paralges pachycnemis* Troues. and *Pterolichus bicaudatus* (Gerv.), both occur simultaneously upon African ostriches and upon South American rheas or nandus, two groups of birds that have remained isolated on different continents since late Mesozoic times.

Mallophaga or biting lice spend their entire existence on the same host, to the hairs or feathers of which the eggs are attached. *Mallophaga* are frequently cited as examples of parasites that manifest a high degree of host specificity (Harrison). They have also been used to elicit evidence of parallel evolution of the hosts and the parasites. This would indicate that the ancestors of the present hosts already harbored identical or ancestral parasites and that the latter have evolved at a slower rate than the hosts. Consequently, a given genus might be represented by different species in hosts that are phylogenetically related to one another. Careful investigation of the parasites may thus lead to the discovery of some possible, unsuspected, phylogenic relationship of the hosts.

Recent investigations, however, while confirming the existence of such intimate host-parasite relationships as postulated, also tend to furnish evidence of numerous exceptions that are mainly due to the possibility of stragglers establishing themselves upon animals other than their normal hosts. This distinctly shows that mallophagan speciation is also due to ecological segregation but that close association among hosts belonging to different groups may permit their parasitic populations to mingle. It is therefore necessary to consider such possibilities before attempting to establish eventual host relationships that tend to differ in too conspicuous a manner from the established classifications of birds and mammals. It is for the same reason also that it is impossible to adopt any so-called law as that proposed by Eichler that tends to enclose the concept of host specificity within restricted limits that are incompatible with the facts.

It must be emphasized that of the two suborders of biting lice, the *Amblycera* constitute a generalized type whereas the *Ischnocera* are more specialized. The former are known to abandon the dead body of a host while the *Ischnocera* never leave the host,

even when it is dead, and remain attached to the fur or to the feathers.

It is therefore easy to understand why each group of hosts, especially birds, possesses characteristic species and genera that may be related to one another and thus demonstrate possible affinities of the hosts (Harrison; Hopkins).

According to its biting lice, the Ethiopean pelican *Pelecanus rufescens* Gm. appears to be more closely related to the Australian *P. conspicillatus* Temm. and to the South American *P. thagus* Molina than to the two other North African species, *P. onocrotalus* L. and *P. roseus* Gm. From a purely morphological standpoint, the Mallophaga from the South American pelicans are sufficiently distinct to warrant their being placed in a separate genus. This is also interesting from another angle, since ornithologists consider *P. thagus* as the type of a distinct subgenus (Bedford). This example clearly shows the effects of ecological segregation of both the parasites and the hosts.

In mammals, similar effects have been observed in certain groups such as the African hyraxes. These live in small, isolated colonies that tend to split up into subspecies and that harbor more than twenty-five species of biting lice in which this same tendency to split up into subspecies has been observed (Webb).

The structure of the spiracular openings of the tracheae in Mallophaga appears to present distinctive features that may be considered as adaptive. There apparently exists a definite relationship between these structures and the tendency for the host to develop an open coat or hairlessness (Webb). The causal agent of such adaptations is attributed to the amount of dust that accumulates upon the animal, and this is greater upon sparsely coated or hairless mammals than it is upon those that have a thick fur.

The conditions mentioned above as to the parasites of pelicans could almost be considered as ideal examples of ecological segregation. It should be borne in mind that straggling frequently occurs, and that consequently mallophagan faunae are liable to become mixed. An investigation of the bird parasites from the Galápagos Islands revealed that their biting lice are hopelessly mixed on account of the different species of birds living promiscuously, since these bare islands do not afford much shelter (Kellogg & Kuwana). Straggling may have occurred in past times and the species became established on a new host.

From evidence available, it is possible to assume

that host specificity in biting lice is caused essentially by two factors, the more important of which is natural segregation of the parasites upon their host. This must have occurred a very long time ago, since most of the bird orders do possess characteristic species and genera of *Mallophaga*.

Isolation of the parasites upon hosts belonging to the same species or to the same order has developed, secondarily, both morphological and physiological characters within the parasites. The frequent presence of stragglers would also indicate that the physiological characters are not so strongly established, since certain species are not only able to survive but also to reproduce upon birds or mammals other than their normal hosts.

Such conditions confirm the view that ecological segregation occurred a long time ago and that it has attained a certain degree of permanence. It is far from absolute and may be secondarily modified as the result of crowding or some other ecological factor.

The existence of physiologically specialized species is also borne out by experiments to rear Mallophaga *in vitro*. Both *Lipeurus heterographus* Nitzsch and *Eumenacanthus stramineus* (Nitzsch) from the fowl have been reared successfully under suitable conditions as to the degree of moisture and temperature, with fowl feathers and dried blood added as food (Crutchfield & Hixon; Wilson). With the first one of the above two parasites, it was found that when the feathers of the little green heron were substituted for those of the fowl, the parasites died. This seems to indicate the presence of some chemical constituent of feathers that appears to be characteristic for a given group of birds and that also differs from one group to another. On the other hand, *Bovicola bovis* (L.), the red cattle louse, can be reared successfully only when yeast is added to the hairs to which the lice are attached (Mathysse).

The origin of Mallophaga is usually assumed to be from psocids, a group of insects that live beneath the bark of trees. Their transfer from this biotope to birds' nests, on twigs, and finally to the birds themselves, can easily be conceived. Moreover it is also supposed that they have passed secondarily onto mammals, but this is not proved; and the presence of one of the most primitive types of Mallophaga on a tree-shrew that is itself a very primitive mammal could indicate that such a transfer might have occurred directly.

Anoplura, or true lice, spend their whole existence upon their host and feed exclusively on blood. They occur solely on mammals and possess certain specialized adaptations in relation to the nature of the hair in which they live. These specialized habitats cause them to become ecologically isolated upon hosts—or even upon distinct parts of the hosts—as for example the human head louse that has given rise to a recognizable variety occurring on the body. The human head louse deposits its eggs in clothing or in the ornaments that replace clothing in certain populations instead of on the hair.

Lice from South American spider monkeys are extremely different from those harbored by African primates, but they are closely related to species discovered on the hair of early American mummies. This would suggest that the spider monkeys may have become infested through contact with man (Ewing).

The human crab louse, *Phthirius pubis* (L.), has a world-wide distribution on man but has also been recovered from the gorilla. It is even possible that the latter might be the original host of the crab louse and that the louse has passed secondarily onto man where it occurs in regions where the individual hair is thick and not unlike that of the gorilla (Fig. 119).

Haematomyzus, the elephant louse, has been reported from both the African and the Asiatic elephants, the Asiatic hosts harboring a variety of the species parasitic on the African hosts. Echinophthiriids contain several distinct genera and occur exclusively upon aquatic carnivores. They also show certain specialized characters already mentioned previously (see page 93). *Haematodipus* has, so far, been reported only from hares and rabbits, the genus occurring both on American and European hares. *Microthoracius*, a genus characteristic of tylopods, occurs upon both Asiatic camels and South American llamas.

Straggling is not frequent but has certainly occurred once and the subsequent isolation of the parasite has given rise to a new species. *Linognathus piliferus* (Burm.) is found on the dog, fox, coyote, and ferret, whereas all the other species of this genus are reported from ungulates. It is probable that the predatory habits of ancestral dogs enabled them to acquire this parasite while gorging themselves upon their victims.

Ecological segregation in sucking lice is obvious, and also their specialized habits appear to cause less straggling than in biting lice. Isolation upon the hosts must have occurred long ago, according to the present-day distribution of the parasites upon their hosts, yet the complete absence of Anoplura upon Australian marsupials would indicate that the latter had already become isolated on that continent before true lice arose as parasites (Kellogg).

2. ENDOPARASITES

All parasites that live normally within their host, either in the gut, natural cavities, organs, or even the blood are considered endoparasites. From the standpoint adopted here, it is not necessary to group the parasites according to their location within the host since in most instances the nature of the host-parasite relationship is found to be approximately the same for all the members of a given group of parasites.

As for ectoparasites, it is also possible to recognize three possible categories of endoparasites, according to whether the larvae or the adults are parasitic or whether parasitism occurs in all the stages of the life cycle.

a. *Larval stages parasitic; adults free-living.*

There does not appear to be sufficient information available on the host-parasite relationship of monstrillids (see page 49) to judge the extent to which these curious copepods are capable of developing either in a single host species or in several. Larval stages of *Monstrilla helgolandica* Claus are found in prosobranch snails whereas those of *Haemocera danae* (Clap.) occur in annelids. The same is also true for the turbellarian genus *Fecampia* (see page 35). The immature stages of *F. erythrocephala* Giard are found in crabs and those of *F. xanthocephala* C. & M. and of *F. spiralis* Baylis in isopods. Both host groups belong to the same phylum.

Larval *Diptera* and *Hymenoptera* occur as parasites in a very great number of insects but, in this case, possible host specificity is due to totally different causes. As mentioned previously (see page 93), it is the adult fly that chooses the host within which it lays its eggs and that, moreover, the fly is definitely attracted to its victim by sense of smell or taste. Consequently, the ensuing host specificity of the maggots might be considered as secondarily ecological, since it is primarily due to an assumed physiological specialization of the adult insects.

The relationship between larval gordiids and their host is essentially and apparently also exclusively of an ecological nature. There does not even appear to be any so-called physiological barrier that might prevent insects other than those normally associated with water from becoming infested (see page 43).

b. *Adults parasitic; larvae free-living.*

Certain adult copepods may be considered as true endoparasites. This is the case for *Xenocoeloma* (see page 53). This genus appears to be extremely rare and it is not possible to affirm that it is strictly adapted to annelids although both of the known species occur in them.

This can also be stated for *Thyonicola* and related genera of endoparasitic snails (see page 32). Although all data available so far tend to show that the species occur exclusively in echinoderms and more especially in holothurians, they are much too incomplete to warrant any definite conclusions as to the existence of a possible host specificity.

c. *All stages parasitic.*

Under this heading are also grouped all the parasitic protozoans in which it is, of course, impossible to speak of adult and larval stages and in which, moreover, the encysted stage is not considered as being free-living.

Protozoa, as a whole, cannot be compared directly with any group of metazoan parasites. The modern tendency is to recognize the major groups of protozoa as phyla.

Entozoic amoebae and trichomonad flagellates show little evidence of host specificity and can be transferred without much difficulty into other hosts. Normal ecological segregation of the parasites in their hosts does not appear to have affected any of their morphological characters but has, however, influenced their reaction to the new environment. Experimentally, physiological races are found to occur but these do not seem to be either very strongly determined or irreversible, since the parasites are able to live normally when re-introduced into their original host (Wenrich). This illustrates the great plasticity of these organisms and also indicates the possibility of their being much more widespread if they were not limited ecologically to certain hosts. Such is also the case for trypanosomes, although these are blood parasites and undergo a passage through insects. Ecological segregation accounts here also for host specificity, since the range of potential hosts is found experimentally to be much greater than that occurring normally.

It is possible that opalinids are not true parasites, and some authors even consider them to be commensals (Harrison). Yet their distribution in their hosts is of particular interest and has even been used in an attempt to discover possible phyletic relationships among the hosts themselves (Metcalf).

The ease with which a species of *Opalina* can be successfully transferred from the rectum of one host to that of another would indicate that ecological factors only are responsible for the distribution of these parasites in their hosts. Since infestation mostly occurs in the tadpole stage, it is easy to understand how segregation can exist, as all species of frogs from a given area do not oviposit simultaneously nor do the different species of tadpoles develop at the same rate. Such complex ecological factors should also include the possibility of the parasites being destroyed within the host by other species of parasites, trematodes (Hazard) or nematodes (Bhatia & Gulati), that feed upon them.

The situation in opalinids is somewhat similar to that in *Mallophaga* (see page 159), namely, an association that has arisen a very long time ago, probably even before modern amphibians had occupied their present geographical areas. In such cases, it is obvious that the greater the degree of isolation of a group of hosts, the greater also the chances for the opalinids to be specific. Yet this would not exclude the possibility of physiological races existing in the sense mentioned above, and such eventualities should be borne in mind when attempting to establish possible amphibian relationships from the study of their parasites.

Sporozoans as intracellular parasites should *a priori* be much more highly specialized than other protozoans. This seems to be the case from the evidence available. For instance, the species of *Plasmodium*, the human malarial parasites, cannot be inoculated successfully into other hosts, even if the latter are primates. Nor has it been possible to establish, in man, malarial parasites occurring in other animals. Normal transmission of malaria, moreover, can take place only with the aid of mosquitoes and this would also imply specialized ecological conditions correlated with the mosquitoes, and more especially with their life cycle.

The species of the coccidian genus *Eimeria* have been reported from different segments of the digestive tract and also from the kidneys of a large number of hosts that include fishes, amphibians, reptiles, birds, and mammals. There appears here also a tendency to form both morphological and physiological "species."

"Evidence rather points to a mutational origin of new characters both physiological and the visible morphological. Mutation may result from definite environmental stimuli and natural selection would determine their survival value" (Wenrich).

Rhizocephala occupy a peculiar situation as to the usual mode of grouping together similar forms of parasites. Although the body of these parasites, containing the reproductive organs and the brood pouch, lies on the surface of the host, the entire root system by which the parasite acquires its nourishment is located within the host. Ontogeny of these forms also reveals that the cypris and first kentrogon stages are ectoparasitic, but that all the subsequent stages are endoparasitic and that the portion of the body bearing the reproductive organs breaks through secondarily as the parasite becomes adult. For these reasons, the *Rhizocephala* are considered here as endoparasites having all their larval stages parasitic. From the somewhat meager statistical evidence available, it is found that host specificity is relatively poorly marked, as an identical species of parasite is liable to occur on several different hosts, all of which are decapod crustaceans. The absence of *Rhizocephala* from hosts that could be considered as being phylogenetically the most primitive might indicate a relatively recent form of parasitism that would have appeared toward the end of the Mesozoic period (see page 64). Moreover, the present distribution of these parasites in their hosts points clearly to an ecological mechanism as responsible for host-parasite relationship.

Pentastomids, at first sight, do not appear to live in a very specialized biotope, since they occur in the lungs of reptiles and in the nasal cavities of mammals. The conditions of both these localizations are somewhat similar to those that would occur in a warm, damp cave, for instance. Yet pentastomids, like cave-dwelling animals, are extremely isolated and from evidence available (see page 109) appear to have been so, within their hosts, ever since they became parasitic during Mesozoic times. Unfortunately, very little experimental investigation has been done with the view of testing the degree of adaptation of a given species to a group of hosts. As pentastomids possess also a rather generalized type of anatomy, this might preclude, *a priori*, any physiological adaptation.

Any attempt to analyze host-parasite relationships in nematodes is rendered difficult, because there are so many possible types of associations of nematodes with other organisms. It is almost possible to establish a continuous series from free-living forms up to highly adapted parasites. Moreover, when such a series is compared with host distribution, no sign whatever of what might be interpreted as parallel evolution is observed.

Nematodes from the body cavity or the tissues of invertebrates are usually assumed to be the oldest parasites among nematodes, yet there does not appear to be any evidence of host specificity to support this. On the other hand, the true parasitic nature of these associations in many cases can be questioned, since most of these nematodes feed upon the dead invertebrate and seem to come much closer to the conception of a predator than to that of a parasite. There does not exist sufficient experimental evidence as to the nature of these associations nor has their necessity been demonstrated. For instance, *Pristionchus aerivorus* (Cobb) was collected originally from the head capsule of termites, yet it is not dependent on entrance into a termite or any other insect to complete its development and has also been found reproducing normally in various habitats and in decaying plant tissue (Christie). *Neoaplectana glaseri* Steiner remains within the gut of Japanese beetle grubs until the latter die, and then feeds upon their tissues. Incidentally, this is one of the few species of so-called parasitic nematode that can be grown for several generations in an artificial medium (see page 105).

As host specificity of plant-parasitic nematodes is of considerable economic importance, it has been much more carefully analyzed than the preceding cases (Steiner). It is found here that distinct populations of the same species of nematode will behave differently toward one host plant. For instance, one population will attack it heavily and another not at all. From experimental evidence it would appear that the degree to which the plant is attacked is correlated with the nature of the host plant upon which the population was previously feeding. Yet, such "physiological races" are never found to be irreversible, and their rate of adaptation is roughly

proportional to the number of nemic generations that have developed upon the original host plant.

Experimental evidence has been furnished showing that plant nematodes are attracted to their hosts apparently by some chemical substance produced by growing roots, and that that substance dissolves in water and diffuses around the plant. For instance, if the root knot nema, *Heterodera radicicola*, be introduced into a confined space in which two distinct host plants such as *Circaea lutetiana* and *C. intermedia* are growing with their roots intermingled, it is observed that the nemas will attack *C. lutetiana* only, but that if the latter be removed the roots of *C. intermedia* are attacked.

Apart from the evident economic importance of such results for the control of plant-parasitic nematodes, they also indicate the presence of a highly specialized type of ecological relationship between the parasites and their hosts. The possible existence of such strains occurring in nematodes parasitic in vertebrates should not be neglected.

Nematodes parasitic in vertebrates furnish evidence of a great variety of habitats within their hosts. Filarioids, for instance, occur throughout the body in connective tissue but not in the gut. Many capillarioids are found in organs such as the liver or the spleen or in the walls of the bladder, or various segments of the digestive tract. Tetramerids occur in the glandular crop of birds, heterakids in the ceca. Many species of strongyles are found exclusively in the lungs, others in the frontal sinuses, although the majority occur in the gut. Strongyloidids are usually regarded as being the most primitive nematodes, yet more than two-thirds of the genera that have been described are reported from mammals, and only a very small number of genera from reptiles and birds. At least half of the spiruroid genera occur in birds, a few in reptiles, and an almost equal number in mammals and in fishes. Whereas in ascaroids most of the genera have been reported from mammals and reptiles, a few are from birds and still less from fishes.

It does not seem possible, under such circumstances, to discover any trace of a parallel evolution of host and parasite, since if this did occur the most primitive genera and species should be found in fishes and not in mammals.

Speciation of the parasites, and apparently also differentiation of generic characters, may be observed in certain groups of specialized hosts. Elephants, for instance, harbor six genera and at least twenty species of strongyles that are not found in any other hosts. Similarly, six genera and some eighteen species have been recorded from rhinoceroses. The nematodes of equines are extremely characteristic and at least eight genera with more than fifty species have been recovered from these hosts.

Diaphanocephalids with three genera and numerous species are found only in snakes and the majority of the camallanids in fishes.

Most of the species parasitic in birds belong to genera that also occur in mammals, and the same species of nematode is liable to be found in birds belonging to distinct orders.

Experimental evidence, however, tends to show that several nematodes parasitic in vertebrates are able to form "physiological" races in the sense mentioned above. Hookworms and *Strongyloides*, for instance, give rise to strains that are specialized for a particular host, but these may be transferred gradually to other hosts belonging to the same group, carnivores for instance. Human and hog ascarids are sometimes considered as a single species, as they are morphologically identical. Yet cross-infestations under normal circumstances fail to yield adult worms. A biochemical analysis of the two "strains" shows that apparently all the constituents are identical but that the carbohydrate fractions composed principally of glycogen are antigenetically distinct (Campbell).

At first sight it is obvious that nematodes are ecologically segregated within their hosts, but this alone does not explain the presence of these physiological adaptations that have been found to exist in several species and that probably also occur in many other forms. Unfortunately, a physiological adaptation can only be discovered experimentally, i.e., by testing the ability for a species to survive and become adult in hosts that are different from its natural group of hosts.

Statistical data available, for obvious reasons, are based entirely on taxonomic work, and in many cases specific identification of the worms is extremely difficult owing to the individual variability in some of the characters upon which the species concept is based. Consequently, there is the possibility of physiological specificity existing in instances where no apparent morphological specificity is found. Until this situation has been investigated in detail, experi-

mentally, nothing very definite can be stated other than that the host-parasite relationship in nematodes is distinctly ecological, but that there may exist possible physiological strains that are masked by the inadequacy of the morphological criteria to distinguish them. Such a condition would also cause nematodes to be practically useless for any attempt at discovering possible host affinities.

In digenetic trematodes, host specificity is liable to occur at all the stages of the life cycle, and therefore will have to be investigated successively in the miracidia, metacercariae, and adults. Since each of these stages possesses its particular ecology, it is obvious that the host-parasite relationship will finally result from a chain of complex actions and reactions that would naturally lead to a high degree of ecological segregation and, consequently, to a marked degree of specificity.

In all cases where the miracidium hatches in the surrounding environment, it is definitely attracted to certain species of snails and not to others, as can be deduced both from the distribution of the cercariae within their hosts and from experimental investigations conducted in the laboratory. The reason for this attraction is as yet unknown and may perhaps be related to the nature of the skin secretions of the snail, part of which might possibly be soluble in water and thus create an aura of specific attraction around each snail. That such a mechanism must be extremely delicate is shown by the fact that the miracidium of *Opisthorchis felineus* (Riv.) is attracted to the prosobranch snail, *Bithynia leachi* Scheff., but not to the closely related species *B. tentaculata* (L.) that also occurs and usually more abundantly in the same biotope (Vogel). The miracidium of *Schistosoma japonicum* Kats. is attracted to oncomelanid snails, whereas that of *S. mansoni* Sambon penetrates only into planorbids. Consequently, miracidia of two different species of the same genus manifest totally different tropisms that are all the more marked here, as the snail hosts themselves belong to two distinct suborders.

It should be borne in mind, however, that penetration of a miracidium into a snail does not necessarily enable it to continue its normal development. It must also be able to overcome successfully the natural defenses that a snail offers to any parasite.

This is also true for miracidia that hatch within the gut of the snail when the latter eats the eggs of the trematode. Consequently it is found that the very first stages of the life history of digenetic trematodes are subjected to the negative influences of natural selection, and that a physiological adaptation, very pronounced in certain cases, has been developed subsequently.

Ecological segregation of the snails, together with the subsequent physiological segregation of the parasites, necessarily influences the distribution of cercariae and consequently also of metacercariae.

Cercariae will naturally be subjected to similar mechanisms as those mentioned above in establishing relations to the organisms into which they penetrate. The metacercarial stage, therefore, will also be limited to hosts in which the larval trematode has successfully achieved its survival. These hosts will be naturally restricted to certain biotopes and, consequently, the final hosts will be the vertebrates that are associated either permanently or occasionally with these biotopes and that feed upon the various members occurring in the host's ecological niche.

A great deal of statistical evidence on the distribution of adult trematodes within their hosts is available, yet relatively few authors have attempted to analyze it.

On the assumption that trematodes have evolved on parallel lines with their hosts, and, consequently, that the most primitive parasites occur in the lowest vertebrates, a classification of amphistomids has recently been proposed (Szidat). Unfortunately unless digenetic trematodes are considered as being polyphyletic, there does not exist any evidence for the *a priori* assumption at the origin of this classification. Moreover, the only genus that has been reported from birds, *Zygocotyle*, is also found in mammals.

In other families, heterophyids for example, the species *Cryptocotyle lingua* (Crep.), has been reported or obtained experimentally from four different orders of birds and from three of mammals. A prosthogonimid, *Prosthogonimus ovatus* (Rud.), occurs in the end gut and sometimes in the oviduct of birds belonging to seven different orders.

It is possible to arrange all the presumed species of the genus *Metorchis* that occur in the gall bladder and bile ducts of many different birds and mammals in a single series without there being any distinct limit between two consecutive specimens.

Since much of this statistical material is based on data obtained from investigations of collections, many of which have been examined by older authors using rather inadequate methods, one might be inclined to consider their results as erroneous interpretations of taxonomy. It is, therefore, of particular interest when an entire family is re-investigated by a single author, using modern methods and basing his results upon the original type materials. This has been done for strigeids, a family of specialized trematodes that are represented in the adult stage in almost all groups of vertebrates with the exclusion of amphibians and fishes (Dubois). Although certain bird orders, such as kingfishers for example, appear to possess their own particular genera and species of strigeids, this is not the case in others. The species *Cotylurus platycephala* (Crep.) has been found in birds that belong to six distinct orders; *Cotylurus cornutus* (Rud.), in avian hosts belonging to five different orders. Several other such instances can be cited. *Alaria mustelae* Bosma, a species from mammals, occurs both in muskrats and otters. Crocodiles from Africa and from Asia harbor species and genera that are distinct from those found in South American alligators.

A careful examination of the various hosts mentioned above shows that they are all ecologically related in one way or another, either by their methods of feeding or by their habitat. All the hosts from which the forty-nine or more genera of strigeids have been recorded are ecologically associated with water and this is especially true for the birds. Moreover, the presence of metacercariae in amphibians and snakes would indicate how certain terrestrial vertebrates such as ophiophagous accipitrines or frog-eating owls are able to acquire their infestation. This is also confirmed by experimental investigations, in the course of which laboratory animals that would not normally occur in the same ecological surroundings as the host may be infested successfully. In this way, several species of strigeids have been obtained in the adult stage in chicks, pigeons, rats, mice, dogs, and cats.

Experimental investigations with trematodes belonging to other families show similar results. *Microphallus opacus* (Ward), a trematode that occurs normally in fresh-water fishes, is found to undergo its metacercarial stage in crayfishes. When such larvae are fed experimentally to reptiles or mammals, it is possible to recover adult worms, but the proportion of successful infestations is variable according to the host. For instance, only two of three experimentally infested turtles harbored adult worms, and then only 18 to 20 per cent of the initial number of cysts. One snake fed fifty metacercarial cysts harbored only four adult worms, while another snake, fed an equal number of cysts, passed out live worms but none became established in its gut. The only mammals that could be infested successfully were young raccoons and opossums, hosts that both belong to species which normally feed on crayfishes (Rausch).

Metacercariae are young trematodes in which all the future organs are already formed, but in which the reproductive organs have not yet reached their maturity. The latter may sometimes occur very rapidly, within a matter of several hours as in certain strigeids, for instance. Precocious sexual maturity in metacercariae has been reported for several species (see page 132) and such progenetic development would indicate that there exist other causes than ingestion of the cysts by the host that can stimulate the attainment of sexual maturity. Under certain circumstances, apparently, metacercariae are able to accumulate sufficient reserve materials to enable them to become sexually mature and to produce eggs. It is possible that this may even occur independently of the metacercaria being swallowed by a host, thus explaining some of the more exceptional results of complete lack of host specificity. It is obvious that from a purely statistical standpoint trematodes with rapidly maturing metacercariae will be considered as less specific than those whose metacercariae become adult more slowly. The former, moreover, may not even establish themselves within the gut of the host but will, nonetheless, be statistically significant if they are found when the host is killed.

Aspidogaster conchicola v. Baer is not a true digenetic trematode (see page 117); it occurs in freshwater clams and possesses a direct life cycle without any intermediate host. This same species has been recovered from the gut of a paddlefish, *Polyodon*, that feeds normally on clams. It is possible to remove these worms experimentally from the clams and to introduce them into the stomachs of turtles where they may survive for several days (Van Cleave & Williams). It may be that in this case the presence of *A. conchicola* in the paddlefish was purely accidental, although nothing is known of its eventual rate of survival in a vertebrate host. The introduction of immature aspidogastrids into *Polyodon*, and the subsequent recovery of mature worms from the gut of this fish, would cause the latter to become a definitive host; and the clam, an intermediate host, and a new type of life cycle would have been born!

From an analysis of the above data, it appears at first sight surprising that there can exist at all a certain degree of host specificity in trematodes. This is, however, largely due to ecological segregation of the larval forms and also to selective feeding habits of the definitive hosts. In certain groups of hosts this last condition is particularly evident. Marine teleosts, for instance, show evidence that each family, or group of species belonging to the same or to closely related genera, has similar ecological habits and that these differ from one family or species group to another. Many species and even genera of trematodes recovered from such fishes show a very distinct host specificity (Manter).

The complete absence of characteristic genera of digenetic trematodes from elasmobranchs, an ancient group of fishes, and also the fact that South American marsupials harbor entirely different trematodes from those of Australian marsupials, appear to indicate that digenetic trematodes are relatively recent parasites and that there exists no justification for considering their having evolved from ancestral forms that supposedly lived in the ancestors of present-day vertebrates. Digenetic trematodes offer the most perfect example of what has been named ecological specificity, the effects of which, in this case, influence not only the adult but also the larval stages (Baer).

A list of acanthocephalans arranged according to their hosts (Meyer) shows that the greatest proportion of genera and species occurs in fishes and especially in fresh-water species. Terrestrial reptiles such as lizards and snakes never harbor adult acanthocephalans, whereas these are found in fresh-water turtles and amphibians. Distinct families are recorded from birds and mammals two of which, moniliformids and pachysentidids, are specific for mammals and one, aporynchidids, for birds. In both gigantorhynchidids and oligacanthorhynchids the number of species reported from birds is larger than that from mammals. Six families have been found exclusively in fishes.

When the host list is examined more in detail, it is seen that there exists no single characteristic genus living in elasmobranchs nor is there even a species that might be considered as typical for this group of hosts. Of the eleven genera reported for marine teleosts, six occur in these hosts only, whereas five genera are found simultaneously in fresh-water teleosts although there is not a single species that is common to both groups.

Among birds and mammals, it is possible to distinguish two host groups, a "land dwelling" group that is ecologically separated from water and another that is ecologically associated with water. Here also, different orders of birds may harbor identical species of acanthocephalans. *Empodius taeniatus* (v. Linst.) has been reported from game birds, bustards, and waders, *Polymorphus striatus* (Goeze) from herons, accipitrines, and ducks, *P. obtusus* Van Cl. from pelicans and herons and *P. mutabilis* (Rud.) from herons, kingfishers, pelicans, and gulls. It would seem however that acanthocephalans from "land" birds are less ubiquitous although the same genera occur in different orders of hosts. The different hosts of the species and genera just mentioned have common ecological surroundings, namely water.

There does not seem to be very much evidence as to the possibility of obtaining adult acanthocephalans in experimental hosts other than their normal hosts. It is not possible, therefore, to find out the degree of intimacy that exists between these parasites and their hosts.

In the cases cited above in which different bird orders were reported as harboring identical parasites, it is not known whether all the specimens were fully mature and normally attached to the gut wall as is always the case within the proper host.

Host specificity is well demonstrated in acanthocephalids from fishes (Van Cleave). For instance distinct families of fresh-water fishes harbor specific genera of acanthocephalans. *Gracilisentis* and *Tanaorhamphus* are found normally only in the gizzard shad, *Dorosoma cepedianum* (LeS.); *Octospinifer* is restricted to catostomids; *Eocollis* to centrarchids.

Speciation in acanthocephalans, as in other parasites, is a consequence of isolation. For instance the Pacific pilotfish, *Kyphosus elegans* (Peters), and the closely related Atlantic pilotfish, *K. secatrix* (L.), each harbors a distinct species of the genus *Filisoma*. The species *Illiosentis furcatus* V. Cl. & Lincic. occurs in *Menticirrhus americanus* (L.) in the Gulf of Mexico and *I. cetratus* V. Cl. in the related Pacific *Menticirrhus undulatus* (Girard), *Roncador stearnsi* (Steind.) and *Umbrina roncador* Jord. & Everm.

Evidence of parallel evolution among acanthocephalans appears to be clear, although the group is not so old as might be expected. The absence of acanthocephalans from elasmobranchs, their relative small numbers in marine teleosts, and their extraordinary speciation in fresh-water teleosts all indicate a fresh-water origin. Of the four genera common to both marine and fresh-water teleosts, it can be said that they possess very generalized types of anatomy and are in no way specialized. This is sufficient evidence for considering them as primitive forms. The absence of acanthocephalans from elasmobranchs can be explained in that these parasites only appeared after elasmobranchs had become detached from the original fresh-water stock of ancestral fishes (see page 149).

More than one hundred years ago, the Danish physician, H. Krabbe, discovered that each bird order apparently possesses its own particular species of tapeworms. This discovery has been substantiated since (Fuhrmann) and extended to other groups of vertebrates (Joyeux & Baer).

Host specificity in cestodes is peculiar in that it attains a high degree of perfection as the hosts themselves become more specialized. Tetrarhynchids and diphyllids occur exclusively in elasmobranchs and, as mentioned previously (see page 150), tetraphyllids may be divided into two distinct categories. One of these is found only in elasmobranchs and possesses the most extravagant types of scolex structure, whereas the other, bearing an ordinary scolex with four suckers, occurs in fresh-water teleosts and in reptiles. Cyclophyllids have been reported from terrestrial vertebrates only and are found in amphibians, reptiles, birds, and mammals. They possess a very specialized type of internal anatomy. Pseudophyllidean tapeworms, which have arisen from another line (see Fig. 161), occur in both marine and fresh-water bony fishes and are also found in mammals, and more rarely in birds and reptiles. There exists here also a very definite type of group specificity. For instance, caryophyllaeids and related families are harbored only by cyprinids and siluroids. *Diplocotyle* occurs in flatfishes; *Abothrium*, *Parabothrium*, *Clestobothrium* in gadids; *Eubothrium* in salmonids; and *Triaenophorus* in pike.

Even among elasmobranchs, there appears to be evidence that sharks and rays harbor separate species of cestodes. The genera *Rhinebothrium*, *Echeneibothrium*, *Lecanicephalum*, and *Polypocephalus* have been reported from rays only and *Calliobothrium* and *Phyllobothrium* from sharks. The genus *Acanthoboth-*

rium occurs in both sharks and rays but with separate species in each.

Tapeworms from snakes are distinct from those found in other reptiles and in amphibians, although all these hosts, harbor similar and closely related genera.

In mammals, each order possesses its characteristic cestodes. Carnivores will not harbor the same species as rodents or insectivores, for instance. Certain genera may even occur in a single group of hosts as *Dipylidium* and *Echinococcus* in carnivores; *Andrya*, *Cittotaenia*, and *Paranoplocephala* in rodents; *Moniezia*, *Thysanosoma*, and *Stilesia*, in ruminants; and *Progamotaenia*, *Hepatotaenia*, and *Triplotaenia* in marsupials. Some genera, like *Hymenolepis*, are found in many groups of both mammals and birds, but with characteristic species in each case.

It is in birds that host specificity attains its highest degree of specialization, since each particular order harbors its own tapeworm fauna. Several genera are found exclusively in certain orders, for example: *Tatria*, *Schistotaenia*, and *Dioecocestus* have been reported only from grebes; *Diplophallus*, *Gyrocoelia*, and *Shipleyia*, from waders; *Cladotaenia* and *Taufikia*, from hawks and vultures; *Schistometra* and *Sphyronchotaenia*, from bustards; *Cyclorchida*, *Dendrouterina*, and *Cyclustera*, from herons.

Tetrabothrium and *Porotaenia*, two genera that have probably been derived from pseudophyllids, are found exclusively in fish-eating birds and mammals, although here again each group possesses its own characteristic species.

Grebes and loons live in identical ecological surroundings, yet harbor distinct species of tapeworms. This is the case for all water birds, herons, ducks, waders, flamingos, and cormorants, that stand about equal chances of swallowing tapeworm larvae harbored by invertebrates. In spite of an evident promiscuity, there is no mingling of the cestode faunae harbored by the different groups.

There occurs, consequently, in cestodes a very particular type of host specificity that is independent of ecological segregation of the hosts and dependent, to some extent, upon the phylogenetic relationships of the hosts themselves. It is for this reason that the term phylogenetic specificity has been proposed (Baer).

It is obvious that exceptions can and do occur but these are found almost exclusively among the parasites of domestic animals and from man, excluding of course all cases of erroneous determinations. The dog tapeworm, *Dipylidium caninum* (L.) and the rat tapeworm *Hymenolepis diminuta* (Rud.) occur occasionally in man. This is also the case for the Old World ape tapeworm, *Bertiella studeri* (Bl.) and the New World howler monkey tapeworm, *Raillietina* (R.) *demerariensis* (Daniels). In the first case there exists a phylogenetic relationship between the hosts, and it is even possible to consider the Old World ape tapeworm as one of the species harbored by primitive man (Baer).

Tapeworm life cycles are less complicated than those of digenetic trematodes, but in this case also the larval stages appear at first to be ecologically segregated. It must be borne in mind that paratenic hosts are liable to occur in most of the pseudophyllidean, tetraphyllidean, and tetrarhynchidean species and consequently, in numerous cases, the original intermediate host may not even be known but must necessarily belong to the organisms that the paratenic hosts swallows with its food. This is particularly evident for several larvae of tetraphyllids and tetrarhynchids that are harbored by cephalopods and bony fishes, being sometimes even found in marine mammals. Such paratenic hosts naturally increase the possibilities for sharks and rays to become infested, but from a statistical standpoint these records are practically useless in the analysis of host-parasite relations.

Human sparganosis, especially the ocular form, occurs almost exclusively in Indo-China yet the adult worm, *Diphyllobothrium mansoni* (Cobb) has been reported from dogs throughout the Orient. Frogs are frequently found to harbor plerocercoid larvae, and as the natives are in the habit of applying freshly killed frog poultices to their sores, especially to the eyes, the plerocercoids migrate out of the frog into the conjunctival sac. Human sparganosis is therefore due entirely to ethnological causes, to the rather peculiar custom of using frogs as poultices!

Genuine oriental pearls usually contain the plerocercoid larva of an elasmobranch tetraphyllidean cestode. The fish hosts of these tapeworms occur frequently on oyster beds and even, occasionally, feed on oysters. The high rate of infestation of the skates and sharks when compared with the comparative scarcity of free pearls seems to indicate that in pearl formation the oyster is a paratenic host that is infested by feeding on planktonic crustaceans, the first intermediate hosts for all tetraphyllidean cestodes.

From experimental evidence, it is clear that not all species of copepods can be infested with equal success. When several different species of fresh-water copepods are fed coracidia of either *Diphyllobothrium latum* (L.) or *Triaenophorus lucii* (Müll.), it is observed that some of the species are more favorable hosts than others and that those in which the procercoid of *D. latum* develops normally may not be a suitable host for that of *T. lucii* (Michajlow). From some unpublished results, this is also the case for the procercoids of *Ligula*, and probably occurs in several other species of pseudophyllids and possibly also tetraphyllids. Consequently, there appears to exist a certain degree of host specificity for these larval forms that is independent of ecological surroundings. This indicates that the presence of an onchosphere in the body cavity of the copepod will, in certain cases, elicit a response from the host's phagocytes and that the latter are thus able to destroy the larvae. The absence of such responses would indicate that a physiological adaptation had occurred, enabling the larvae to survive and develop normally in certain species of hosts but not in others.

The existence of such a reaction within the intermediate host's body has also been recorded in flea larvae that were infested experimentally with onchospheres of the dog tapeworm, *Dipylidium caninum* (L.). In this case, phagocytes tend to enclose the larvae completely and inhibit their development, even destroying some of them. However, when the flea larva pupates, the phagocytes abandon the cestode larvae in order to participate in the mechanism of pupation, and during this time the cysticercoid larvae can develop. Consequently, viable larvae are found in the adult flea as soon as it emerges from the pupa (Chen). It is not known whether this occurs also in the dog louse, *Trichodectes*, which can equally well be an intermediate host for this cestode.

Several species of cysticercoids can accomplish their development in different host groups. Those of *Hymenolepis gracilis* (Zed.), for example, occur in both copepods and ostracods; *H. anatina* (Kr.), in amphipods and ostracods. The common rat tapeworm, *Hymenolepis diminuta* (Rud.), has been reported as occurring spontaneously or has been obtained experimentally in four different orders of insects and in myriapods. On the other hand, cysticercoids belonging to two distinct species of *Hymenolepis* from European water shrews have been found simultaneously in amphipods.

Cysticerci-larvae of the carnivore genus *Taenia* do not occur indiscriminately in all vertebrates. Those of *Taenia taeniaeformis* (Batsch), the cat tapeworm, are found in the liver of rodents and have not been reported from other hosts, although it has been claimed that this larva has been found in bats. *Taenia pisiformis* (Bloch) develops in leporids, *T. tenuicollis* in ruminants, and *T. solium*, adult, in man, has larvae in the hog but also in man himself and in the dog. The dwarf dog tapeworm, *Echinococcus*, has been found in a great number of mammals and even in birds.

An interesting, though exceptional case is that of the dwarf rat tapeworm, *Hymenolepis nana fraterna* (Stiles), that normally develops directly in the intestinal villi of the initial portion of the jejunum of rats and mice. In certain instances that appear to be in some way related to specific strains of this worm, insects may serve as intermediate hosts, and the subsequent cysticercoid differs from that usually formed within a villus of the intestine by having a very large caudal appendage. Since a direct life cycle is a secondary acquisition for cestodes, it is possible to interpret this potential intermediate host as being a reversion to the original type of life cycle.

From the evidence presented above, it is clear that both larval and adult tapeworms are associated with their hosts in a very intimate fashion. It is obvious that ecological segregation of the hosts originally produced isolation of the parasites in the different vertebrate groups. Yet, on the other hand, cestodes appear to be highly specialized from a physiological standpoint and to have become adapted to their hosts a very long time ago, as is shown by their present-day distribution. It is not possible, even experimentally, to break down this host specificity, as can be done for other parasites (trematodes). The data indicate that ecological specificity has here been replaced by phylogenetic specificity, a much more intimate type of association that arose thousands of centuries ago when cestodes first became parasitic in the ancestors of the species which today serve them as hosts.

This general analysis of host specificity brings clearly to light the effects of ecological segregation of the parasites upon or within their hosts. From this standpoint, ectoparasites are particularly favorable examples, since t e effects of isolation are often reflected in morphological changes that occur in the parasites. In several instances where straggling is prevented normally, a careful study of parasite speciation may indicate possible host relationships but such methods should be applied only in cases where the numerous sources of error have been reduced to a minimum.

Although endoparasites usually have complicated life cycles, the fundamental causes for host specificity are the same as in ectoparasites. But ecological segregation instead of affecting only the host which harbors the adult parasite also exerts its effects upon all the stages of the life cycle. In certain groups, such as digenetic trematodes, it even appears as if ecological segregation of the infestive metacercariae might be the primary cause for the distribution of the adult worms in their hosts. This also has obviously occurred originally in cestodes, although here absence of a gut and the subsequent highly specialized mode of feeding have produced physiological segregation, and since the latter has evidently occurred when vertebrates first split up into the present-day groups, the result is a phylogenetic specificity.

Copepods are by far the most diversified parasites and also the only ones that are found in the adult stage on both invertebrates and vertebrates. They have been reported from mollusks, echinoderms, serpulids, annelids, ascidians, and fishes, and no other group of parasites possesses so great a range of hosts. As most of the genera appear to be adapted to hosts belonging to distinct phyla, and since free-living larval stages are known to occur, it might be possible to interpret this as an indication that copepods are probably the oldest parasites actually known. It is possible, moreover, that they share this position with prosobranch snails and myzostomids, both of which have been recorded as fossils.

It is evident that the higher the degree of host specificity, the greater the value the parasites will have for revealing possible phylogenetic relationships among the hosts. But this must not be taken too literally since host-parasite relationship can furnish only indications of possible affinities that must be confirmed by results from workers investigating the same problem from other angles.

For instance, a South American bird, *Cariama cristata* (L.), occupies a very isolated position in bird taxonomy and has been shifted from one order to another until some of the more recent taxonomists finally placed it in a special order. From a parasitological standpoint, *Cariama* is found to harbor several species of helminths that belong to the four principal groups, *viz.*, nematodes, trematodes, acanthocephalans, and cestodes. In its feathers, there is found a species of biting louse that cannot, unfortunately, be considered as a species characteristic for this host. An analysis of the helminths can be summed up in Table 5.

TABLE 5. Host Relations of the Worm Parasites, *Cariama*.

PARASITES	OTHER HOSTS BESIDES *Cariama*
Trematodes:	
Strigea vaginata (Brand.)	South American snake-eating eagles
Acanthocephalids:	
Oligacanthorhynchus taenioides (Dies.)	None (genus occurs exclusively in South American fish-eating eagles)
Nematodes:	
Subulura allodapa (Crep.)	Eurasian bustards
Subulura suctoria (Mol.)	
Cestodes:	
Chapmania brachyrhyncha (Crep.)	None (genera occur also in Eurasian bustards)
Idiogenes horridus (Fuhrm.)	

The ecological specificity of trematodes and acanthocephalans is clearly shown in the foregoing analysis. Infestive larval forms of these parasites occur in snakes and *Cariama* also feeds on snakes. Consequently, neither trematodes nor acanthocephalans can be of any use in determining ecological specificity.

The presence of two identical species of nematodes in both *Cariama* and Eurasian bustards may seem at first sight peculiar, and one might feel inclined to interpret this as coincidental.

The cestode genera *Chapmania* and *Idiogenes* are both specialized davaineids and their presence in both host groups is significant. Moreover, it is not possible to assume that the presence of these genera in two so geographically separated bird groups might be due to convergence. From what has been stated earlier as to phylogenetic specificity in tapeworms, it would appear that *Cariama* and bustards must be related. This conclusion is also found in the most recent work on bird taxonomy (Peters).

An example like this demonstrates both the possibilities and also the limits of the host-parasite relationship method for establishing phylogenetic affinities among the hosts. On the other hand, in regard to nematodes, it vindicates the possible existence of physiologically adapted species of worms that may occur in different host groups and that are, morphologically, identical.

Migration of eels is a biological problem that can be studied from several angles and that has even been used to substantiate the Wegner hypothesis of continental drift. All the known species of eels can be grouped into four categories according to whether leptocephala are borne by the Kuro-Siwo current in the north Pacific, the Notonectian current in the south Pacific, or the Gulf Stream in the north Atlantic. The European eel is the only species that requires three years of marine life before entering fresh water, although both American and European eels spawn in practically the same area. When carried by the Gulf Stream along the coast of North America, leptocephala of the American eel enter into the rivers of this country, whereas the European eels continue their journey in salt water.

From a parasitological standpoint, both species of eels harbor the same fresh-water tapeworm, *Ichthyotaenia macrocephala* (Crep.), which is absolutely characteristic for eels. On the other hand, both Japanese and European eels contain related species of a marine tapeworm genus *Bothriocephalus*, but this never occurs in American eels. The reason for this is to be found in the life cycle of *Bothriocephalus claviceps* (Gze.) from European eels. The latter become infested while sojourning in the estuaries, before migration into the rivers, as Conger eels that live in the estuaries harbor the same species of cestode. Consequently, the absence of *B. claviceps* from North American eels can be explained since these do not remain in the estuaries but pass immediately into fresh water.

This would indicate, according to parasitological evidence, that both European and North American eels had a common ancestor, as is witnessed by their possessing the same species of fresh-water tapeworm, but that subsequently the life cycles of the two species of eel became modified. That of the American eel appears to have been shortened, rather than that of the European eel lengthened, as the proponents of Wegner's theory supposed. A physiological mutation occurring in the North American eel has impelled the latter to migrate into fresh water at least two years earlier than his European travelling companion. Since European and North American eels

do not harbor a single species or even a genus of acanthocephalans in common, one is forced to admit that the latter parasites are younger than tapeworms, and consequently invaded secondarily and independently both species of eels after these had become definitely separated.

REFERENCES

BAER, J. G. 1940. The origin of human tapeworms. *J. Parasit*, 26:127–34.

———. 1946. Le Parasitisme. 231 pp., 138 figs., 4 pls. Lausanne et Paris.

———. 1948. Les helminthes parasites des Vertébrés. Relations phylogénétiques entre leur évolution et celle de leurs hôtes. Conséquences biologiques et médicales. *Ann. Franche-Comté et de l'Université de Besançon*, 15 pp.

BEDFORD, G. A. H. 1931. Description of three new species of *Tetrophthalmus* (Mallophaga) found on pelicans. *Parasitology*, 23:236–42, 6 figs.

BHATIA, B. L., & GULATI, A. N. 1927. On some parasitic ciliates from Indian frogs, toads, earthworms and cockroaches. *Archiv. f. Protistenk.*, 13:505–23.

BYCHOWSKY, B. 1933. Die Bedeutung der monogenetischen Trematoden für die Erforschung der systematischen Beziehungen der Karpfenfische. *Zool. Anz.*, 102:243–51.

CAMPBELL, D. H. 1939. The immunological specificity of a polysaccharid fraction from some common parasitic helminths. *J. Parasit.*, 23:348–53.

CHEN, H. T. 1934. Reactions of *Ctenocephalides felis* to *Dipylidium caninum. Zeitschr. f. Parasitenk.*, 6:603–37, 29 figs., 1 pl.

CLAY, TH. 1947. A preliminary key to the genera of the Menoponidae (Mallophaga). *Proc. Zool. Soc. London*, 117:457–77, 40 figs.

CHRISTIE, J. R. 1941. Parasites of invertebrates. *Introduction to nematology*, Part 2 (2):246–66, figs. 165–78.

CRUTCHFIELD, C. M., & HIXON, H. 1943. Food habits of several species of poultry lice with special reference to blood consumption. *Florida Entom.*, 26:63–66.

DUBOIS, G. 1938. Monographie des Strigeida. *Mém. Soc. Neuch. Sc. Nat.*, vol. 6, 535 pp., 345 figs.

EICHLER, W. 1949. Some rules in ectoparasitism. *Ann. Mag. Nat. Hist. Ser.*, 12, 1:588–98.

EWING, H. E. 1926. A revision of the American lice of the genus Pediculus, together with a consideration of the significance of their geographical and host distribution. *Proc. U. S. Nat. Mus.*, vol. 68, 30 pp., 3 pls.

———. 1938. Sucking lice of American monkeys. *J. Parasit.*, 24:13–33, 6 figs.

FUHRMANN, O. 1932. Les ténias des Oiseaux. *Mém. Univ. Neuchâtel*, vol. 8, 381 pp., 147 figs.

HARRISON, L. 1928. Host and parasite. *Proc. Linn. Soc. N. S. W.*, vol. 53, 31 pp.

HAZARD, F. O. 1941. The absence of opalinids from the adult green frog, *Rana clamitans. J. Parasit.*, 27:513–16.

HOPKINS, G. H. E. 1942. The Mallophaga as an aid to the classification of birds. *Ibis*, 6:94–106.

JOYEUX, CH., & BAER, J. G. 1936. Cestodes. *Faune de France*, vol. 30, 613 pp., 569 figs.

KELLOGG, V. L. 1914. Ectoparasites of mammals. *Am. Nat.*, 48:257–79.

KELLOGG, V. L., & KUWANA, S. I. 1902. Mallophaga from birds. *Proc. Wash. Acad. Sc.*, 4:457–91.

MANTER, H. W. 1947. The digenetic trematodes of marine fishes of Tortugas, Florida. *Am. Mid. Nat.*, 38:257–416, 152 figs.

MATHYSSE, J. G. 1946. Cattle lice. Their biology and control. *Bull. Cornell Univ. Agric. Exp. Sta.*, vol. 832, 67 pp., 41 figs., 4 pls.

METCALF, M. M. 1923. The opalinid ciliate infusorians. *Bull. U. S. Nat. Mus.*, 120.

———. 1941. Further studies on the opalinid ciliate infusorians and their hosts. *Proc. U. S. Nat. Mus.*, 87: 465–634.

MEYER, A. 1932–1933. Acanthocephala. *Bronn's Kl. Ord. Tier.*, 4 (2), 582 pp., 281 figs., 1 pl.

MICHAJLOW, W. 1938. Ueber die Bedurfnis einer Vereinheitlichung der Forschungsmethoden, die sich auf die Copepoden als Zwischenwirte der Cestoden beziehen. *Zool. Pol.*, 3:15–22.

NIGRELLI, R. F. 1935. On the effect of fish mucus on *Epibdella melleni* a monogenetic trematode of marine fishes. *J. Parasit.*, 21: *Supp.* 438.

NIGRELLI, R. F., & BREDER, C. M. 1934. Susceptibility and immunity of certain marine fishes to *Epibdella melleni*, a monogenetic trematode. *J. Parasit.*, 20:259–69.

PETERS, J. L. 1934. Check list of birds of the world, vol. II. Cambridge.

RAUSCH, R. 1947. Some observations of the host relationships of *Microphallus opacus* (Ward, 1894). (Trematoda: Microphallidae). *Trans. Am. Micros. Soc.*, 66:59–63.

REULING, F. H. 1919. Acquired immunity to an animal parasite. *J. Inf. Dis.*, 24:337–46.

ROTHSCHILD, M., & CLAY, TH. *In press.* Bird Parasites. *New Naturalist Series.*

REVERBERI, G., & PITOTTI, M. 1942. Il ciclo biologico e la determinazione fenotipica del sesso di Ione thoracica Montagu. Bopiride parassita di Callianassa laticauda Otto. *Pubb. Staz. Zool. Napoli*, 19:111–84, 27 figs.

STEINER, G. 1925. The problem of host selection and host specialization of certain plant infesting nemas and its applications to the study of nemic pests. *Phytopathology*, 15:499–534, 8 figs.

SZIDAT, L. 1940. Beiträge zum Aufbau eines natürlichen Systems der Trematoden. I. *Zeitschr. f. Parasitenk.*, 11:239–83, 12 figs.

VAN CLEAVE, H. J. 1947., The Eoacanthocephala of North America, including the description of *Eocollis arcanus* new genus and new species, superficially resembling the genus Pomphorhynchus. *J. Parasit.*, 33:285–96, 8 figs.

VAN CLEAVE, H. J., & WILLIAMS, C. O. 1943. Maintenance of a trematode *Aspidogaster conchicola* outside the body of its natural host. *J. Parasit.*, 29:127–30.

VOGEL, H. 1934. Der Entwicklungszyklus von *Opisthorchis felineus* (Riv.). *Zoologica*, vol. 33, 103 pp., 45 figs., 8 pls.

WAGNER, J. 1939. Aphaniptera. *Bronn's Kl. Ord. Tier.*, 5(3), 114 pp., 100 figs .

WEBB, J. E. 1946. Spiracle structure as a guide to the phylogenetic relationships of the Anoplura (Biting and Sucking Lice), with notes on the affinities of the mammalian hosts. *Proc. Zool. Soc. Lond.*, 116:49–119, 216 figs.

———. 1947. Spiracle structure in the Siphunculata genus *Prolinognathus* Ewing (with notes on the affinities of the hosts, the Procaviidae). *Ibid.*, 116:575–78.

WENRICH, D. H. 1935. Host-parasite relations. *Proc. Am. Phil. Soc.*, 75:605–50.

WILSON, F. H. 1934. The life cycle and bionomics of *Lipeurus heterographus* Nitzsch. *J. Parasit.*, 20:304–11, 1 fig.

CHAPTER FOURTEEN

The action of parasites upon their hosts

From the definition of parasitism given in the first part of this book, it is evident that both the parasite and the host react upon one another. In the majority of cases, however, the nature of this reciprocal reaction is unobserved since it does not manifest itself in a visible form. This does not mean that it is nonexistent, but only that the present methods of investigation are not precise enough to discover it. This consequently means that only the exceptional cases, where visible changes occur, are reported and are sometimes investigated experimentally.

The reaction of the host's body to a parasite is usually found to be identical whatever the species of parasite, as long as the location in or on the host is the same. This also indicates that the effects of a parasite upon its host are, primarily, the consequence of the reactions of the host's body to the parasite. Such reactions may be localized at the site where the parasite is attached or may be more generalized involving serological reactions that affect the entire organism.

Although the fundamental reactions to parasites are identical in both invertebrates and vertebrates, the effects are more easily visible, sometimes even spectacular, in the former than in the latter. This is due to the fact that in many invertebrates, parasites affect the normal activity of organs that control important functions. These activities are sometimes only partly but at times completely inhibited with immediate and visible effects upon the host. From a practical standpoint, the effects of parasites upon invertebrates and upon vertebrates are examined separately.

1. EFFECTS OF PARASITES UPON INVERTEBRATES

Nearly all the cases of parasites affecting invertebrates have been recorded for arthropod hosts, and these are almost exclusively crustaceans and insects.

If such obvious consequences as result from dipteran or hymenopteran larvae feeding upon their hosts be excepted, it is possible to examine separately the effects of parasites upon two of the most important functions of the host, namely, growth and metamorphosis and sex determination.

Effects upon growth and metamorphosis of insects

Various observations indicate that larval insects parasitized by braconid or chalcid larvae forego a diapause and pupate immediately so that the pupae of parasitized larvae sometimes appear several months earlier than normally (Varley & Butler).

Since a normal diapause may be interrupted and development proceed under the effects of both physical and mechanical stimuli, it is assumed that the parasites exert similar effects, and consequently the development of insect larvae is accelerated.

The presence of a nematode, *Aproctonema entomophagum* Keilin, in the body cavity of larvae of *Sciara pullula* Winn. (*Diptera*) appears to cause a quite different reaction within its host. Metamorphosis is delayed to the extent that two generations of the nematode are produced in the body cavity. This effect can be understood, since the parasites are free to roam about within the insect's body, and moreover, increase in size, thus indicating that they absorb nourishment. Curiously enough, all the parasitized imagines of *S. pullula* were found to be females, but lack of fresh material makes it impossible to state whether males are actually parasitized but die off early, or whether parasitism of the larval stage brings about some change leading to the production of the female sex only (Keilin & Robinson).

The presence of parasites in the body cavity of insects must exert not only a mechanical effect but also modifies the whole metabolism of the insect. There is evidence that this is the case in certain instances where the lipoid content of the blood has been increased (Salt).

Effects upon sex determination of insects and crustaceans

Indirect effects of nematodes on the sex of chironomids have been reported at different times (Rempel). But as explained below, there does not appear to exist any direct connection between destruction of the gonads and the so-called secondary sexual characters. Although in infested males the testes are completely eliminated, there do not appear any outward female characters. In a similar manner, female intersexes have been attributed to destruction of the ovaries. The presence of parasites must exert a general effect on the insect since here also the lipoid content of the haemolymph is increased.

Such results together with those occurring in crustaceans were formerly brought together under the rather inappropriate heading of "parasitic castration." This implies destruction by the parasite of the host's gonads and eventual repercussion on the organism as modifications of what might be considered as secondary sexual characters.

The expression "parasitic castration" currently employed in textbooks is unfortunate, since all recent investigations on the subject tend to show that in invertebrates the so-called secondary sexual characters are independent of the gonads. Experimental removal of the latter in no way affects the sexual phenotype.

Moreover, several distinct phenomena appear to be involved here and make it very difficult to establish the exact role of the parasite (Reverberi). By far the most spectacular effects of parasitism upon sexual characters have been observed in crustaceans, as here sexual characters are particularly pronounced on account of the modified appendages of the female in relation to oviposition and incubation. There is often also a marked difference in size and shape of the pincers and of the abdomen of both sexes.

As mentioned previously (Chapter 6), both rhizocephala and parasitic isopods absorb their nourishment directly from the host's blood, but the same species of parasite does not necessarily cause identical phenotypical changes in all its hosts. For instance, when the rhizocephalid *Gemmosaccus sulcatus* (Lillj.) parasitizes male hermit crabs belonging to the species *Anapagurus chirocanthus* (Lillj.), the latter becomes completely feminized even to the shape of its pleopods. The transformation is, however, much less marked when the same host is parasitized by *Peltogaster paguri* Rathke. However, both of these rhizocephalids evoke exactly the same degree of feminization upon the hermit crab *Eupagurus cuanensis* (Thomps.). When *Peltogaster paguri* Rathke parasitizes *Pagurus pubescens* Krøy., no phenotypical changes are observed although the ovaries are destroyed in the female crabs (Reinhard). Curiously enough, masculinization of female crabs by parasites does not seem to have been observed and the phenotypical changes always occur in male crabs.

From a physiological standpoint, the blood of crabs parasitized by sacculinids contains large amounts of fat, and that of feminized male crabs carries a proportion of the latter that is much closer to the amount found in normal females than to that occurring in males. It has been claimed recently that the liver of male *Pagurus pubescens*, parasitized by *Peltogaster paguri*, contains less fat than that of normal males (Reinhard & v. Brand). Yet, in this case, as mentioned above, no feminization of males has been observed.

Several theories have been proposed to explain this action of the parasites upon male crabs, yet none has, so far, furnished a satisfactory explanation. A recent and very careful biometrical study of normal and parasitized species of *Callianassa laticauda* Otto and *C. truncata* G. & B. has revealed the complete independence of phenotypical sexual characters from the gonads (Reverberi). Moreover, this study also brings out the extreme lability of sex in crustaceans, many of which are cryptic hermaphrodites and others, have sex which is not determined irreversibly. The immediate effect of the parasites upon their hosts has not yet been determined, but it may be assumed that they upset the normal metabolism and perhaps, also, secrete toxins which pass into the blood of the host.

Similar toxic effects have been postulated to explain the occurrence of intersexes in wasps and bees parasitized by stylopids (Salt) and also for the presence of feminized males in membracids parasitized by *Diptera* (Kornhauser).

2. EFFECTS OF PARASITES UPON VERTEBRATES

Following in the wake of Pasteur's fundamental discoveries in the field that was to become bacteriology, there arose a new science known as immunology.

The immediate practical application of this both to human and veterinary medicine retarded its spread into other fields, especially into that of biology.

Immunology today deals with the molecular structure of complex proteins and carbohydrates and, consequently, with cellular metabolism. Formerly considered as a special branch of science, immunology is now found to be only a particular aspect of properties common to all living matter.

The use of antigens other than those provided by bacteria is of comparatively recent origin and has been followed rapidly by attempts to apply these to the field of parasitology. From a practical standpoint, most workers have sought to obtain specific antigens to be used for serological diagnosis of parasites, but they have also investigated the possibility of protecting an organism against parasites by vaccination.

The absence of parasites in certain hosts is often referred to as natural immunity, but this expression can be extremely misleading if not used carefully. The problem of host specificity has been discussed in the preceding chapter and its nature, in regard to ecological and phylogenetic factors, examined. Consequently, a host that is naturally uninfested does not necessarily possess antibodies that protect it from parasites. Its apparent freedom from the latter may well be due to ecological causes, especially to its not having come into contact with infestive larval stages. Natural immunity is an expression that should be avoided when statistical data are being investigated, since it can only be applied to results from unsuccessful experiments to infest a given host with parasites.

From both factual and theoretical data it is possible to state that most organisms possess a natural capacity for preventing mass infestation by parasites, and that this depends both on the location and the nature of the parasite. From a purely philosophical standpoint such a mechanism as is postulated here protects the host and, at the same time, the parasite. It represents the quantitative expression of the physiological equilibrium, as defined earlier, that arises between the host and the parasite and that represents also the outcome of selective influences which have enabled the parasite to become adapted to its host. There is consequently some evidence of a mechanism that normally restricts the number of parasites and which, in the case of intestinal parasites, appears to be totally different from any of the usual immunological reactions.

It is obvious that the presence of the parasite within its host will stimulate antibody formation, in as much as eventual antigenic substances liberated by the parasite are able to come into contact with the humors or the tissues of the host. Consequently, parasites that normally live in the digestive tract do not cause antibody formation unless they enter the gut wall and by so doing destroy the cells.

Another factor that must be taken into consideration is that of the age of the host. Experimental infestations with intestinal parasites indicate that after a certain age, hosts are less susceptible to becoming parasitized than are younger ones. This may be due primarily to the fact that young organisms are less specialized than adults. Blood groups for instance become evident only after birth and their specificity gradually increases until a certain age where it reaches its maximum. What might be also a chemical factor, and has been described as an "age resistance" factor, is found in chickens infested with the common fowl roundworm. This will be discussed later (Part 4).

A certain amount of evidence points to birds and perhaps mammals also being infested when still in the nest by food supplied by their parents. However an interesting exception to this is the European cuckoo that is never found to harbor the same parasites as its foster parents and that consequently must acquire them after it is full-fledged.

Many of the examples of age resistance to parasites that are reported in the literature, especially in medical textbooks, can be explained in another way. They mostly fail to take into consideration the fact that young animals or children usually have a much higher carbohydrate diet than do adults, and that this is again the case for old people or for inmates of public institutions. A change in diet can exert almost immediate effects on intestinal parasites, on protozoans as well as on helminths. A high protein diet in rats causes the number of their trichomonad flagellates to decrease considerably (Hegner) and also protects dogs from acute amebiasis (Faust). On the other hand, it is a well established fact that a rich carbohydrate diet and a low protein content of the food favor the development of *Enterobius*. These mechanisms described in man and in domestic animals probably hardly ever occur in wild animals. They indicate, nonetheless, possible causes to which abnormal parasitic infestations may be attributed and also show to how great an extent parasites are dependent upon their host's feeding habits.

Intestinal parasites

The metabolism of intestinal parasites, especially of helminths, naturally produces substances that are no longer in a form available for the parasite and that are consequently discharged. In most cases, such end products are evacuated, but if a large number of parasites are present, or if the host is particularly sensitive, such end products diffuse into the gut wall and either excite the sympathetic nerves of the Auerbach system or pass into the blood stream. But instances such as these have been reported from clinical parasitology only, seldom from veterinary pathology, and so far never from wild animals.

A host that harbors tapeworms cannot generally be superinfested with worms of the same species. This is especially true for the larger worms of man, such as *Taenia saginata* and *Diphyllobothrium latum*. But the mechanism is in no way related to an immunological reaction, since reinfestation can take place almost immediately after the tapeworms of the first infestation have been evacuated. It is for this reason that the mechanism is spoken of as premunition. It bears perhaps a certain resemblance to what is known as crowding among species in the same ecological association. That this interpretation may be correct can be surmised from the results observed when a large number of larvae are swallowed simultaneously, or at least in one meal. In this case, a large number of adult worms are recovered but their size is more or less proportional to the number of worms present, or, in other words, to the available supply of food. Similar effects of crowding have also been observed in an acanthocephalan, *Moniliformis dubius* Mey. from the intestine of rats (Burlingame & Chandler). Consequently, premunition would result from a definite relationship between the size of the gut and the number of parasites. On the other hand, many hosts are found to harbor, simultaneously, different species of tapeworms with different types of life cycles, thus excluding the possibility of a single, mixed infestation. In such instances, it is observed that the localization of the parasites within the gut varies with each species. For instance, in foxes, *Taenia*

crassiceps Rud. occurs in the anterior portion of the jejunum and *T. polyacantha* Leuck. in the posterior portion. This is also the case in dogs, for *T. pisiformis* Block and *T. multiceps* Leske respectively. In rats, *Hymenolepis diminuta* Rud. is found in the anterior segment of the intestine and *H. nana fraterna* Stiles in the posterior segment. When the intestine of a bird is opened carefully, instead of being flushed out with water, a similar condition can be observed. These observations should not be interpreted as an example of the parasites making use of the available space to attach themselves, for in infestations with a single species the worms will be found attached to the intestinal wall in the same location as when other species are also present.

The practically complete independence of intestinal parasites from serological reactions, as might result from injections of antigen, is demonstrated by several unsuccessful experiments to vaccinate animals against tapeworms.

Although it has been claimed that dogs, immunized by injections of dried hydatid cyst, do not harbor so many adult *Echinococcus* as the controls (Turner, Berberian, & Dennis), these experiments are open to criticism and the results are in no way conclusive. Similar negative results have been obtained after implanting live specimens of *Hymenolepis diminuta* into the peritoneal cavity of rats and infesting these subsequently with cysticercoids, or also by feeding them first dried, powdered worms (Chandler).

Rats and mice infested with *Hymenolepis nana fraterna* are immune to superinfestation and such immunity may be transferred from the mother to her offspring via the milk. Consequently, there exist antibodies that appear in the blood and that pass into the milk. By repeatedly injecting fresh worm antigen into mice, it is observed that the percentage of worms from a subsequent infestation is reduced (Larsh).

These apparently contradictory results are explained by the life cycle of the dwarf rat tapeworm. The onchospheres penetrate into the villi and develop into cysticercoids and the latter, when fully formed, break through the wall of a villus and fall into the gut lumen. Larval stages of this parasite are comparable to somatic parasites that elicit serological reactions, since they are antigenic. Induced antibody formation, by injections of fresh worm antigen, therefore inhibits development of the cysticercoids and, subsequently, of the tapeworms. This interesting experiment clearly shows the difference, stressed previously, that exists between somatic and intestinal parasites in their respective reactions upon the host.

A somewhat similar example of resistance to superinfestation by a parasite is that occurring in *Trichinella*. An infested rat, harboring encysted larvae in its muscles, is immune to reinfestation. The establishment of such an immunity has been approached from the experimental angle with the following interesting results. If rats are infested with either male or female larvae alone (Roth) or with larvae previously exposed to X-rays (Levin & Evans), the adult worms will not produce any larvae although they penetrate into the gut wall as do normal worms. Subsequent infestation with normal *Trichinella* larvae, however, shows that an immunity has been produced and that the larvae are eliminated from the gut without being able to become adult. Moreover, as in *Hymenolepis nana fraterna* Stiles, immunity so produced is not permanent but lasts from six to seventeen weeks. Quite similar results can also be obtained by injecting into the rats dried, heat-killed, powdered larvae. When the rats are kept on a vitamin-A-deficient diet, however, no immunity is developed (McCoy). It would be worthwhile repeating these experiments using purified protein and polysaccharid antigens, as those have been successfully isolated with the aim of establishing a reliable skin test for trichinella (Meicher).

The common fowl nematode, *Ascaridia galli* Schrank, on hatching from the egg in the gut of the host, burrows deeply into the mucosa and remains there until it has reached the third larval stage (Chapter 7). Attempts to build up an artificial immunity against the adult worms by antigen injections into the host have either failed or yielded inconclusive results, although ring tests showed that antibodies were present in the serum (Eisenbrandt & Ackert). These results appear to indicate that the larvae that penetrate into the mucosa probably feed on cells, but that the amount of antibody that they thus swallow is too sma l to have any effect. That this interpretation is probably correct can be assumed from results obtained by introducing live worms into specifically immunized chicken serum. A precipitation of the serum occurs around the mouth of the worms and is all the more marked if the worms are younger, and it is most violent when larval worms extracted from the mucosa, are used (Sadun).

All these experiments indicate that no immunity develops from the presence of intestinal parasites as long as all their stages of development occur in the lumen of the gut. As soon as larval stages penetrate into the gut wall, they elicit the formation of antibodies in the blood which inhibit further development of the larvae.

The mode of feeding of the parasites, and especially the lesions that they may cause to the tissues, will also affect the host. Yet from an anatomo-pathological standpoint, parasites in their normal hosts rarely cause violent reactions, since the latter would exert a selective influence and the parasites would be eliminated. Practically, there appears to be a single species of intestinal protozoan that can cause pathological lesions, and that is *Endamoeba histolytica*, the agent of amebic dysentery in man and other animals. The presence of healthy carriers and the natural resistance to lesions in many experimental hosts appear to indicate that the pathology of amebiasis is closely related to the environment, to the conditions present in the bowel. The effects of a rich protein diet, or the increase of carbohydrates, have already been mentioned, as well as their indirect effect upon the pathology of the parasite.

Although acanthocephalans burrow into the mucosa, they hardly ever cause a host reaction, or even an afflux of leucocytes. Nematodes possessing buccal capsules, or certain trematodes such as strigeids, feed upon predigested food and very often destroy the surface of the intestinal mucosa. In such cases the surrounding tissues are always greatly infiltrated by eosinophilic polynuclears, thus demonstrating a local, antigenic reaction.

Several helminths provoke the formation of intestinal diverticula within which they are either completely enclosed, as in the trematode *Balfouria* from African storks, or only partly so, as in *Parorchites zederi* Baird, a tapeworm from penguins, or even as in *Heligmosomoides polygyra* (Duj.), a roundworm from wild rodents.

Hymenolepis microstoma (Duj.), a rat tapeworm, is usually found with the whole anterior end of the strobila inserted in the gall bladder of its host and only the ripe segments in the lumen of the gut. This also occurs in *Stilesia hepatica* (Wollfh.) from sheep and in *Progamotaenia festiva* (Rud.), a tapeworm from kangaroos. Under the influence of these parasites, the walls of the bile ducts or gall bladder react and chronic inflammatory lesions are produced. These are particularly well known for liver fluke infestations and can, in certain cases, as for instance when the trematode *Opisthorchis felineus* (Riv.) is present, degenerate into adenomatous growths or even into typical carcinomatous formations. Cancer of the stomach has also been reported for rats infested with *Capillaria gastrica* (Baylis), a species of nematode that lives in the wall of the stomach. Yet in none of the above cases where cancerous growths have been discovered could these be attributed to the presence of parasites only. (For a general summary of pathological changes due to parasites see Baer.)

Somatic parasites

Under this heading are included all the larval parasites together with adult helminths such as filarioids and blood flukes. Most protozoan parasites reported from the blood or the tissues should also be included. The latter, however, have been investigated almost entirely from a medical standpoint and their reactions within the host are fully described in textbooks on tropical medicine.

Larval parasites that migrate from the gut into the body cavity or into the surrounding tissues do not cause lesions but insinuate themselves in between the cells. The possibility of their carrying with them intestinal bacteria and inoculating them into the blood of the host has been postulated. This, however, does not seem to be the case and it is even possible to demonstrate that helminth extracts exert a bacteriostatic action, *in vitro*, upon intestinal bacteria (Joyeux; Joyeux & Baer).

Parasites that develop in close contact with the tissues of the host must necessarily act as antigens. It appears that the specificity of the latter is not very marked, but this is probably due to the fact that these antigens had not been prepared according to the more recent biochemical methods.

Experimental hosts have been immunized against larval, somatic parasites by using extracts of the same species of worm as an antigen. The larva of *Taenia taeniaeformis* Batsch develops normally in the liver of rats and the latter can be protected from infestation by previous inoculations of antigen prepared from worm extracts. Passive immunity may be carried on into the offspring which will be protected from experimental infestations in proportion to the intensity of the original immunization of the mother.

Antigens prepared from adult worms removed from cats are able to protect rats against the larvae. Yet when adult worms belonging to different species are used as antigens, no protection is afforded. This result may be due to some other cause, such as the method of preparation of the antigen, since if pieces of live *Taenia pisiformis* Bloch from the dog are inserted into the peritoneal cavity of rats, the latter are protected against larvae of the cat tapeworm (Miller). Similar results are obtained when extracts of the dog tapeworm, *T. pisiformis* Bloch, are injected into rabbits that normally harbor the larval forms; they are protected after the inoculation (Kerr).

Both from statistical and from experimental evidence, it is seen that many hosts are protected naturally against development of larval parasites and, consequently, that their blood contains natural antibodies. For instance, the larvae of *Taenia crassiceps* Rud. occur normally in the body cavity of voles and field mice. They may be inoculated and continue to develop by budding in the peritoneal cavity of mice and hamsters, but are destroyed in the body cavity of rats and rabbits (unpublished results).

CONCLUSIONS

The more general conclusions that can be drawn from the foregoing summary are that all animals, whether vertebrate or invertebrate, possess a normal mechanism that protects them from superinfestation by parasites that are already harbored either in the larval or in the adult stages.

Such a mechanism, according to evidence deduced from experimental infestations, not only protects the host but it also assures the survival of the parasites by limiting their number to the amount of nourishment available.

The appearance of specific antibodies is a property inherent in all living organisms, although their detection, in small amounts, escapes all but the very refined methods of analysis.

A great deal more research work is necessary along these lines before the problem of host-specificity in its physiological form may be reduced to terms of biochemistry. But even now, the mechanism that maintains a state of equilibrium between the host and the parasite is evident.

The very peculiar effects of certain parasites upon invertebrates such as crustaceans and insects should be considered as secondary. This is due, in the first place, to the host itself, to the normal lability of the gonad that appears in many cases to be potentially bisexual. By drawing attention to the change in outward sexual characters of their hosts, parasites have also contributed an important share to new lines of research in general biology.

REFERENCES

BAER, J. G. 1932. La pathogénie de quelques helminthiases. *Rev. suisse Zool.*, 39:251–60.

BURLINGAME, P. L., & CHANDLER, A. C. 1941. Host parasite relations of *Moniliformis dubius* (Acanthocephala) in albino rats, and the environmental nature of resistance to single and superimposed infections with the parasite. *Am. J. Hyg.*, 33:1–21.

CHANDLER, A. C. 1940. Failure of artificial immunization to influence *Hymenolepis diminuta* infections in rats. *Am. J. Hyg.*, 31:17–22.

EISENBRANDT, L. L., & ACKERT, J. E. 1940. On the resistance of chicks to the intestinal nematode *Ascaridia lineata* (Schneider) following immunization. *Am. J. Hyg.*, 32:1–11.

FAUST, E. C., SCOTT, L. C., & SWARTZWELDER, J. C. 1934. Influence of certain foodstuffs on lesions of *Endamoeba histolytica* infection. *Proc. Soc. Exp. Med. Biol.*, 32:540–42.

HEGNER, R. 1937. Parasite reactions to host modifications. *J. Parasit.*, 23:1–12.

JOYEUX, CH. 1907. Recherches sur le pouvoir antibactérien de l'extrait de cestode. *Arch. Parasit.*, 11:409–18, 2 pls.

JOYEUX, CH., & BAER, J. G. 1929. Recherches expérimentales sur la larve plérocercoide de *Diphyllobothrium ranarum* (Gastaldi, 1854). *C. R. Soc. Biol.*, 29: 1125–26.

KEILIN, D., & ROBINSON, V. C. 1933. The morphology and life history of *Aproctonema entomophagum* Keilin, a nematode parasite in the larva of *Sciara pullula* Winn. (Diptera-Nematocera). *Parasitology*, 25:285–95, pls. 19–20.

KERR, K. B. 1935. Immunity against a cestode parasite, *Cysticercus pisiformis*. *Am. J. Hyg.*, 22:169–82.

KORNHAUSER, S. I. 1919. The sexual characteristics of the membracid, *Thelia bimaculata* (Fabr.) I. External changes induced by *Aphelopus theliae* (Gahan). *J. Morph.*, 32:531–636, 54 figs.

LARSH, J. E. 1944. Studies on the artificial immunization of mice against infection with the dwarf tapeworm *Hymenolepis nana* var. *fraterna. Am. J. Hyg.*, 39:129–32.

LEVIN, A. J., & EVANS, T. C. 1942. The use of Roentgen radiation in localizing an origin of host resistance to *Trichinella spiralis* infection. *J. Parasit.*, 28:477–83.

McCOY, O. R. 1939. Immunity to Trichiniasis in rats. *Vol. Jub. Yoshida*, 2:339–41.

MEICHER, L. R. 1942. Immunological studies on a polysaccharid and protein fraction isolated from *Trichinella spiralis. J. Parasit.*, 28: *Supp.* 20.

MILLER, H. M. 1932. Acquired immunity against a metazoan parasite by use of non-specific worm materials. *Proc. Soc. Exp. Med. Biol.*, 29: 1125–26.

REINHARD, E. G. 1942. Studies on the life history and host parasite relationship of *Peltogaster paguri. Biol. Bull.*, 82:401–15, 1 pl.

REINHARD, E. G., & BRAND, TH. V. 1944. The fat content of Pagurus parasitized by Peltogaster and its relation to theories of sacculinization. *Physiol. Zool.*, 17:31–41, 2 pls.

REMPEL, J. G. 1940. Intersexuality in Chironomidae induced by nematode parasites. *J. Exp. Zool.*, 84:261–89.

REVERBERI, G. 1943. Sul significata della "castrazione parassitaria." La transformazione del sesso nei Crostacei parassitati da Bopiridi e da Rhizocephali. *Pubb. Staz. Zool. Napoli*, 19:225–316, 51 figs., pls. 6–9.

ROTH, H. 1943. The role of the intestinal phase of Trichina infection in the establishment of immunity to reinfection. *Am. J. Hyg.*, 32:99–111.

SADUN, E. H. 1949. The antibody basis of immunity in chicks to the nematode, *Ascaridia galli. Am. J. Hyg.*, 49:101–16.

VARLEY, G. C., & BUTLER, C. G. 1933. The acceleration of development of insects by parasitism. *Parasitology*, 25:263–68.

PART FOUR

Physiology of parasites

The physiology of parasites embodies some of the most interesting problems of biology since it leads to investigating the possible ways in which parasitism has arisen, whether certain organisms became strictly adapted to such a mode of life, or were preadapted to it. As stated in the first part of this book, the analysis of associations between two different species must be considered from a physiological standpoint if its true nature is to be investigated, namely, its absolute necessity for either one or the other of the two partners or for both of them. Commensals are physiologically· independent from one another, symbionts physiologically mutually dependent, whereas parasites depend entirely upon their host.

Such definitions, upon this basis, avoid the difficulty that often arises when there exists a considerable difference in size between two partners of a symbiotic association, or when a host is not very much larger than its parasite.

It is, of course, obvious that only experimental investigations make it possible to discover the physiological necessity for such associations but, pending such experiments, the concepts of symbiosis and parasitism should not be confused and, especially, not considered as synonymous. This tendency has occurred on two occasions recently, once in a textbook (Steinhaus) and once in a review of parasitic nematodes (Dougherty). No amount of scholastical reasoning will alter the facts that symbiosis and parasitism correspond to two physiological conceptions that are fundamentally distinct.

The physiology of parasites has, for obvious reasons, been almost exclusively investigated from the clinical standpoint with the purpose of discovering substances that might be therapeutically active. It is only in comparatively recent years that the problem has been investigated from the biological angle and, also, that attempts have been made to obtain the survival of parasites outside their hosts in artificial media, or even to culture them under known conditions.

From the preceding chapters it clearly stands to reason that the environmental conditions of a parasite are much more diverse than is usually supposed, although one can, in a general way, divide the biotopes into categories. For instance, ectoparasites might be divided into two groups according to whether they occur upon aquatic or terrestrial vertebrates, and then the former group could be considered in regard to the hosts that occur in fresh water or in the sea.

It would be much more difficult to classify the different environments of endoparasites under less than three headings, namely, blood, somatic, and intestinal parasites. Of these three categories, blood would appear to be the most constant throughout a given organism or group of organisms belonging to the same species. Somatic parasites, on the other hand, would imply the presence of parasites somewhere within the tissues of the host and, in such a case, a considerable variety of conditions necessarily occur. This is also borne out by the several localizations of somatic parasites, whether they are larval or adult. As for intestinal parasites, grouping into categories is even more difficult since each of the different segments of the digestive tract corresponds to a particular type of environment that possesses its own peculiar physicochemical particularities. Endoparasites occur in the esophagus, stomach, duodenum, anterior jejunum, posterior jejunum, cecum, colon, rectum, cloaca, urinary bladder, as also in the bile ducts, gall bladder, and pancreatic ducts. In this way, each segment constitutes its own peculiar biotope as can also be witnessed by specific parasites occurring there and not elsewhere. Moreover, the normal physiological and physicochemical conditions that reign in all these ecological niches are mostly unknown. A few general statements, based exclusively on conditions occurring in man and in domestic animals, are found in the literature and have been summarized recently (Hobson). They stress the considerable variation encountered in the same host and also the inadequacy of the data in regard to the actual gut contents, especially as to the protein, fat, and carbohydrate that the parasite would be able to utilize.

On the assumption that there is no oxygen present

in the gut, intestinal parasites have been considered as anaerobic, and it is only recently that it has been demonstrated that certain parasites are capable of utilizing oxygen for their respiration within the gut of their host. Consequently, many statements that occur currently in the literature will have to be revised before anything approaching a general survey that embraces the whole problem can be furnished.

In many groups of parasites, practically nothing whatever is known about the physiology of the species other than what may be surmised from their host relationships. Practically the only groups from which any amount of data is available are the protozoans and the helminths, both of which are of economic importance for man.

In many other groups of parasites, however, fundamental problems remain unsolved, such as for instance the presence of an oxyhaemoglobin in the fat body of botfly larvae that certainly is used for respiration during the larval stages since it disappears after pupation (Keilin). Parasites that feed upon the blood of their hosts do not all break up the haemoglobin molecule in the same way and, consequently, although their feeding habits are identical, their physiology is quite different (Wigglesworth; Sproston & Hartley). It is also obvious that results such as these substantiate the presence of physiologically specialized parasites, as have been postulated elsewhere from data supplied by their host relationships.

A review of the physiology of parasites will necessarily be fragmentary for the reasons stated previously, yet the writer hopes that it will stimulate others to enter into this field of research which is, as yet, practically untilled.

CHAPTER FIFTEEN

Physiology of parasitic protozoa

Using the localization of the parasites as a physiological basis, it is possible to distinguish two groups of protozoan endoparasites, those that live in the blood and blood-forming tissues and those that live within the gut.

1. BLOOD PARASITES

Although the species of *Leishmania* are morphologically identical, they may be separated on a clinical basis even though intermediate stages have been reported (Kirk). They occur naturally in the dog and the cat in addition to man, and have also been successfully inoculated into rodents, jackals, and *Macacus*.

Leishmania can be successfully cultivated in the Nicolle, Novy, and MacNeal medium, but since this is not of a known or constant composition, nothing much can be deduced from the standpoint of essential growth requirements.

Using a basic medium of glucose and silk peptone in order to eliminate all possible introduction of growth factors, M. Lwoff has cultivated *Leishmania* in a purely synthetic medium and has found that the species are unable to synthesize either thiamine (Vitamin B$_1$), ascorbic acid (Vitamin C), hematin, or cholesterol. It is possible, also, that the latter constitutes the so-called X-factor observed by various authors in serum. An attempt to isolate this factor from serum has shown that it is not an albumin, or a globulin, that it is destroyed at 100° C. but only partly so at 70°C., that it cannot be dialyzed and is lost during fractioning (Senekjie & Lewis). These properties might perfectly well coincide with those of cholesterol.

A growth inhibiting factor has been reported from the serum of patients harboring *Leishmania* (Culbertson), and it is possible to assume that this might well be due to the fact that the parasites have used all the available cholesterol that normally occurs in serum, so that growth would not be inhibited by the presence of a special factor, but by the absence of an essential one.

In an attempt to elucidate the growth requirements of free-living, semiparasitic, and parasitic trypanosomes, M. Lwoff has used the above medium. Her conclusions show that all the species, either free-living or parasitic, need thiamine and also that within a given genus, *Strigomonas*, the species do not all have the same growth requirements. In this genus, hematin appears to be essential to all the species except those that occur in plants, in plant-feeding insect larvae, and in the gut of non-bloodsucking flies; these species are able to synthesize their own hematin. Yet even here exceptions may occur and *Strigomonas culicidarum culicis* Lwoff is so far the only known blood-feeding dipertan that can synthesize hematin, whereas *Strigomonas culicidarum anophelis* Lwoff has lost this power.

The need for ascorbic acid apparently exists only in trypanosomes from vertebrates, the other species being capable of synthesizing their own. Such observations are also in keeping with the theory that parasitic trypanosomes in vertebrates originated as insect parasites and have passed secondarily into warm-blooded hosts, since the species occurring in insects that are not blood feeders are precisely those that have the power of synthesizing thiamine, ascorbic acid, hematin, and the X-factor from serum.

The loss of the power to synthesize thiamine is not a result of parasitism since it also occurs in several free-living forms among the colorless flagellates. It would seem that the biological evolution of trypanosomes has proceeded on parallel lines with physiological evolution, such as the loss of power to synthesize certain growth factors. It is even possible to assume that parasitism in the blood of vertebrates, where the necessary factors occur normally, has permitted trypanosomes to survive and to become successfully established. This is also borne out by the almost complete lack of specificity as to the hosts of such species as *T. rhodesiense* Stephens & Fantham and *T. gambiense* Dutton.

T. evansi (Steel) is one of the species from vertebrates that has lost most of its important physiological functions and contains only very few enzymes, no pepsin or trypsin but a cathepsin and a carboxypolypeptidase, none of which are very active. It does not even contain a carbohydrase and must, consequently, rely for its energy entirely upon the hexoses contained in the blood sugar of its host (Krigjsmann in Lwoff). So great a degree of physiological degradation would imply a specialized habitat, and it is possible that the inability of *T. evansi* to live in an insect host for any length of time could be attributed to this physiological specialization that requires an almost direct transfer from one host to another. Unfortunately, *T. equiperdum* Dofl. which is transferred by direct contact has not been investigated in the same way; it might furnish the necessary evidence in support of this theory.

The carbohydrate metabolism of parasitic trypanosomes is high, as can be deduced from the drop in level of the blood sugar of the host. Injections of glucose increase the number of parasites in experimental animals whereas insulin causes their number to decrease considerably. When rats infested with *T. equiperdum* are fed glucose, their life is prolonged for several hours and also the number of trypanosomes found at death is considerably above the average in such cases (Hoppe & Chapman).

Investigations of the respiratory mechanism of parasitic trypanosomes shows that cyanide inhibits respiration in some species but not in others. On the basis of such facts, two groups can be distinguished which, curiously enough, correspond to a morphological and biological classification proposed previously (Hoare & Coutelen). The first group, in which cyanide acts as an inhibitor, corresponds to the so-called *T. lewisi* group that contains species easily cultivated and that are transmitted from one host to another by the feces of the intermediate host. The second group, that is insensible to cyanide, contains all the pathogenic forms that are cultured with greater difficulty and that are transmitted either by contact or by bloodsucking flies. This would indicate that the species of the first group contain an enzymatic system that is normally catalyzed by heavy metals such as iron, and also that this system would be absent from the second group

(Brand & Johnson; Brand & Tobie). The only heavy metal possibly present upon which cyanide could exert an influence would be iron. This appears all the more probable that hematin, the only molecule containing iron, cannot be synthesized by trypanosomes of the second group, and consequently the latter would remain insensible to cyanide. The fact that the trypanosomes in the gut of flies that have fed upon mammals infested with species of the second group are unable to resist the effects of cyanide, would indicate that the technique employed by the authors did not furnish enough blood for the parasites to obtain hematin. On the other hand, inhibition of respiration by cyanide in trypanosomes of the first group might indicate that these have retained their power to synthesize hematin. Whether this is true or not remains unsettled until further investigations along these lines have been reported.

There is no need for including in this chapter the several successful methods for culturing pathogenic trypanosomes, as they can be found in most textbooks, and all except those mentioned above make use of media of uncontrolled constitution that cannot be employed for the kind of investigations outlined previously. Physiological requirements of parasitic protozoans can be determined only in synthetic culture media, and all other media, in spite of their evident importance from a medical standpoint, do not come up to these critical requirements.

Physiology of intracellular sporozoans is practically unknown and the most important investigations have been made on malarial parasites. Several simple and also a few very complicated media have been devised for culturing *Plasmodium* (see Trager; McKee *et al.*) and although successful results have been obtained, none of the methods are adequate to discover the necessary growth requirements of these parasites. Even the simplest techniques that come closest to a synthetic medium contain such chemically undefinable substances as chick embryo extract and red blood cell extract (Trager).

Consequently it should be stressed that results obtained so far as to certain physiological requirements are based on malarial parasites that develop within red blood cells, the survival of which is assured by the medium.

In this way *Plasmodium knowlesi* Coggs. from monkeys and *Pl. lophurae* Coggs. from chicks and ducks have been kept alive for several days on condition that the medium be frequently renewed.

The glucose consumption of parasitized red blood cells is much greater than that of normal blood, since within half an hour of starting the experiment, glucose has completely disappeared. It may however be accounted for in the form of lactate and pyruvate (McKee *et al.*). Parasitized red blood cells are found to be twenty-five to seventy-five times more active glycolytically than normal cells. There is also evidence that parasitized cells are able to utilize lactate in the presence of air, a reaction that apparently never exists in normal red blood cells. Consequently, it is suggested that the parasites contain an enzyme which is absent from normal cells. In such cultures, the addition of certain plasma fractions, rich in fat-soluble, biotin-active material, inhibits multiplication of the parasites in the same way as a high oxygen tension. Certain vitamins of the B group have been found indispensable. These are, for *P. knowlesi*, para-aminobenzoic acid and for *P. lophurae*, calcium pantothenate. Certain heterocyclic compounds as pyrimidines and purines are also essential for *P. knowlesi* but, curiously enough, not for *P. lophurae*. As the latter species is a malarial parasite of birds, it might be suggested that these compounds are provided by the destruction of the nuclei in the red blood cells.

A duck that has recovered from a malarial infestation becomes immune to reinfestation, yet its blood, when used in cultures, supports growth as well as that of normal, nonparasitized birds (Trager). This has not been satisfactorily explained so far, but it is possible to assume that the absence of leucocytes from the cultures could account for this, since, if a true immunity reaction occurs here, the entire phagocytic system would be sensitized.

The extrahaemocytic forms of *P. lophurae* have been successfully cultured for as long as eighty-nine days in roller tissue cultures of chick organs (James & Tate in McKee), but, here again, such experiments, in spite of their evident interest, do not contribute much to an understanding of the physiology of malarial parasites. The problem of successful cultures in the absence of red blood cells has not yet been solved although it is more than likely that it would indicate new approaches to the chemotherapeutic aspect of the question.

2. INTESTINAL SYMBIONTS AND PARASITES

The association of protozoans with organisms that feed almost entirely upon cellulose is of particular interest, as has already been stressed in the first part of this book. From a physiological standpoint, investigations of such associations are of great interest since they clearly show the reason for their existence in such peculiar surroundings.

The association of termites and flagellates has received much attention from various authors, and the necessity of these flagellates for the host is amply demonstrated. Yet, apparently, not all of the species present in a single association possess identical physiological properties since certain flagellates do not even feed upon cellulose (Cleveland). For instance, *Strebilomastix strix* Kofoid & Swezy feeds solely on dead flagellates that occur in the gut of *Termopsis*. When *Termopsis* has been defaunated by being exposed alternately to high oxygen tensions and to periods of starvation, this species of flagellates usually survives but it is incapable of maintaining its termite host alive.

Indirect evidence, that is evidence obtained from flagellates removed from the host's gut but not from cultures, indicates also that certain species as *Trichonympha campanula* K.& S. contains glycogen when fed wood, but that *Trichomonas termitis* (Cutl.) does not. Further investigations would be interesting to show whether, in this case, the flagellates possess enzymes that could break the glycogen down to glucose since the latter of course escapes detection by the iodine technique previously employed.

Unfortunately, no cultures of these flagellates outside the body of the host have been successful so far, and consequently, information on the physiological properties and on the metabolism of the different species is lacking.

The ciliates and flagellates from the rumen of ruminants and the cecum of other ungulates are particularly interesting subjects for experimental research because of their large size and their presence in enormous quantities.

The first successful attempts to obtain cultures of cattle ciliates were relatively crude, since they consisted of inoculating cellulose-splitting bacteria into hay infusions before introducing the ciliates (Margolin). Later, it was discovered that oxygen is lethal for these protozoans and that the cultures have to be free from air. Oxygen has been replaced by methane, a gas that occurs normally in the paunch of ruminants. A growth factor has also been found necessary and is furnished by filtered fluid from the rumen (Westphal).

By using more refined methods, such as obtaining

cellulose from pure cotton and a gaseous mixture of 95 per cent nitrogen and 5 per cent carbon dioxide, together with dried grass and paunch fluid, satisfactory cultures can be obtained (Hungate). The growth factor present in fluid from the paunch has not yet been identified but it is not found in either peptone or in beef extract. It might be assumed that this factor is thiamine since the latter is known to occur in the paunch of ruminants where it is synthesized by bacteria. It has also been suggested that necessity for strict anaerobiosis is due to the absence of a catalase in the ciliates.

Cultures obtained from individual clones of several species of *Diplodinium* and *Entodinium* show that the former contain cellulase and also cellobiase and are therefore able to split up the cellulose molecule into glucose. *Entodinium*, on the other hand, contains neither cellulase nor cellobiase and must rely entirely on the products resulting from hydrolysis of cellulose through bacterial action.

Consequently, there appear here also two groups of ciliates, both occurring in the same biotope, yet each one is adapted physiologically in its own manner. From a purely morphological standpoint the genus *Entodinium* is considered more primitive than *Diplodinium*, and the latter is supposed to have been derived from the former. Should this assumption be correct, and there is no reason to believe that protozoologists are mistaken, then it will be necessary to assume that *Entodinium* has lost the power of synthesizing cellulase and consequently, that its survival as a species has been made possible only through its association with cellulose-splitting bacteria.

On the other hand, as has been stressed previously, there is no necessary association between the morphological and the physiological evolutions of a species. *Diplodinium*, while morphologically more evolved, can perfectly well have retained an ancestral physiological trait, namely the power to synthesize cellulase.

Evidence as to physiological requirements of such symbiotic ciliates is not yet very extensive, especially in regard to the large number of species and genera that have been reported. Yet it is clear that all these organisms are anaerobic.

It seems difficult to imagine that anaerobic organisms arose by mutation since, even if this were possible, they would invariably die unless such mutations were caused by the environment, by their presence in the paunch of ruminants.

Ruminants are relatively old mammals that have become differentiated somewhere in Tertiary times. Moreover, their symbiotic fauna tends to indicate that such families as the camels and llamas must have become isolated at an early date (Dogiel).

It is not known whether the primitive ancestors really ruminated, or when such a mechanism was first introduced, but the warm, swampy plains of the Tertiary most certainly were covered with thick grass growing on a layer of bacterial decay that produced both methane and carbon dioxide. Protozoans may have flourished in such an environment and their transfer from the grass to ruminants could have occurred frequently. Being preadapted, they were able to establish themselves in their new surroundings.

As the climate of Tertiary times grew colder and the swamps dried up, the association of protozoans and bacteria disappeared gradually, so that the only surviving species would have been those that became established in ruminants. It is also possible to assume that rumination appeared at the same time and that consequently ruminants were forced to rely upon the protozoans and bacteria for their own survival.

The physiology of protozoans occurring in the gut of mammals other than ruminants has been approached from a very different angle, and at least in regard to flagellates and ciliates no really synthetic medium has been devised for cultivating them. Consequently their essential growth requirements are unknown.

The ease with which intestinal flagellates can be cultivated is somewhat disconcerting, and one is inclined to believe that they are not at all true parasites but commensals that find in the gut contents their essential food requirements.

By using a relatively simple standard medium containing salts, mucin, and dried blood serum, it is possible to obtain cultures of various species of *Trichomonas* obtained from both man and other mammals. Yet none of these cultures are sterile and, consequently, the role of bacteria in modifying the medium has not been investigated (Wenrich). The same medium also permits cultivation and growth of species belonging to the genera *Retortomonas* and *Monocercomonoides* that occur in insects, amphibians, and rodents. Several of these cultures survived for more than a year without any attention.

Tritrichomonas batrachorum (Perty) obtained from different hosts appears to represent distinct strains of flagellates, judging from the irregular results of survival of the species in cultures. There is evidence in such cultures that different species of flagellates may be antagonistic toward one another. For instance, *T. augusta* Alexieff is able to survive only a short time unless *T. batrachorum* be first removed. *T. augusta* Alexieff also requires a greater amount of nutritional material. Nutrient materials and pieces of host tissue must be added frequently to the culture.

None of the essential food requirements of trichomonads could be investigated using the above techniques. It is known, however, that *T. columbae* (Riv.) and *T. foetus* (Riedm.) are able to synthesize hematin, and that this is also the case for *Eutrichomastix serpentis* (Dobell), an intestinal parasite that may pass into the blood (Cailleau in Lwoff).

An essentially bacteria-free medium for rearing *Trichomonas vaginalis* Donné has been described recently (Johnson), but this also contains complex substances of unknown composition such as liver infusion and blood serum and agar. Moreover, a mixture containing fourteen different growth factors is added. This is found to be sufficiently active, even when diluted six to twelve times the original concentration. The necessity for a growth factor supplied by serum is rediscovered, thus confirming previous workers (Cailleau). By increasing the serum content of the medium, liver infusion may be dispensed with and this is also the case when peptone is replaced by trypticase. Also unidentified fractions (cholesterol?) that appear essential for growth have been isolated from ether-extracts of serum.

For reasons easily understood, the species *Endamoeba histolytica* Schaud. is the only one that has been frequently investigated as to its physiological requirements.

Many culture media have been devised, some quite simple, others extremely complicated (Shaffer *et al.*). Yet none of these media are sterile and bacteria must be inoculated before the media are able to support growth of the amebae. This same difficulty occurs for an almost synthetic medium that has been proposed recently (Hansen & Anderson). In none of the above media are special precautions taken to provide anaerobiosis. When this is the case, however, the physiological needs of the amebae seem to be different and especially remarkable is their extreme sensitiveness to air, which even in small amounts proves lethal (Snyder & Meleney). The addition of rice starch is essential to all media, although its role has not been investigated in detail. It is true, however, that amebae feed upon the starch grains and are even able to hydrolyze them.

The essentially synthetic medium mentioned above contains ten vitamins of the B complex and when these are omitted, the amebae die out after the fourth transfer. But no investigations have been attempted, so far, with the aim of examining the possible requirements of isolated vitamins for this group.

Under anaerobic conditions, it is found that the culture medium can be simplified by substituting cysteine as a reducing agent for aerobic bacteria and also by adding 1.10^{-6} cholesterol to the peptone Ringer solution with rice starch. An anaerobic species of bacillus, isolated from the original cultures, is found to be necessary to maintain the culture. Curiously enough, the latter is destroyed when exposed to air for one hour.

The physiology of amebae is singularly complicated by the presence of bacteria in all of the media, since they introduce an unknown factor whose effects have not been discovered. It has been suggested that the bacteria reduce the oxidation-reduction potential of the medium, as a low potential is a condition for successful growth (Chang).

It is clear that none of the above culture methods are adequate for investigating the essential food and growth requirements of *E. histolytica*, yet such a study might be extremely enlightening as to possible methods of treating amebiasis.

The high carbohydrate diet that is so favorable for producing experimental amebiasis in animals may bear a direct relationship to the bacterial flora in the intestine and especially to that which develops subsequently in the cecum and the colon where the parasites are normally located. There exists, perhaps, some connection between bacterial fermentation of carbohydrates in this segment and the amebae, the latter profiting by the hexose sugars thus produced.

Nothing definite is known as to the pathogenicity or the inocuity of *E. histolytica* or the way that these parasites attack the surface of the mucosa.

CHAPTER SIXTEEN

Physiology of parasitic helminths

A very considerable amount of literature has accumulated on the physiology of parasitic helminths, but much of this originates from investigations that were undertaken several years ago before the present biochemical methods of analysis were available. Consequently, many of the results obtained formerly must be questioned and cannot be incorporated in a general review without careful criticism.

Very complete bibliographies have been published recently on the physiology of tapeworms (Smyth), nematodes (Hobson), and acanthocephalans (Bullock), whereas trematodes have been studied by various authors especially as to their survival and culture in artificial media.

The physiology of helminths is considerably complicated by their passing through invertebrate or vertebrate hosts before becoming adult in the gut of the final host and, consequently, it is important to examine separately the physiological requirements of the larval and of the adult forms.

Several authors, more physiologists than zoologists, who have worked with larval forms have extrapolated their results to apply them to the adult worms. For instance, cysticerci that live in the tissues of their host not only possess different morphological structures, but also physiological requirements distinct from the adult worms that occur in the gut of the final host. It is obvious that if the physiological requirements of helminth larvae were the same as those of the adult worms, there would be no need for them to pass into a final host! Yet such elementary facts appear to have been overlooked by quite a few investigators.

Quantitative analyses of helminths, although possessing a certain interest, do not furnish much information as to their metabolism. Also, such investigations reveal a considerable variation in identical species that may be caused by the food of the host as, for instance, the higher glycogen content in hog ascarids from Denmark than in those of the United States (v. Brand).

Both in nematodes, and in cestodes, such quantitive analyses stress the fact that the protein content of the species examined was very low, lower in fact than the sum total of the carbohydrates and the fats.

In a general way, nearly all investigations have been carried out on a small number of species, that is, species that can be obtained easily and in quantity and that are sufficiently large to be manipulated without difficulty.

Before attempting to draw general conclusions as to the physiology of parasitic helminths, it will be necessary to examine each group individually. Such a dogmatic arrangment is justified, however, by the fundamental differences that exist between the different groups of helminths studied. This is especially true as to the structure of the body wall, nematodes, acanthocephalans, cestodes, and trematodes possessing different structures although the latter two are somewhat similar. Then also, both nematodes and trematodes possess an intestine, whereas neither cestodes nor acanthocephalans ever have one. It is obvious that such differences will influence their metabolism and modify their physiological requirements.

1. SOMATIC HELMINTHS

a. Cestodes

Larval tapeworms, as has been seen earlier (Part 3, Chapter 12), can be grouped into two categories according to whether they belong to the plerocercus-plerocercoid type or to the cysticercus-cysticercoid type. The former occur almost exclusively in aquatic vertebrates and invertebrates and rarely in land vertebrates (*Sparganum*, *Tetrathyridium*) and the latter group of larvae belong to the cysticercus-cysticercoid type, in warm-blooded vertebrates and in invertebrates.

Such host segregation indicates that besides fundamental morphological distinctions, the physiological requirements of the larvae must be different also.

Plerocercoid and plerocercus larvae are found in the body cavity of their host, or in thin-walled cysts on the surface of the internal organs, where they are usually inconspicuous and in no way affect the host's metabolism. Plerocercoids of *Ligula* and *Schistocephalus*, however, that occur in the body cavity of fishes, though still in the larval stage have attained their maximum growth. The abdomen of the host is so distended that the body wall becomes very fragile; such fishes frequently burst when caught in a net or even when roughly handled. The presence within the body cavity of such large larvae naturally compresses the organs and, sometimes, may prevent the gonads from developing normally so that a mechanical castration results.

Evidence from observations in the field indicates also that closely related species belonging to the same genus may have different nutritional requirements during their larval stage, even if the adult worms both occur in the same host. For instance, plerocercoid larvae of *Triaenophorus lucii* (Müll.) are found in thin-walled cysts on the surface of the liver of burbots (*Lota*) and those of *T. crassus* Forel in the epiaxonic muscles of whitefish both in Europe and in this country. The adults of both species occur in pike.

Such plerocercoid and plerocercus larvae are able to survive for several days in balanced saline solutions to which is added glucose at 15° C. Under oligaseptic conditions, plerocercoid larvae of *Diphyllobothrium latum* and *Ligula intestinalis* have been maintained for as long as 260 hours at 15° C. in Ringer-Locke medium alone, and in the same solution to which is added 1 per cent glucose and fish broth. Under such conditions, the glycogen content of the larvae has been studied and found to decrease very rapidly when R-L is used alone (Markow). It was reduced to 66 per cent of its original level after 38 hours, and when the temperature is raised to 37° C., the glycogen content, measured after 72 hours, is reduced to 6 per cent of its original level. When the experiment is repeated with glucose added to the medium, there is no drop whatever in the glycogen level. The latter is even increased and has been found in *Ligula* to have increased 11 per cent above its original value.

It should be remembered, however, that in cestodes the carbohydrates are not entirely stored as reserve glycogen, but an important quantity of it is intricately bound to protein from which it cannot be detached without denaturing the latter (Kent). Consequently, the results mentioned above probably involve only the free glycogen.

Glycogen metabolism is extremely complex and not yet explained in a satisfactory manner. It is usually assumed that in cestodes it is hydrolyzed by enzymes under anaerobic conditions and the waste products are partly excreted as fatty acids. On the other hand, from experimental evidence it is found that the glycogen molecule cannot pass through the cuticula of the body wall, whereas the glucose molecule can. Consequently, there must exist an enzymatic source that is able to build up glycogen from glucose.

Plerocercoid larvae of *Triaenophorus lucii* and *Diphyllobothrium latum* have been found to be facultatively anaerobic. Their respiratory quotient is increased by the addition of glucose, and, moreover, cyanide does not inhibit respiration entirely as would be expected since cytochrom-C has been observed in the larvae (Friedheim & Baer). These results indicate that such larvae as occur on the surface of the organs or in the body cavity of fishes are able to utilize the very small amounts of oxygen present and do not rely entirely upon their carbohydrate reserves. The reserves are maintained at a certain level adequate for their metabolic energy. This, of course, is necessarily very low during the larval stage of their existence.

Metabolism of cysticercoid larvae is practically unknown on account of the small size of such larvae and the experimental difficulty in obtaining results that might be statistically significant. From indirect evidence, however, in a single case it seems that certain larval structures, such as the tail of the cysticercoid, might play a certain part in procuring nourishment for the larva. As mentioned previously in Chapter 12, the cestode *Hymenolepis nana fraterna* possesses two possible life cycles. The cysticercoids recovered from the warm-blooded vertebrate host are different from those occurring in the insect host. The essential difference lies in the development of the tail, which is enormous in the larva from insects and inapparent in that removed from the intestinal villus of the rat. It is suggested that this difference might be significant and related to the metabolism of the larvae, as for instance, absorption of nourishment. This might also explain why the caudal appendage in cysticercoids varies so greatly according to the intermediate host in which the larva occurs.

Physiological conditions for larvae of the cysticercus type are entirely different. Such larvae occur only in warm-blooded vertebrates and almost exclusively in mammals. Their presence invariably produces a host reaction that tends to enclose the larva within a capsule of connective tissue that forms the so-called outer wall of the cyst. Since the tapeworm larva develops and grows within the cyst, nourishment must be absorbed through the wall of the latter.

When a cysticercus is carefully dissected, it is seen that there exists between the cyst wall and the bladder a small amount of fluid that may be regarded as a transudate from the host. On the other hand, the fluid that is contained within the bladder is of an entirely different composition than that mentioned above. This indicates that the larval membrane cannot be compared to an ordinary semipermeable membrane (Schopfer). Histologically, the structure of the larval membrane is complex. It contains glycogen, muscle fibers, and numerous cells. The cystic fluid contains glucose and also the usual products of glycogenolysis such as succinic, valeric, propionic, acetic, and lactic acids. The selective effect of the larval membrane is shown by the very much smaller proportion of protein present in the cystic fluid than in the surrounding liquid enclosed by the cyst wall. This also indicates that the larval bladder membrane is impermeable to the larger proteic molecules, as also to glycogen. It would be worthwhile repeating these investigations using more recent methods of analysis so as to determine with greater precision the nature of the larval proteins as compared to those of the host and also to compare them with the proteins from the adult worms. Such investigations would be all the more interesting since the cystic fluid contains markedly antigenic substances.

The osmotic pressure of the cystic fluid is only very slightly higher than that of the host's blood. There is also evidence that the fat deposits that have been found in *Echinococcus*, and also in other larvae, are only waste products resulting from glycogenolysis (Smyth).

Respiration of cysticercus larvae has been investigated in a single species only, namely *Taenia taeniaeformis*, the larva of the cat tapeworm that occurs in cysts in the liver of rats and other species of rodents.

This larva, however, differs from all other cysticerci by possessing a very long strobila and an exceedingly small bladder. It has been suggested that this larva possesses a hydrogenase which acts upon a substrate of glycogen (Wilmoth).

b. *Nematodes*

Several genera and species of adult nematodes occur normally in the tissues of their hosts but their metabolism is practically unknown. They are found essentially in the connective tissues and may either wander around or remain permanently in the same place.

It is not clear whether nematodes absorb nourishment through the mouth and gut or through the body wall. The evidence in support of the former has been obtained from *Ascaris*, a species that possess a particularly thick body wall, the structure of which is very different from that of filarioids. Nonetheless, when radioactive antimony is injected into the blood of dogs harboring the heartworm, *Dirofilaria immitis*, (Leidy), it is observed that thirty-six hours later much of this has accumulated in the liver, thyroid, and parathyroids of the host, and that the worms contain ten times more antimony than does the blood of the host. The radioactive antimony has not been regionally localized within the worms, although this would have been particularly interesting since antimony salts, in blood flukes for example, are deposited in the gonads and destroy them. (Brady *et al.*)

Litomosoides carinii (Trav.), a filarioid from the pleural cavity of the cotton rat, *Sigmodon* sp., has been found to possess an extremely high rate of aerobic and anaerobic glucose metabolism (Bueding). In the presence of air, 30 to 45 per cent of the glucose utilized is converted into lactic acid, 25 to 35 per cent into acetic acid, and 10 to 20 per cent into a stored polysaccharid (glycogen?). In the absence of air, over 80 per cent of the total carbohydrate utilized is metabolized into lactic acid and the remainder into acetic acid. Since respiration is completely inhibited by cyanide, there is no cytochrome in these worms.

It is exceptional to discover an adult worm possessing so great an adaptation to both aerobic and anaerobic metabolism. This possibly may be a general property of filarioid worms and would also explain their peculiar habitat.

Respiration in larval nematodes has been investigated in *Eustrongylides ignotus* (Jägersk), a species that occurs encysted on the surface of organs within the body cavity of top minnows (*Fundulus spp.*) (v. Brand). These larvae are found to lead a purely aerobic existence and are able to tolerate a temperature range from 5° C. to 45° C., the oxygen uptake increasing with the temperature. This is, however, not very surprising since the adult worms of this species occur in the gut of herons that normally possess a high body temperature. Moreover, larval eustrongilids have been found to contain hemoglobin that is dissolved in the body fluid of the worms. It is very likely that this plays an important part in the respiratory mechanism, since no organic acids, such as those resulting from glycogenolysis, have been detected in the fluids surrounding the larvae.

These larvae have also been kept *in vitro* for as long as thirty months but without manifesting any signs of growth (v. Brand & Simpson). It is true that the latter investigators claim to have found in their cultures a single worm that had molted into a preadult male. This, however, is not proved since preadult larvae showing the principal differential characters of the sexes have been recorded from top minnows in this country (Chapin).

c. *Trematodes*

Blood flukes can be considered somatic worms but there is not very much information as to their metabolism. Certain species, however, such as *Schistosoma japonicum* Kats., have been maintained outside their host in a relatively simple culture medium for as long as four months (Chu). Unfortunately, no observations were made either on metabolism or on respiration. It is significant, however, to find that egg laying is impaired under such conditions.

Sterile cercariae of *Diplostomum flexicaudum* (Cort & Brooks), which are consequently free from any enveloping microorganisms, have been found to transform into metacercariae within the lenses of fish eyes that were kept in a simple culture medium (Ferguson), but no determination as to a possible carbohydrate metabolism was made nor were any other physiological properties of the larvae investigated.

d. *Acanthocephala*

Practically nothing is known about the metabolism of acanthocephalan larvae that occur in the body cavity of their hosts.

It has been observed that glycogen accumulates within the acanthor before the egg is hatched but that it disappears completely after the acanthor is liberated and becomes an acanthella. Later, the amount of glycogen again increases and is stored inside the larva. These experiments have been made with *Macracanthorhynchus hirudinaceus* (Pall.) larvae obtained experimentally in the larvae of Japanese beetles. Moreover, there is no relationship whatever between the amount of glycogen that is stored up in the acanthella and the amount present in the experimental host (Miller).

2. INTESTINAL HELMINTHS

Intestinal helminths have always been regarded with considerable awe as being extraordinary organisms that have fled the light of day to live within a warm, slimy tunnel, where they seem to resist digestion in a somewhat miraculous way. Their metabolism has been variously interpreted according to the precision with which the chemical analyses have been made. It is, unfortunately, hardly possible to utilize today data that have been obtained by methods that are now known to be fraught with errors and that are, consequently, inadequate.

a. *Cestodes*

Since tapeworms never possess a gut, the structure of their body wall is of particular importance. It is usually assumed that the cuticula of cestodes, as that of trematodes, is secreted by subcuticular cells, and perhaps also by cells contained in the parenchyma.

Formation of the cuticula in cestodes has never been studied in detail histochemically, but from work done on trematodes (Kruidenier) it might be assumed that in cestodes also, the cuticula is a polymerized mucoprotein. This is, of course, purely hypothetical as to tapeworms and can only be used as a theoretical basis for further research.

A recent study of the proteins of a single species of cestode, *Moniezia expansa* (Rud.) from sheep, had revealed some entirely unsuspected facts that are extremely interesting (Kent). It has been possible to isolate, without denaturing them, three distinct types of proteins that are all "cenapsed" with other molecules. This means that the accessory molecules cannot be separated from the protein without denaturing the latter. These three fractions are as follows:

1. A protein bound together with cerebrosids and bile salts. The nature of the latter has not been

determined exactly, but this is of considerable importance since it shows that the host supplies certain important substances that are incorporated by the parasite into necessary molecules.

2. A protein bound with glycogen containing 40 per cent protein and as much as 60 per cent glycogen; this has been named baerine.

3. Also a protein bound with glycogen, but containing 89 per cent protein and 11 per cent glycogen that has been named moniezine. Finally, a residue that represents 36 per cent of dried and delipidated worm material was found to be made up entirely of scleroproteins.

The above complex protein-glycogen molecules represent the bound glycogen that probably does not play any part in the normal carbohydrate metabolism, but that has been calculated together with the total glycogen content since all previous investigations have used techniques that destroy the proteins.

The carbohydrate metabolism of cestodes appears to be much more complicated than was formerly supposed. It is dependent upon the available supply of glucose in the gut of the host, and this also explains the considerable quantitative differences found by various authors, even when investigating the same species of worm. For instance, in *Moniezia expansa* (Rud.), taking into account the remarks mentioned above, analyses of individual worms have yielded a glycogen content that varies from 9 per cent to 49 per cent (v. Brand).

The free glycogen accumulates in the parenchyma where it can be detected by the usual methods and consequently the amount compared quantitatively with the results from chemical analysis. It has been suggested that *Taenia hydatigena* Pall. removed from dogs that have received a rich carbohydrate diet for eight weeks contain nearly twice as much glycogen as worms from dogs fed upon a normal diet for the same length of time (v. Brand).

A similar experiment but on a larger scale, using a fowl tapeworm, *Raillietina cesticillus* (Mol.), shows that after a period of starvation of twenty hours the mean glycogen content of the worms is about 20 per cent lower than in worms from normally fed chickens (Reid). Furthermore, there exists a daily peak in the glycogen content that occurs in this case at 6 P.M. and a daily low at 6 A.M. It has been suggested that this daily fluctuation of the glycogen content corresponds to a cyclic form of metabolism, and that this also corresponds to a daily rhythm of proglot-

tids being shed. The latter may even be modified by changing the feeding time of the host.

Cysticercoids of *Hymenolepis diminuta* (Rud.), a rat tapeworm, when fed to rats on a carbohydrate-free diet develop into stunted worms. Moreover, the number of worms that become successfully established in such cases is about 50 per cent lower than in normally fed rats used as controls (Chandler).

Fat in tapeworms appears as a waste product of glycogenolysis and if its distribution be investigated with either osmic acid or Sudan III, it is found to parallel that of free glycogen. Moreover, if cestodes possessed a fat metabolism, they would also possess a lipase, yet this has never been discovered. Consequently, the phospholipids that can be extracted from all tapeworms are no doubt bound into complex molecules that mask the lipids in ordinary histological techniques.

It has been suggested that vitamins and other specific factors are essential for the growth of tapeworms (Hager; Addis & Chandler). The evidence put forward has been obtained from experimental infestations of rats with *Hymenolepis diminuta* (Rud.).

When rats are fed upon a diet deficient in vitamins of the B (G) group, it is found that egg output of the worms ceases. If the rats are females, the worms are stunted, but in males growth is normal. Diets deficient in vitamins A, D, E, or B$_1$ cause the worms to increase in size.

Such data, however, cannot be used to study the eventual vitamin requirements of cestodes, since the vitamin deficient diets affect the host's metabolism, and this, secondarily, affects, or at least does so apparently, that of the tapeworms, although the direct causal relationship has not been demonstrated in a satisfactory manner. The same can also be said of experiments tending to demonstrate the influence of hormones (Addis). When worms are stunted in castrated rats on normal diets and growth is resumed, after feeding or injections of testosterone, this does not prove the action of testosterone upon the worms. There is, so far, no single clear case of a vertebrate hormone affecting directly an invertebrate, as the latter do not possess the necessary receptor cells.

These experiments only show that cestodes develop normally in animals that possess a normal metabolism, but that when the latter is upset, either by a vitamin deficiency or removal of the sexual glands, the resulting change affects the parasites indirectly and only insofar as it modifies the physiological conditions in the intestine.

It is well known to all helminthologists who have studied materials from collections, that if tapeworms are not immediately removed from the dead host they undergo a so-called maceration or partial digestion. This is also true for dead tapeworms, killed by an anthelminthic, for instance, in the intestine of a living host.

It has been frequently suggested that tapeworms possess anti-enzymes or, more correctly, enzyme inhibitors. Evidence gained from adding mashed tapeworms to active enzymes has supposedly shown that under such conditions enzymatic activity is inhibited. This evidence, however, is far from convincing, because mashing up the worms denatures the proteins, and the resulting mixture is not in the least comparable to the molecular structure of a living tapeworm. Many substances, by combining with the prosthetic group in the enzyme, inhibit the latter's activity. But such substances have never yet been reported from cestodes.

There is evidence, on the other hand, that the cuticular layer of the body protects the worm from being digested. Living segments of *Taenia saginata* when introduced into artificial digestive fluid resist the attack of enzymes, but if the cuticula be cut or bruised, digestion results almost immediately (de Waele).

As mentioned previously, it has been postulated provisionally, pending the necessary investigations, that the cuticula of tapeworms is also, as in trematodes, a polymerized mucoprotein. Recently, it has been shown that the three different proteins isolated from *Moniezia expansa* react in different ways in the presence of crystallized trypsin under optimum conditions (Kent). For some undiscovered reason, the cerebrosid-bile salt-protein complex activates digestion in the presence of lipids, but in the absence of the latter, not more than 50 per cent of the nitrogen is hydrolyzed. A mixture of baerine and moniezine, on the other hand, when exposed under similar conditions inhibits hydrolysis after twenty hours, and it is found that not more than 37 per cent of the total nitrogen that should be digested is hydrolyzed. It has been suggested that the loosely coiled protein molecule is protected from the effects of the enzyme by the glycogen molecules which probably envelop it.

Digestion of dead worms, or worms in which the cuticula has been torn or cut, would thus be explained by the denaturing of the protein-glycogen molecules. Glycogen would thus be dissolved and leave the protein molecule to suffer the effects of the enzymes.

The presence of enzymes in the tissues of tapeworms has been claimed by several authors but has never been proved in a satisfactory manner. Glycogenolytic enzymes have also been reported but never yet isolated.

By using a technique that does not denature the proteins to too great an extent, it has been found possible to prepare from tapeworms an antigenic extract that elicits the appearance of antibodies when injected into rabbits. If the resulting antiserum is diluted sufficiently, it will precipitate only with the specific antigen. Consequently, using a given antiserum, it is possible to test different antigens, and it is found that the nearer the homologous titer to the heterologous titer, the greater the relationship between the two antigens and therefore, also, the physiological similitude of the species that furnished the antigens. This method is an application of serological reactions to species determination that has often been applied in the past to both animals and plants.

The above technique, with delipidated antigens that contain both protein and carbohydrate, has been used for tapeworms with the following results (Wilhelmi). A homologous titer of 1:6000 is specific, but heterologous titers must be considerably higher and, consequently, less diluted, for the ring test to be positive. For instance, *Moniezia expansa* (Rud.) tested against *Dipylidium caninum* (L.) was positive at 1:400 and against *Taenia taeniaeformis* Batsch at 1:50. On the other hand, with an undetermined species of *Tetrabothrium*, no positive ring test was obtained at all. Between two closely related species, *Moniezia expansa* (Rud.) and *M. benedeni* (Moniez) homologous titers were determined as 1:4000 and heterologous titers as 1:1000 (Mahr).

As a result of these experiments the following definition of a species has been proposed: "Species of helminths may be defined tentatively as a group of organisms the lipid-free antigen of which, when diluted to 1:4000 or more, yields a positive precipitin test within one hour with a rabbit anti-serum produced by injecting 40 mg. of dry weight, lipid-free antigenic material and withdrawn ten to twelve days after the last of four intravenous injections administered every third day" (Wilhelmi).

Such a definition would apply probably equally well to all species of animals and plants. It has the advantage, however, of drawing attention to the possibility of using serological reactions to support taxonomic definitions of species. The precision of such tests lies almost entirely in the way in which the antigen is prepared, and will be all the higher if the specific protein molecules are not denatured. Moreover, it is possible, as in other parasites, that the carbohydrate fractions are also antigenic, so that differential reactions could be observed with either one or the other of the two antigens. It has been stated previously that in human and pig *Ascaris*, the protein antigen is identical, and consequently, generic, whereas the carbohydrate antigens are different and, therefore, specific. In bacteria, proteins provide the specific antigens whereas carbohydrates-polypeptides provide the type-antigens.

A great many more experimental results will have to be obtained from different species before this technique can be applied to eventual phylogenetic affinities of any of the parasites. It is premature to suggest that the cestode genus *Dipylidium* should be more closely related to *Moneizia* than to the genus *Taenia*. Each of these three genera represents a different family as recognized by taxonomists, and all belong to the *Cyclophyllidea*. The only affinities that might be invoked between *Moniezia* and *Dipylidium* are that both possess reduplicated genital organs (convergence) and also have larval forms that develop as cysticercoids in arthropods.

It is, however, significant to discover that none of the above three genera reacts with the genus *Tetrabothrium*. This genus belongs to a family whose taxonomic position is a moot question, but all the species of which occur exclusively in fish-eating birds and, more rarely, mammals. Assuming that the proteins of tapeworms are built up from materials supplied by the hosts, this might explain why a positive reaction does not occur. Nothing, of course, can be stated definitely but it is possible that this new approach, when used with the proper care by qualified biochemists, may lead to interesting conclusions.

b. *Nematodes*

Nematodes usually possessing a complete digestive system and showing evidence of intestinal absorption must necessarily swallow their food. The nature of the latter has been incompletely investigated.

By feeding the host substances that may be easily recognized, as powdered charcoal for instance, it is possible to demonstrate that ascarids feed on host gut contents (Li). This is also borne out by the presence of barium, visible on X-ray photographs in the gut of the human *Ascaris*.

It is probable that most of the food swallowed by ascarids is already partly dissolved, and that the esophageal glands are responsible for this. This explains, also, why it is comparatively rare to find organized debris in the gut of these worms. An indirect proof of the nature of the food is found in the following experiments. When fowls are deprived of all food but receive every eight hours an injection of a 25 per cent glucose solution, they remain perfectly healthy, and when infected with *Ascaridia galli*, the common fowl ascarid, the worms develop normally during the first period of their existence. This, it should be remembered, is spent buried in the mucosa. But, when the preadult worms become free in the lumen of the gut, their growth is inhibited in glucose-injected fowl and the worms become stunted (Ackert *et al.*). This is correctly interpreted as being due to the absence of nourishment in the host's gut. When glucose is added to a 30 per cent solution of sea water containing *Ascaris*, the glucose concentration of the latter's body fluid increases. If, however, the experiment is repeated and the extremities of the worms ligatured, no absorption of glucose results, thus indicating that this occurs via the gut and not through the body wall (Hobson *et al.*). A similar experiment, using radioactive phosphorous, leads to the same conclusions (Rogers & Lazarus). Ascarids definitely also feed on blood, as hemoglobin is found in their body fluid. Although never permanently attached to the mucosa, these worms are provided with three lips which enable them to attack the tissues. Not all species that are occasional blood feeders necessarily absorb hemoglobin, as will be seen later.

Trichuroids are said to feed by osmosis, their gut being used exclusively for excretion (Müller), but no experimental evidence has so far substantiated this assumption.

Strongyloids possess a powerful mouth capsule, into which empty "proteolytic" glands that apparently digest part or all of the tissues sucked into the mouth capsule. This is clearly visible in sections of the whole worm attached to the mucosa. Frequently these abrasions of the mucosa denude capillary vessels and blood flows into the mouth capsule. When the gut of anesthesized dogs harboring hookworms is opened, it is found that the pharynx of the worms pumps the blood into the gut from where it flows almost continuously out through the anus (Wells). The blood passes too rapidly to be digested, and there exists a considerable amount of evidence that this is accidental and that strongyles feed on other substances contained in the gut of the host, even though some species appear to be capable of digesting hemoglobin, since hematin has been detected in their gut (Rogers).

These results indicate that digestive enzymes may possibly exist in the gut of nematodes and that not only the esophageal glands but also the gut cells are able to secrete them.

Former experiments that were based on whole worm extracts are totally inadequate by modern standards to be of any value. Recent investigators, however, have made use of extracts from isolated guts, from which the esophagus had also been removed, and have been able to demonstrate the presence of enzymes (Enigk; Rogers). Lipase has been reported from *Strongylus equinus* (Müll.) and *St. edentatus* Looss, horse parasites, and also from the hog *Ascaris*. It is apparently absent from the gut of *Graphidium strigosum* (Duj.), a species that occurs in the stomach of rabbits. Proteinase has been found in all of the above species and has, moreover, been reported from the dog ascarid, *Toxocara canis* (Werner). On the other hand, a carbohydrase (amylase) is present only in the gut of *Gr. strigosum* (Duj.), *St. edentatus* Looss, and *Ascaris*. It is more than probable that these enzymes will also be found in other species of nematodes when the material difficulties inherent in such experiments have been overcome. It also seems that the activity of these enzymes is not the same for all the species. For instance, the lipase and proteinase of *St. edentatus* Looss present a much greater activity than those of *Ascaris*. This might have been expected *a priori* since these species possess a mouth capsule and consequently destroy a greater part of intestinal mucosa than does *Ascaris*.

When powdered charcoal is fed to rabbits harboring *Graphidium strigosum* (Duj.), it is later found in the cells of the mid-gut region (Enigk). Consequently the cells of this region are able to absorb food particles, but it is not known whether they also

secrete enzymes. The pH of the anterior portion of the mid gut is 4.4 to 4.8, while farther back and also in the hind gut it is somewhat lower than 7.0.

Although a considerable amount of research has been done upon the cuticle of nematodes there still remain several unexplained facts. It is obvious however, that the cuticle is not an inert layer and that, consequently, its permeability depends on its own particular metabolism in the same way as that of the skin in higher animals. For this reason, also, experiments that aim to discover the permeability of the cuticle and that are based upon worm "cylinders" of scraped cuticle cannot yield results comparable to those from living worms. That this is true is demonstrated by the fact that glucose, that does not normally diffuse through the living cuticle, does so when the hypoderm has been scraped away (Hobson). This would indicate that the hypodermal layer among other properties possesses that of rendering the cuticle semipermeable.

A chemical analysis of the various layers of the cuticle in *Ascaris* has shown that they are all combinations of mucoproteins, no doubt elaborated by the hypodermis and also staining with metachromatic stains (Kruidenier, unpublished). A global analysis yields a high sulphur content, and this has caused several investigators to consider the outer layer of the cuticle as formed by keratin. This layer also resists both gastric and pancreatic digestion, although the latter is known to attack keratin!

Several investigators, basing their conclusions on experimental work, have postulated the presence of "nezymes" or enzyme inhibitors that protect nematodes from being digested. These investigators, however, have used whole worm extracts that in no way correspond to the actual situation found in living worms. With identical techniques, it has even been possible to prepare enzyme inhibitors with earthworms. Moreover, since the cuticle of all free-living nematodes possesses the same fundamental structure as that of the parasitic species, it would be interesting although difficult on account of their small size to examine also their eventual resistance to digestion. It should be remembered that many free-living nematodes are saprozoic and, as such, live in decomposing organic substances that certainly contain enzymes. Moreover, it is very interesting to discover that nematodes are digested by certain plant enzymes such as papain, ficin, and bromelin. Plants that normally possess these enzymes, the papaya, certain gums, and the pineapple, should, *a priori*, be protected from nematodes. Ficin has even been used as an anthelminthic, but its proteolytic activity is so powerful that it also attacks the intestinal mucosa.

Curiously enough, there does not appear to be any clear evidence as to the function of the excretory system in nematodes. Several investigators have found ammonia, as much as 11 to 30 mg. per 100 gm. in *Ascaris*. The excretory function of the excretory system has even been questioned and no definite proof has been, as yet, brought forward in favor of either alternative. The so-called phagocytic cells described in *Ascaris*, and that occur also in other species, have been found to possess a respiratory function of which more will be said later (Hurlaux).

Fats and carbohydrates appear to be stored as "reserve" materials but nothing is known of the true nature of the fats. The interpretation of histological stains, especially the so-called fat specific stains, is delicate and does not yield sufficiently adequate results. It is found that 1 to 1.8 per cent of fat can be extracted from whole ascarids and that the greater part of this consists of nonvolatile fatty substances from which ascaryl-alcohol has been isolated. The latter apparently occurs only in female worms where it supposedly is used to build up the inner egg membrane (Fauré-Frémiet).

Histologically, it seems that both fat and carbohydrate occur in the same parts of the worms, yet no work appears to have been done on an eventual fat-carbohydrate metabolism, except in a case to be mentioned later. Fat also occurs within the the intestine but its resorption has not been studied in details and this is all the more surprising since lipase has been recorded from the gut.

Some investigators claim that fat does not constitute a reserve source of energy for the worms. When *Ascaris* is starved in ordinary saline, the fat content remains invariable and is found to be the same at the beginning and at the end of the experiment (v. Brand). It is true, however, that the period of starvation was perhaps too short to warrant such conclusions.

There exists, on the other hand, distinct evidence of a fat metabolism and this may possibly depend upon the presence of oxygen. The assumption that intestinal worms must lead an anaerobiotic existence is hard to combat and, moreover, there is evidence that they certainly use oxygen and that *Ascaris*, for instance, possesses oxydase (Hurlaux). Conse-

quently, the entire problem of fat metabolism should be reconsidered on the basis of renewed experimentation.

At least all investigators agree as to the presence of carbohydrates, although their metabolism is not completely known. When several analyses of carbodrates are compared, they are found to vary to an extraordinary extent that can be attributed only to faulty techniques. It is also necessary to consider the time that elapses between the moment when the worms are removed from the dead host and when they are subjected to analysis. Then also, as stated previously, the food of the host may affect the initial amount of carbohydrate present. In support of this view are results obtained with the fowl ascarid, *Ascaridia galli* (Schrank). When the host is starved, the glycogen content of the parasites falls very rapidly and within forty-eight hours represents less than 90 per cent of the initial amount present. Moreover, at this stage, the worms abandon their host and are evacuated (Reid).

Glycogen is found in the hypodermis, in the non-contractile portion of the muscles, in the ovary, in the unripe eggs, and also in the spermatids of most of the species examined. According to Fauré-Frémiet, the appearance of glycogen in the oocytes is preceded by that of fat or at least by a substance which stains like fat with osmic acid. It has also been found that glycogen granules within the intestinal cells break up and disappear when the worm is starved (*Ascaris*). In the horse ascarid, *Parascaris equorum* (Goeze), glycogen disappears more rapidly from the myoblasts when oxygen is present than under anaerobic conditions. Moreover, there is evidence that *Ascaris*, in the presence of oxygen, is able to synthesize glycogen, but only part of the amount lost under anaerobiosis (v. Brand).

It is obvious that the above results have been obtained from a very small number of species, but they stress the fact that nematodes are facultatively aerobiotic. Consequently it is not surprising that they possess also a distinct respiratory mechanism which, to some extent, is independent of the carbohydrate metabolism.

Hemoglobin has been reported from the fluid from the body cavity in several species of nematodes, and its origin has also been a matter for much discussion, since some investigators consider it as identical with that of the host although others find it to be spectroscopically distinct. Cytochrome has also been discovered in the hog ascarid and in *Camallanus trispinosus* (Leidy), a species from the gut of turtles.

Hemoglobin from the body fluid of *Parascaris equorum* (Goeze) is identical to that of the horse and this would imply that it is able to pass from the latter's blood through the intestinal wall of the parasite. The peroxidasic properties of both horse and worm hemoglobins are also identical (Hurlaux).

The so-called giant phagocytes present in the body cavity of *Parascaris* have been found to contain catalase. They are also continuously bathed by the body fluid of the worm, and for this reason they are considered as respiratory organs that enable the worms to lead a true aerobic existence but also to utilize oxygen under low tensions (Hurlaux). These results appear to be supported by the fact that several species of nematodes from sheep are unable to survive anaerobiosis even for periods as short as four hours (Davey).

There appears to be no doubt that by far the greater part of the glycogen that disappears is used up as a source of energy.

"While there is some doubt about the importance of an oxidation-breakdown of glycogen in the metabolism of such nematodes as *A. lumbricoides* it is generally agreed that the principal energy-producing mechanism must be one which is able to work in the absence of oxygen. The details of this mechanism have not yet been fully elucidated" (Hobson).

On the other hand, under both aerobic and anaerobic conditions *Ascaris* produces the same waste products, which has led to the conclusions that fermentation processes continue even when oxygen is present (v. Brand). A similar process appears to exist in *Trichinella* larvae also (Stannard). Experimental evidence, however, is far too scanty and too inadequate to permit these results to be applied to all nematodes. It is impossible to extrapolate results when almost the sole experimental material is furnished by three or four different species belonging to the same suborder.

A substance that possesses toxic properties and is soluble in 50 per cent alcohol is not dialyzable nor precipitated by trichloracetic acid has been isolated from the hog ascarid. A dose of 2 mg. is sufficient to kill a guinea pig (Macheboeuf & Mandoul). It has been suggested that this substance might perhaps be a polypeptid.

A similar substance has also been isolated from other species of nematodes, from a cestode, flukes, and also leeches and botfly larvae (Deschiens). There is, however, no reason to believe that such substances occur normally or that certain well known effects occurring in ascaridiasis are due to them. The nonspecific origin of these substances would imply that they correspond to molecular arrangements which may also occur elsewhere and bear no relationship whatever to parasites. It has been suggested that these substances might be capable of either liberating histamine or of forming this substance (Deschiens).

Among substances elaborated by the host and that exert an unfavorable influence upon the nematodes is found the so-named growth-inhibiting factor produced in the duodenal goblet cells of fowls infested with *Ascaridia galli* (Ackert *et al.*). The number of duodenal goblet cells increases with the age of the fowl and it has been suggested that this "age-resistance factor" is responsible for the failure to infect adult chicks with these nematodes.

This factor, however, is not specific, but is also found in both dog and swine mucus and, consequently, is produced in the absence of nematodes altogether. Neither prolonged washing nor heating destroys it, and it is the writer's contention that addition of this mucus to "cultures" of *A. galli* probably causes the mucus to combine with some essential factors present. Consequently, these are removed from the medium or, at least, are combined in a way that they are no longer available to the worms. This appears possible since when worms, on the point of dying, are removed from the medium to which mucus had been added and placed in a fresh solution without mucus, they immediately revive. It is somewhat difficult, under such circumstances, to understand in what way the effects of duodenal mucus could be related to host specificity.

c. *Trematodes*

Very little information is available as to the physiology and the metabolism of trematodes. Here more than in other helminths, the variety of food is much greater since trematodes occur in the blood, lungs, frontal sinuses, gall bladder, bile ducts, intestine, and cloaca of their hosts. They also possess a mouth and a gut and there is certain evidence that they are able to absorb nourishment through their body wall (Stephenson).

It has been suggested that the common liver fluke, *Fasciola hepatica* L., a parasite of the bile ducts, feeds exclusively on blood. The blood is concentrated in the worm's gut, the fluid portion being absorbed and the hemoglobin being transformed into acid hematin. A small portion of the latter is absorbed by the intestinal cells and the rest excreted as feces (Stephenson). This would, however, indicate that these flukes feed exclusively upon serum and that the transformation of hemoglobin into hematin is only secondary. Moreover, bile ducts infested with flukes possess thickened, fibrous walls with very few capillaries, and the latter would, practically, only exist in the submucosa. In infested bile ducts there is also an increased production of mucus mixed with the bile and, if liver flukes were only blood feeders, it is not easy to understand why they enter the bile ducts at all and do not remain in the liver tissues where they penetrate as young, immature flukes.

By adding glucose to an alkaline salt solution having a pH 8.4, a medium is obtained in which liver flukes survive for as long as sixty hours at 36° C. But their metabolism can hardly be studied under such circumstances. It has been found, however, that the absence of air decreases the length of survival and, consequently, that the worms thrive better under aerobic conditions.

Another liver fluke, *Clonorchis sinensis* (Cobb), has been kept for as long as five months in a frequently renewed medium of 1/2 Tyrode's solution to which serum is added. The addition of substances such as glycogen, cysteine, lecithin, hemoglobin, or bile had no apparent effect upon the worms. Glycogen, estimated by the Best method, was found to be present in approximately the same amount at the beginning of the experiment as at the end of five months (Hoeppli & Chu). This would seem to indicate that survival of the Chinese liver fluke was due to the fact that all of its essential food requirements were furnished by the serum. No particular precautions were taken to avoid aerobiosis nor were the cultures sterile, since a bacteriostatic (sulfamids) was added to keep down an excess of bacterial growth. All the cultures were maintained at 37° C.

The considerable difference in the results observed between two trematodes that both occur in the bile ducts of their hosts is curious. It is possible, however, that this may be due to the enormous difference in size of the two species. Since serum alone appears to provide the necessary factors, it is possible that the quantity available in the first experiments was insufficient.

In *F. hepatica*, fat droplets have been observed by some investigators in connection with the excretory ducts. They have been attributed to carbohydrate metabolism. It is not clear how these droplets of unsaturated fatty materials pass from the parenchyma into the excretory system, since it is claimed that there are no flame cells (Stephenson).

The function of the body wall of trematodes, in relation to their physiology, has not yet been established. The structure and origin of the cuticula in *Paragonimus* shows distinctly that the cuticula is built up of mucopolysaccharids that are no doubt polymerized to a considerable extent by the possible effects of the host's fluids upon them. This would also imply that, under certain conditions that have not yet been determined experimentally, the cuticula may be removed by the enzymes present in the gut, but that it is also being re-formed by the subcuticular glands and perhaps also by secretions from glands within the parenchyma (Kruidenier).

Hemoglobin has been reported from *Telorchis robustus* Goldb. and from *Alassostoma magnum* (Stunk.), two species which occur in turtles. It has been found to be spectroscopically different from that of the host and it seems also that cytochrome is present in *A. magnum* (Wharton). Nothing is known of the eventual respiratory function of hemoglobin in trematodes. It probably occurs in many other species from various hosts, judging from the markedly pink color of many living trematodes.

An interesting contribution to the formation of the eggshell in *F. hepatica* has been made recently (Stephenson). It has been known for some time that the yolk glands contribute to forming the eggshell and that the so-called shell gland, or Mehlis' gland, has another function that is not yet quite clear although it has been suggested that its secretion facilitates the passage of eggs into the uterus. The vitelline globules which flatten out to form the eggshell contain an orthodihydroxyphenol and a protein, as has been ascertained by histochemical reactions (Romanini). This polyphenol is later oxidized into a quinone so that finally the eggshell is made up of a quinone-tanned protein that is said to be similar to that of sclerotin produced by insects.

d. *Acanthocephala*

Only a very few investigators have attempted to make an analysis of the metabolism of *Acanthocephala*. The peculiar anatomy of these helminths, the complicated structure of their body wall, the absence of a gut and their mode of implanting themselves in the mucosa, place the acanthocephalans in a group by themselves.

It is only recently that a more complete attempt than any previously has been made on a histochemical basis to determine the presence and distribution of the most important substances (Bullock).

Previous workers, for reasons easily understood on account of the size of the worms, worked with *Macracanthorhynchus hirudinaceus* (Pall.) (v. Brand), whereas the above mentioned investigations were carried out on *Echinorhynchus coregoni* Linkins, *E. gadi* (Zoega), *Neoechinorhynchus cylindratus* (V.Cl.), and *Pomphorhynchus bulbocolli* Linkins, all occurring in fishes, and *Neoechinorhynchus emydis* (Leidy) from the slider turtle.

It should be borne in mind that histochemical techniques must be carefully controlled, especially when dealing with such soluble substances as glycogen and perhaps others also. When investigating organisms with so thick a body wall as acanthocephalans, it is doubtful whether certain fixatives, such as chromic acid for instance, are able to penetrate with sufficient rapidity to immobilize the substances brought out subsequently by the stains. It would seem that the only satisfactory technique for this sort of work would be the freezing-sectioning-fixing technique described recently (Adamstone).

The fat metabolism, judging from the distribution of lipids, is unique among the helminths since in no other group has so great an amount of fatty substances ever been described. Neutral fat is distributed in practically every tissue of the body and especially in the subcuticular muscle layer where it occurs in both the noncontractile and in the contractile portions. No fat has been found previously in the muscles of *M. hirudinaceus* (Pall.) (v. Brand). On the other hand, there appears to be no fat in the muscular receptaculum, within which the proboscis is withdrawn. The inner subcuticular layer that contains also the lacunar system (see Fig. 131) also contains the greatest amount of fat, although there is no fat within the vascular system itself. The subcuticula of the proboscis and neck regions contains large amounts of fat that occur in submicroscopic and microscopic globules. Such globules, curiously enough, also occur at the bases of the hooks. Fat is present in the lemnisci, although this had been denied by previous authors who had used only osmic

acid for its detection. The reproductive organs contain considerable amounts of fat, the latter occurring even in the lumen of the female genital ducts. In the egg balls, fat appears at first but later, as the eggs are formed, decreases and finally has disappeared completely from the mature larva.

Phospholipids occur in abundance in the subcuticula but more in the outer layer than in the others. They are also present around the lacunae of the vascular system. A small amount of cholesterol is found in the middle and inner layers of the subcuticula.

Lipase is present in the subcuticula of the trunk and also in the lemnisci, but not in the subcuticula of the proboscis. A similar distribution has been observed for phosphatase. Curiously enough, both the enzymes appear to be lacking in the two species of *Neoechinorhynchus* and, moreover, no enzyme whatever could be discovered in any of the species when whole worms were mashed up and tested. This cannot be explained in a satisfactory way except that no data are available on how long the fish containing the parasites had been on ice. Although the acanthocephalans appeared to be alive and in good condition, it is possible that this might account for these discrepancies.

The greatest amount of glycogen appears to be distributed in the subcuticular layers although the cuticula itself is always glycogen free. There is a small amount of glycogen in almost all of the organs in the body. In the muscles, it is found in the noncontractile portions and, to some extent also, in the contractile portions of the subcuticular muscles and also in the wall of the receptaculum. There appears to be some evidence, also, that the embryos, formed within the egg, contain a polysaccharid other than glycogen which might possibly be galactogen (v. Brand & Sauerwein).

Nothing whatever is known of the respiratory mechanism in *Acanthocephala* and, consequently, both the fat and the carbohydrate metabolisms remain obscure. It seems difficult to assume that such large amounts of fat are composed entirely of waste products derived from the carbohydrate metabolism, as would be the case if the worms lived entirely in anaerobiosis. On the other hand, if they are able to use oxygen, and such a possibility should not be excluded *a priori*, they could also burn up the excess fat. Or in other words: "Either the fat is going in to fulfill a nutritional requirement of the parasite or it is going out as a waste product of carbohydrate metabolism" (Bullock).

CONCLUSIONS

From the foregoing pages it is clear that many of the essential facts about the physiology of parasitic helminths are as yet obscure or even unknown. It seems, however, that the old concept considering parasitic helminths, *ipso facto*, as obligate anaerobic organisms must be abandoned. All helminths are able to utilize oxygen and, moreover, it even seems that in certain nematodes the presence of oxygen is essential. The fact that hemoglobin occurs in both nematodes and trematodes also indicates the presence of an oxydasic system that has, so far, been demonstrated in *Ascaris* only.

Parasitic helminths appear to be able to adjust themselves to very low oxygen tensions, such as occur normally in the gut. They are also dependent upon the host's gut contents for their nourishment, glycogen being the essential source of energy. This is used up very rapidly and the reserves exhausted, if it is not continually built up from glucose furnished by the gut contents. There is no evidence of any helminth being able to utilize glycogen as a source of nourishment. It must be broken down to hexose sugars and then synthesized. The intensity of the glycogen metabolism may be judged from the fact that both nematodes and cestodes, if deprived of nourishment by starvation of the host, are either eliminated or the strobila broken.

The synthesis of glycogen from hexose sugars has not yet been established, although it must necessarily exist. In worms without an intestine, the seat of this synthesis appears to be either the body wall or its immediate vicinity and this may even be the case in trematodes. On the other hand, in nematodes the body wall does not seem to be the seat of such a process, at least in the species investigated.

The carbohydrate metabolism is apparently also linked up with that of the proteins, and complex molecules have been isolated from tapeworms. It is very likely that these will also be discovered in trematodes and that they occur perhaps in other helminths.

The mucopolysaccharid nature of the cuticula in cestodes and in trematodes may also explain their resistance to digestion. There is, moreover, some evidence that this occurs in nematodes, although the outer layer of the skin in the latter is considered

as being formed of keratin. It is interesting, however, to remark that no clear-cut case of so-called "anti-enzymes" being secreted has yet been reported although this has been claimed by some investigators.

No true fat metabolism has apparently been observed. It has even been suggested that, in parasitic helminths, fat is not an energy reserve substance but a waste product which is usually eliminated in the form of fatty acids.

Practically nothing is known of the function of the excretory system or of the nature of the excreta although it has been claimed that in nematodes, for instance, waste nitrogen products have been observed in crystalline form within the excretory ducts and in trematodes, in the form of fat droplets.

Enzymes have been reported from the gut of nematodes and their presence postulated, although never proved, in cestodes and in trematodes. A phosphatase and a lipase have been discovered in acanthocephalans.

Metabolism of parasitic helminths is far more complex than was formerly supposed. Most investigators who have attempted to investigate the problems seem to have failed to recognize this. The recent progress of biochemistry, especially as to carbohydrate and protein molecules, shows clearly the importance of their complex combinations, such as mucoproteins and mucopolysaccharids.

Osmotic pressure, on which much stress was laid formerly, is less important than has been supposed, since most helminths are able to adjust themselves to osmotic changes such as occur frequently within the gut. This is also true for the hydrogen-ion concentration since the pH in the host intestine is liable to vary to a considerable extent before or after meals.

Future investigators should take into consideration, more than has been the case so far, the biological conditions that should be preserved throughout the experiment. Mashing up worms to discover enzymes or to effect chemical analyses should be a thing of the past. The progress of histochemistry makes it possible today to locate, under certain controlled circumstances, many types of fats, carbohydrates, and enzymes. But even then, these techniques almost invariably destroy the real nature of the chemical structure that can be obtained from comparative biochemical analyses only.

The discovery of specific glycoproteins in tapeworms has perhaps opened an entirely new field of research, but one that must remain, for the present at least, in the hands of biochemists. Here is, perchance, the first indication, on a biochemical level, of the nature of host specificity. It is too early to assume this to be true, but the evidence is significant and authorizes such speculations.

REFERENCES

ADAMSTONE, F. B., & TAYLOR, A. B. 1948. The rapid preparation of frozen tissue sections. *Stain Technology*, 23:109–16, 9 figs.

ADDIS, J. C. 1946. Experiments on the relations between sex hormones and the growth of tapeworms (*Hymenolepis diminuta*) in rats. *J. Parasit.*, 32:574–80.

BUEDING, E. 1949. Studies on the metabolism of the filarial worm *Litmosomoides carinii*. *J. Exp. Med.*, 89:107–30.

*BULLOCK, W. L. 1949. Histochemical studies on the Acanthocephala. *J. Morphol.*, 84:185–223, 2 pls.

BRADY, F. J., LAWTON, A. H., COWIE, D. B., NESS, A. T., & OGDEN, G. E. 1945. Localization of trivalent radioactive antimony following intravenous administration to dogs infected with *Dirofilaria immitis*. *Am. J. Trop. Med.*, 25:503–15.

BRAND, TH. V., & SAUERWEIN, J. 1942. Further studies upon the chemistry of *Macracanthorhynchus hirudinaceus*. *J. Parasit.*, 28:315–18.

BRAND, TH. V., & JOHNSON, E. 1947. A comparative study of the effects of cyanide on the respiration of some trypanosomidae. *J. Cell. & Comp. Physiol.*, 29:33–50.

BRAND, TH. V., & TOBIE, E. 1948. Further observations on the influence of cyanide on some trypanosomes. *J. Cell. & Comp. Physiol.*, 31:49–68.

CHANG, S. L. 1946. Studies on *Entamoeba histolytica* IV. The relation of oxidation-reduction potentials to the growth, encystation and excystation of *Entamoeba histolytica* in culture. *Parasitology*, 37:101–12.

CHAPIN, E. A. 1926. *Eustrongylides ignotus* in the United States. *J. Parasit.*, 13:86–87.

CHU, H. J. 1938. Certain behavior reactions of *Schistosoma japonicum* and *Clonorchis sinensis* in vitro. *Chinese Med. J. Supp.*, 2:411–17, 1 fig.

CLEVELAND, R. R. 1925. The effects of oxygenation and starvation on the symbiosis between the termite, *Termopsis*, and its intestinal flagellates. *Biol. Bull.*, 48:309–26, 1 pl.

CULBERTSON, J. T. 1941. Immunity against animal parasites. x + 274 pp. New York.

DESCHIENS, R. 1942. Données biologiques relatives aux substances toxiques vermineuses. *Bull. Soc. Path. Exot.*, 35:115–22.

———. 1948. Les substances toxiques vermineuses, leur pouvoir pathogène, leur identification. *Ann. Inst. Past.*, 75:398–410.

DOGIEL, V. A. 1927. Monographie der Familie Ophryoscolecidae. *Arch. f. Protistenk.*, 59:1–228, 134 figs.

DOUGHERTY, E. C. 1949. The phylogeny of the nematode family Metastrongylidae Leiper (1909): a correlation

of host and symbiote evolution. *Parasitology*, 39:222–34, 27 figs.

FERGUSON, M. S. 1943. In vitro cultivation of trematode metacercariae free from microorganisms. *J. Parasit.*, 29:319–23.

HANSEN, E. L., & ANDERSON, H. H. 1948. An essentially synthetic medium for *Entamoeba histolytica*. *Parasitology*, 39:69–72.

HOARE, C., & COUTELEN, F. 1933. Essai de classification des trypanosomes des mammifères et de l'homme basé sur leurs caractères morphologiques et biologiques. *Ann. Parasit.*, 11:196–200, 1 pl.

*HOBSON, A. D. 1948. The physiology and cultivation in artificial media of nematodes parasitic in the alimentary tract of animals. *Parasitology*, 38:183–227.

HOEPPLI, R., & CHU, H. J. 1937. Studies on *Clonorchis sinensis* in vitro. *Festschrift Nocht*: 200–203.

HOPPE, J. O., & CHAPMAN, C. W. 1947. Role of glucose in acute parasitemic death of the rat infected with *Trypanosoma equiperdum*. *J. Parasit.*, 33:509–16.

HUNGATE, R. E. 1942. The culture of Eudiplodinium neglectum, with experiments on the digestion of cellulose. *Biol. Bull.*, 84:157–63.

———. 1943. Further experiments on cellulose digestion by the protozoa in the rumen of cattle. *Biol. Bull.*, 84:157–163.

HURLAUX, R. 1947. Recherches sur les cellules dites phagocytaires de l'ascaride du cheval (*Parascaris equorum* Goeze). *Ann. Sc. Nat. Zool.* (11), 9:155–225, 24 figs., 2 pls.

JOHNSON, G. J. 1947. The physiology of bacteria-free *Trichomonas vaginalis*. *J. Parasit.*, 33:189–98.

KEILIN, D. 1944. Respiratory systems and respiratory adaptations in larvae and pupae of Diptera. *Parasitology*, 36:1–66, 54 figs., 2 pls.

KENT, F. H. N. 1947. Etudes biochimiques sur les protéines des *Moniezia* parasites intestinaux du mouton. *Bull. Soc. Neuch. Sc. Nat.*, 70:85–108, 1 fig., 1 pl.

KENT, F. H. N., & MACHEBOEUF, M. 1948. Existence de sels biliaires et de cérébrosides associés à des protéines chez *Moniezia expansa* (Recherches biochimiques sur les cestodes.) *Experentia*, 4:193–94.

———. 1949. Recherches sur les protéines du cestode *Moniezia expansa* II. Etudes de la digestibilité des diverses fractions protéiques par la trypsine. *Schweiz. Zeitschr. Path. u Bakt.*, 12:81–84.

KIRK, R. 1949. The differentiation and nomenclature of Leishmania. *Parasitology*, 39:263–73.

KRUIDENIER, F. J. 1948. Metachromatic determination of mucoprotein distribution in *Paragonimus kellicotti*. *J. Parasit.*, 34, Supp: 22.

LWOFF, M. 1940. Recherches sur le pouvoir de synthèse des flagellés trypanosomides. *Monogr. Inst. Past.*, 213 pp.

MACHEBOEUF, M., & MANDOUL, R. 1939. Tentatives d'isolement de la substances toxique contenue dans l'extrait d'*Ascaris megalocephala*. *C. R. Soc. Biol.*, 132:124–26.

MAHR, M. M. 1942. Precipitin reactions and specificity of *Moniezia expansa* and *Moniezia benedeni*. *Biol. Bull.*, 83:88–90.

* Contains references not mentioned here but cited in the text.

MARGOLIN, S. 1930. Methods for the cultivation of cattle ciliates. *Biol. Bull,* 59:301–5.

McCoy, O. R., DOWNING, V. F., & VOORHIS, S. N. VAN. 1941. The penetration of radioactive phosphorus into encysted *Trichinella* larvae. *J. Parasit.,* 27:53–58.

McKEE, R. W., ORMSHEE, R. A., ANFINSEN, C. B., GEIMAN, Q. M., & BULL, E. G. 1946. Studies on malarial parasites VI. The chemistry and metabolism of normal and parasitized (*P. knowlesi*) monkey blood. *J. Exp. Med.,* 84:569–82.

———. VII. Methods and techniques for cultivation. *Ibid.,* 84:583–606, pls. 23–24.

———. VIII. Factors affecting the growth of Plasmodium. *Ibid.,* 84:607–21.

MILLFR, M. A. 1942. Studies on the developmental stages and glycogen metabolism of *Macracanthorhynchus hirudinaceus* in the Japanese beetle larva. *J. Morph.,* 73:19–41, 3 figs.

ROGERS, W. P., & LAZARUS, M. 1949. The uptake of radioactive phosphorus from host tissues and fluids by nematode parasites. *Parasitology,* 39:245–50, 5 figs.

———. 1949. Glycolysis and related phosphoros metabolism in parasitic nematodes. *Ibid.,* 302–13.

ROMANINI, M. G. 1947. Contributo all conascenza istochimica dei vitellogeni di Distoma hepaticum. *Monit. Zool. Italiano,* 56:16–19.

SENEKJIE, H. A., & LEWIS, R. A. 1945. An inquiry into the growth factor or factors of certain blood and tissue flagellates. *Am. J. Trop. Med.,* 25:345–48.

SHAFFER, J. G., & FRYE, W. W. 1948. Studies on the growth requirements of *Endamoeba histolytica* I. Maintenance of a strain of *E. histolytica* thru one hundred transplants in the absence of an actively multiplying bacterial flora. *Am. J. Hyg.,* 47:214–21.

SHAFFER, J. G., RYDEN, F. N., & FRYE, W. W. 1948. Studies on the growth requirements of *Endamoeba histolytica* III. The growth and multiplication of two strains of *E. histolytica* in a transparent medium without the addition of rice starch or other particulate matter

and without demonstrable bacterial growth. *Am. J. Hyg.* 47:345–50.

*SMYTH, J. D. 1947. The physiology of tapeworms. *Biol. Rev.,* 22:214–38.

SNYDER, T. H., & MELENEY, H. E. 1942. Anaerobiosis and cholesterol as growth requirements of *Entamoeba histolytica. J. Parasit.,* 28 *Supp:* 11.

SPROSTON, N. G., & HARTLEY, P. H. T. 1941. The ecology of some parasitic copepods of gadoids and other fishes. *J. Mar. Biol. Assn.,* 25:361–92, 2 figs.

STEINHAUS, E. A. 1947. Insect microbiology. 763 pp. Ithaca, N. Y.

*STEPHENSON, W. 1947. Physiological and histochemical observations on the adult liver fluke *Fasciola hepatica. Parasitology,* 38:116–44, 7 figs., 2 pls.

TRAGER, W. 1941. Studies on conditions affecting the survival in vitro of a malarial parasite (*Plasmodium lophurae*). *J. Exp. Med.,* 74:441–62, pl. 23.

———. 1947. The development of the malarial parasite *Plasmodium lophurae* in red blood cell suspensions in vitro. *J. Parasit.,* 33:345–50.

WENRICH, D. H. 1946. Culture experiments on intestinal flagellates. I. Trichomonad and other flagellates obtained from man and certain animals. *J. Parasit.,* 32:40–43.

———. 1947. Culture experiments on intestinal flagellates. II. Additional observations on flagellates from man, rodents and insect larvae. *Ibid.,* 33:25–28.

———. 1947. Culture experiments on intestinal flagellates. III. Species from amphibia and reptiles. *Ibid.,* 33:62–70.

WESTPHAL, A. 1934. Studien ueber Ophryoscoleciden in der Kultur. *Zeitschr. f. Parasitenk.,* 7:71–117.

WHARTON, G. W. 1941. The function of respiratory pigments of certain turtle parasites. *J. Parasit.,* 27:81–87.

WIGGLESWORTH, V. B. 1943. The fate of haemoglobin in *Rhodnius prolixus* (Hemiptera) and other blood sucking arthropods. *Proc. R. Soc. B.,* 131:313–39, 6 figs.

WILHELMI, R. W. 1940. Serological reactions and species specificity of some helminths. *Biol. Bull.,* 79:64–90.

CHAPTER SEVENTEEN

In vitro cultures of parasitic helminths

Many attempts have been made to grow parasitic helminths, *in vitro*, under either sterile or oligaseptic conditions. Such methods would of course be ideal for studying their metabolism in the same way as has been done for flagellates. To this day, however, very few investigators have achieved any notable results, even in spite of the considerable literature that has been published on this subject. This is largely due to the fact that, in most cases, the so-called cultures are nothing else than a medium in which the worms are able to survive for a variable length of time and in which oviposition, if it does occur, usually yields sterile eggs.

All helminths possess energy reserves that usually take the form of glycogen stored in the body of the parasite. These reserves account for the time of survival, under optimum conditions of hydrogen-ion concentration, osmotic pressure, and temperature. It is usually found that an increase in the temperature shortens the length of survival time since it also increases the metabolic rate of the worms, and consequently the latter use up their reserves more rapidly.

Saprozoic nematodes have been successfully cultured ever since the beginning of the present century, with the aim of establishing their sexual behavior and the conditions of their hermaphroditism (Maupas). Usually, a drop of water containing some decaying organic material heavily infected with bacteria makes an excellent medium. In sterile peptone solutions, growth is suspended but continues normally if bacteria are introduced into the culture. On the other hand, a saturated gelatin solution supports growth, but only for two to three generations of worms. In solutions containing tyrosin or leucin,

growth is retarded. Although the larvae become adult, the production of eggs is considerably curtailed (Potts).

No successful attempts have been made, to the writer's knowledge, to culture free-living nematodes in sterile media, although certain investigators have been able to culture the free-living stages of nematodes parasitic in vertebrates but without obtaining any significant results (Lapage).

Forms closely related to free-living nematodes from the body cavity and intestine of insects have been cultured successfully for a considerable length of time (Glaser). *Neoaplectana glaseri* Steiner that occurs in Japanese beetle larvae has been reared on veal infusion with living yeast or with fresh rabbit kidney. Yet even in such cultures fecundity of the worms gradually declines, in some strains after only five or six transfers and in others after twenty transfers. In such cases, however, passage of the culture through beetle larvae restores the original degree of fecundity. Similar results were also obtained when dried yeast or dried powdered Japanese beetle larvae were added to the medium.

The related species *Neoaplactana chresima* Glaser *et al.* has also been grown successfully on rabbit kidney in sterile media.

Unfortunately, experiments conducted under such circumstances do not furnish any information as to the metabolism of the worms. This was not the aim of the investigators, but these results do show that, under suitable circumstances, a synthetic medium could be found in which it would be possible to culture both free-living species and also those that occur in insects.

The above results raise the question as to whether or not the nematodes that occur in insects are true parasites. The relative ease with which they can be cultured and the close phylogenetic relationship with free-living species appear to indicate that they are more of a saprozoic than parasitic nature. In the absence of information regarding their metabolism, and especially regarding the extent to which they have lost their power to synthesize essential nutritional requirements, one cannot reach valid conclusions. But it is suggested that they are not true parasites any more than are the nematodes which live in plants. Apparently, also, like the latter, they form strains that are adapted to particular hosts. Until further research establishes their true physiological status, the question must remain open.

Such a conclusion naturally applies also to cultivation together in sterile media of tomato plant seedlings and the root nematode, *Heterodera marioni* (Cornu). The latter produce the characteristic swellings on the roots within six weeks (Ferguson).

No successful culture of nematodes parasitic in vertebrates has been reported so far. In every case, even when growth does occur, it is later inhibited and ceases altogether.

Bacterially clean *Trichinella* larvae introduced into tissue cultures of chick or rat embryos develop as far as sexually differentiated stages, but the molts are incomplete and molting ceases completely after four days (Weller). When *Trichinella* larvae are inoculated into the amniotic sac of chick embryos within the egg, and are incubated with the latter, they undergo development and become sexually mature, although remaining below normal size. Attempts to culture the larvae in sterile amniotic fluid, *in vitro*, failed completely (McCoy).

These experiments, however, have not been carried out under controlled conditions. They are interesting in themselves but furnish no answer to the question of why growth is abnormal or what are the nutritional requirements of the larvae.

It seems astonishing that the results obtained by Glaser and his collaborators have never been repeated nor extended. This would be particularly interesting as to the necessary growth factors required—the presence of which is postulated from the above results. It would appear that all the elements are united for obtaining a perfect biochemical analysis of the problem of growth in *Neoaplectana*, and it is to be hoped that some future investigator may be able to investigate this again from a purely scientific standpoint without having to consider the possible economic applications of his results.

The structure of larval tapeworms does not usually make them useful objects for experimentation, since all larvae except certain plerocercoids must undergo metamorphosis before the strobila even begins to grow. The plerocercoid of *Diphyllobothrium latum*, for instance, requires considerable increase in size and, also, must undergo some kind of metamorphosis that is expressed, physiologically, by the sloughing off of the posterior half of the larva. On the other hand, plerocercoid larvae of *Ligula intestinalis* and of *Schistocephalus solidus* are unique in that they have attained their full growth while still within the body cavity of the fish intermediate host. These larvae, moreover, are very thick and "fleshy" and possess a high glycogen content. It is not unusual to observe such larvae with their genital organs completely outlined but not yet functional, an indication that sexual maturity is attained within a relatively short time after the larvae have been swallowed by a suitable final host. This was discovered as far back as 1876 by Duchamp, who ascertained experimentally that not only were the worms sexually mature within four days when fed to ducks, but also that the worms were almost immediately evacuated from the host after oviposition. The same investigator obtained adult worms by feeding larvae to pigeons, and was able to demonstrate that similar results were obtained when larvae were introduced into the peritoneal cavity of dogs, and even when the larvae were cut into pieces.

These experiments by Duchamp were later substantiated and extended with the result that adult worms were also obtained by feeding larvae to cats and dogs, although larvae failed to develop in rabbits. Moreover, larvae introduced into the abdominal cavity of cats became adult, even when cut into several pieces, and produced about 75 per cent of viable eggs. On the other hand, in the peritoneal cavity of rabbits, the larvae also became adult, but only three eggs out of 2300 laid were fertile (Joyeux & Baer). Using saline serum, with or without addition of ascites fluid and the usual precautions as to asepsis, it is possible to obtain maturation of the genital glands and oviposition, *in vitro*, within six to twelve days. But in no case has it been possible to obtain any viable spermatozoa, and histological controls show that spermatogenesis has been curtailed (Joyeux & Baer).

A later investigator has repeated these experiments and also extended them to *Schistocephalus solidus*, but with the same results in both cases. Namely, fertile eggs were absent although, in this case, spermatogenesis appears to have proceeded normally (Smyth). The absence of fertile eggs is attributed to the fact that the conditions of the experiment prevented the worms from copulating. Recently, the same investigator, with the same technique, has obtained 6 per cent of viable eggs, although the worms have been cultured individually, thus confirming the well known fact that tapeworms are self-fertilizing.

The present writer does not believe that any of these experiments should be considered as successful demonstrations of *in vitro* cultures. They indicate that optimum conditions for survival of the larvae were realized and that, thanks to the large amount of reserve materials, especially glycogen, at the outset, metabolism has proceeded normally to the extent of maturation of the gonads. Unfortunately no analyses of glycogen have been made either before or after the experiment to check this possibility. Moreover, the scarcity of fertilized eggs is significant and it is obvious that a substance available in the intestine of dogs and cats and also in the peritoneal cavity of the latter is lacking in the media used. This substance, which is apparently responsible for the normal maturation of the genital glands, is also absent from the intestine and the peritoneal cavity of rabbits. No attempt, so far, has been made to isolate it.

Growth, *in vitro*, of young *Crepidobothrium loennbergi* (Fuhrm.) removed from the gut of mud puppies and introduced into sterile salt-dextrose-broth has been claimed. At the end of thirty-two days, the length of the worms had increased three to fourfold and the proglottids appeared abnormal but remained sterile (Stunkard). In tapeworms, this does not mean that growth actually occurred, unless the number of segments had increased proportionally, but this is not stated.

Trematodes, by their size and the relative ease with which it is possible to obtain metacercariae possessing well developed genital anlagen, would seem to be a very favorable material for culturing experimentally.

Few attempts have been published with the aim of determining the length of survival of adult trematodes, apart from that of Stephenson already mentioned in the previous chapter and a more recent experiment with *Watsonius watsoni* (Conyh.), an amphistome from primates and from man (Deschiens & Pick).

Metacercariae of strigeids apparently share with *Ligula* and *Schistocephalus* larvae the property of becoming very rapidly adult in the final hosts, and they should therefore constitute a useful experimental material.

Securing *in vitro*, metacercariae of *Diplostomum flexicaudum* (Cort & Brooks) from cercariae that had penetrated into the lens of the eye of fishes (Ferguson) is not, in the true sense, a culture since no control over the experiments was established, and that the "medium," fisheye lenses, does not correspond to any known chemical composition.

It has been found possible to free metacercariae of the species *Posthodiplostomum minimum* (MacC.) from their cysts with solutions containing pepsin and to maintain them under sterile conditions in a medium of Tyrode-chick serum-yeast extract at 39° C. The larvae matured within ten days and oviposited, but all the eggs produced remained sterile, and here also it was possible to observe that spermatogenesis did not occur (Ferguson).

Under oligaseptic conditions, metacercariae of *Microphallus opacus* (Ward) become adult and oviposit in various media within six days (Rausch). The fertility of these eggs has not been examined. It is interesting, however, to discover some kind of correlation between the ease with which these metacercariae may be cultured and the very wide range of hosts in which the adult worms have been obtained, a fact that lends considerable support to the theory that in trematodes, host specificity depends to a certain extent upon the rate of maturation of the gonads.

There do not appear to be any published records of attempts to culture larval acanthocephalans, although the relative ease with which it is possible to obtain such material would make them interesting to study.

From the above results it is clearly evident that, so far, no single, true culture of any parasitic helminth can be claimed. The field remains open and should yield important results as to the possible support from the physiological angle of host specificity. Concerning the latter, the culturing of nematodes from both insects and plants will no doubt furnish helpful information as to the minimum physiological conditions to which these worms are able to adapt themselves. Consequently, it may also lead to a better understanding of the complex problem of adaptation of nematodes to parasitism.

It should be borne in mind that these investigations should, as far as possible, be carried out on larval forms in which growth can be estimated objectively. To state that larval echinococci increase in size is no indication of growth, since a change in osmotic pressure produces exactly the same results.

REFERENCES

ACKERT, J. E., TODD, A. C., & TANNER, W. A. 1938. Growing larval *Ascaridia lineata* (Nematoda) in vitro. *Trans. Am. Micros. Soc.*, 57:292–96.

CHU, T. C. 1936. Studies on the life history of *Rhabdias fuscovenosa* var. *catanensis* (Rizzo, 1902). *J. Parasit.*, 22:140–60, 8 figs.

DESCHIENS, R., & PICK, F. 1948. Conservation de *Watsonius watsoni* (Conyham, 1904) amphistome de l'homme et des primates dans des conditions extérieures à l'hôte. *Bull. Soc. Path. Exot.*, 41:490–94.

FERGUSON, M. S. 1940. Excystment and sterilization of metacercariae of the avian strigeid trematode, *Posthodiplostomum minimum*, and their development into adult worms in sterile cultures. *J. Parasit.*, 26:359–72, 8 figs.

———. 1943. In vitro cultivation of trematode metacercariae free from microorganisms. *Ibid.*, 29:319–23.

———. 1948. Culture experiments with *Heterodera marioni. Ibid.*, 34, *Supp.*, 32.

GLASER, R. W. 1940. The bacteria free culture of a nematode parasite. *Proc. Soc. Exp. Med. & Biol.*, 43:512–14.

GLASER, R. W., McCOY, E. E., & GIRTH, H. B. 1940. The biology and economic importance of a nematode parasitic in insects. *J. Parasit.*, 26:479.

———. 1942. The biology and cultures of *Neoaplectana chresima*, a new nematode parasitic in insects. *Ibid.*, 28:123–29.

GLASER, R. W., & STOLL, N. R. 1938. Sterile cultures of free living stages of the sheep stomach worms, *Haemonchus contortus. Parasitology*, 30:324–32, 3 figs.

HOBSON, A. D. 1948. The physiology and cultivation in artificial media of nematodes parasitic in the alimentary tract of animals. *Parasitology*, 38:183–227.

JOYEUX, CH., & BAER, J. G. 1942. Recherches sur l'évolution de la Ligule intestinale. *Bull. Mus. Hist. Nat. Marseille*, 2:1–32.

LAPAGE, G. 1935. The behaviour of sterilized exsheathed infective Trichostrongylid larvae in sterile media resembling their environment in ovine hosts. *J. Helminth.*, 13:115–28.

MAUPAS, E. 1900. Modes et formes de reproduction des Nématodes. *Arch. Zool. Exp.* (3), 8:463–624, pls. 16–26.

McCOY, O. R. 1934. The development of adult Trichinae in chicks and rat embryos. *J. Parasit.*, 20, *Supp.*, 333.

POTTS, F. A. 1910. Notes on the free living nematodes. *Quart. J. Micros. Sc.*, 55:433–84, 11 figs.

RAUSCH, R. 1947. Some observation of the host-relationships of *Microphallus opacus* (Ward, 1894) (Trematoda: Microphallidae). *Trans. Am. Micros. Soc.*, 66:59–63.

SMYTH, J. D. 1946. Studies on tapeworm physiology. I. Cultivation of *Schistocephalus solidus* in vitro. *J. Exp. Biol.*, 23:47–70, 5 figs., pls. 2–3.

———. 1946. Studies on tapeworm physiology. II. Cultivation and development of *Ligula intestinalis* in vitro. *Parasitology*, 38:173–81, 4 figs., pls. 6–8.

———. 1948. Development of cestodes *in vitro:* Production of fertile eggs; Cultivation of plerocercoid fragments. *Nature*, 161:138, 2 figs.

STUNKARD, H. W. 1932. Attempts to grow cestodes in vitro. *J. Parasit.*, 19:163.

THOMAS, L. J. 1941. Effects of testosterone on nematodes. *J. Parasit.*, 27, *Supp.*, 37–38.

WELLER, T. H. 1943. The development of the larvae of *Trichinella spiralis* in roller tube tissue cultures. *Am. J. Path.*, 19:503–15.

PART FIVE

Origin of parasitism

The ecological approach to the study of parasitism clearly shows that many organisms appear to have been predisposed to becoming parasitic, and that they were preadapted to a different mode of life that has enabled them to establish themselves successfully in a new ecological niche.

The idea of preadaptation, as conceived by modern biologists, in no way implies the existence of a preconceived plan, of a directed form of evolution outside the scope of human discernment. Preadaptation means that organisms living in a given environment may possess, besides their normal adaptive characteristics, other potentialities that may never, normally, become manifest. If, however, for some accidental cause the environment be modified, fresh water becoming brackish or drying up for instance, the organisms that possessed such potentialities are able to survive in the new environment and would, therefore, be considered as preadapted. Preadaptation may be either physiological or morphological, and it also implies that such organisms are able to pass from a generalized type of environment to a more specialized one.

Cave-dwelling arthropods (mites, dipterans, and other insects) have passed secondarily onto bats. From leading a purely guanophilic existence they were prepared to become blood feeders, since they were accustomed to a high nitrogen content in their diet. Richer food was advantageous for the species, whose reproduction rate increased in consequence. Once arthropods were established physiologically, morphological changes could be evolved and, naturally, those that were best adapted for the particular type of existence stood the greatest chance of surviving. It is obvious that the individuals that were physiologically adapted, but not morphologically, were gradually eliminated by selection.

The origin of lice, and probably also of fleas, can be explained in similar manner although here the free-living ancestors were no doubt insects dwelling in the bark of trees. Subsequently, as in lice, the entire life cycle occurred upon the host.

Two very good instances of constitutional preadaptation are that of fly larvae and of worms like nematodes that normally feed upon decaying organic matter, and, in this case, physiological adaptation appears to have been more important than the subsequent morphological adaptation. The latter does not even appear to have occurred in fly larvae and exists, moreover, in only a few groups of parasitic nematodes.

It has been demonstrated that adult flies lay their eggs in certain places or upon certain animals to which they are attracted by odor, and also that the nature of this attraction is liable to be conditioned. Consequently, maggots will grow in different hosts but the selective influence that will eliminate unfavorable hosts will also, but inversely, affect conditioning of the adult flies to the most favorable hosts.

Since free-living nematodes and scavenger beetles both feed upon decaying organic material, it is easy to understand in what way the former have become established in the latter species. It is probable that nematodes became established in the intestine of vertebrates either directly or via insects, but, in any case, they were physiologically preadapted to living in an atmosphere with a low oxygen tension. Many of the present-day species of nematodes that live in the cloaca of reptiles, and that reproduce continuously without leaving their hosts, should be considered as illustrating one of the stages through which the free-living forms passed before becoming parasitic.

All the known ecological niches have been populated accidentally and this is especially true for parasites. The number of unsuccessful attempts must have been enormous and were doubtless due, primarily, to the inability of the species to become physiologically adapted, since among parasites there does not appear to be any evidence of competition for survival as the food supply is generally plentiful.

From the outset, parasitism benefits the species that has adopted this mode of life, boosts its fertility, and thus increases the chances for the invasion of new hosts. Parasitism also exerts a conservative influence on the species because lack of competition is particularly favorable for the survival of a much larger proportion of mutations than would persist among free-living organisms.

Life cycles involving intermediate hosts have no doubt arisen secondarily, since they are corollary to an increased fertility; but here, of course, ecological factors are of primary importance in establishing the nature of the intermediate hosts.

The distribution of parasites, as found today, is clearly the outcome of hundreds and thousands of unsuccessful experiments, in the course of which species or individuals have been eliminated. There is no evidence of ectoparasites being older than entoparasites; both types have evolved independently and sometimes side by side. Ectoparasites are frequently a cause of irritation to their hosts, that scratch and bite themselves to get rid of these undesirable animals and, in so doing, swallow their parasites. Yet this has never led to the parasites becoming established in the intestine of the host.

All turbellarians are hermaphroditic and from this stock have arisen some of the most successful lines of parasites, such as monogenetic trematodes, digenetic trematodes, cestodarians, and cestodes, although some of these have become secondarily diecious. It can be easily understood to what extent hermaphroditism is able to benefit a species, since it increases its chances of invading new niches. For each freshly established bisexual parasite, the corresponding number of hermaphrodites is many times greater.

One of the most evident consequences of the parasitic mode of living is the appearance of neoteny that mostly affects the male sex only or, more rarely, both sexes as in certain mites. Neoteny has also been reported from free-living organisms although much less frequently. The cause for neoteny is undetermined, but its relative frequency among parasites might indicate that it is in some way related to the quality of the food available and to the presence, in the latter, of certain essential substances.

As previously stated, physiological adaptation has been a condition *sine qua non* for organisms to be able to become parasitic, and even more so for entoparasites than for ectoparasites. Parasitism affects an organism in two totally different ways, physiologically, through causing it to lose the power to synthesize part or all of its essential nutritional requirements, and morphologically, through the loss of all superfluous organs. The greater the effect of either one or of both of these factors, the more

highly specialized and therefore the more intimately adapted to its host will the parasite be.

It is certain that parasitism has appeared at frequent intervals in the course of the thousands of centuries during which plants and animals gradually occupied all the available niches. In several groups, such as arthropods, nematodes, and protozoans, parasitic forms arose from species that had already become differentiated, and consequently that had evolved along distinct lines. This is clearly evident in the actual parasitic mites and in the nematodes.

Indirect evidence, as stated previously, leads to the conclusion that flagellates have been associated with termites and other wood-eating insects ever since the Paleozoic, and that during the same period the crinoids harbored myzostomids and perhaps the echinoderms, parasitic snails. The ancestors of cestodes and acanthocephalans have disappeared, together with their primitive fish hosts but, unlike the latter, they unfortunately did not leave their impression in the stone.

Primitive, mid-Tertiary mammals harbored fleas that showed all the characteristics of the group as it is known today, and parasitic tachinid larvae developed from maggots that fed upon these same dead animals.

It is obvious that new ecological niches for parasites appeared as the vertebrates evolved into their ultimate orders and families, and that the parasites invaded these new territories, some successfully, others less so. Subsequent isolation of both the host population and the parasites led to speciation and also to segregation of the larval forms. In physiologically highly specialized parasites like tapeworms that also require metamorphosis of the infestive larvae, there is every evidence that parallel evolution of the hosts and the parasites has occurred and has been maintained in spite of different hosts occupying identical biotopes. This is primarily due to the peculiar nutritional requirements of the parasites. It is possible that a similar mechanism may have existed originally for all helminths, but, in the groups other than tapeworms, the infestive larval forms do not need to undergo metamorphosis in the final host, and also the parasites appear to be less specialized from a physiological standpoint. Consequently, ecologically similar hosts are apt to harbor the same species of parasites and the distribution of these parasites will also be ecological as opposed to the phylogenetic distribution of cestodes.

It has often been stated that groups of hosts or host species that are isolated geographically, or for other reasons, harbor parasites that tend to split into a great number of subspecies. Examples of such instances are the lice and tapeworms of hyraxes and the tapeworms of African green pigeons and also of guinea fowls. Inbreeding of isolated populations tends to preserve small genetic variabilities that disappear when random mating occurs. This is especially true for hyraxes and also for the two groups of birds mentioned previously, which tend to subspeciate to a degree that is alarming to taxonomists.

Lice that live upon these isolated populations inbreed freely and, consequently, small genetic variations are preserved and are considered by taxonomists as of sufficient importance for distinguishing species. Tapeworms are mostly self-fertilizing and, consequently, the conditions are particularly favorable for preserving all the genetic variations that may occur. Since the intermediate host is, necessarily, an arthropod that occurs in the same territory as the host, the chances of these genetic variations being preserved are considerable, much more so, in fact, than if the hosts were spread over entire continents.

This also shows that it is impossible to ignore the host when studying the parasites, and that slight variations from a given morphological type may lead to interesting conclusions. In the cestode genus *Hymenolepis* for example, the combination of mor-

phological characters of the species is considerably smaller than in other genera, owing to the fact that there are only three testes and that the rostellum is usually armed with a small number of hooks, the shape of which varies slightly even within a given species. This genus contains a very great number of species, many of which occur exclusively in ducks and these hosts, although migratory, breed in ecologically similar surroundings. Moreover, during the breeding season they form distinct populations which explains also the extraordinary variations found in their parasites.

From the foregoing conclusions it is clear that parasites no longer appear as organisms that have escaped from the effects of selection and sought a secluded existence within another organism, the host. Parasites are probably as old, if not older, than most of their present hosts, and a definite physiological preadaptation has enabled them to invade such peculiar ecological niches as the digestive system, natural cavities, the skin, the gills, etc., of other animals where they have become successfully established. As new hosts appeared and new niches became available, the parasites also invaded them, yet in the process they have continually been subjected to the same laws as all other ving organisms, except that the rather peculiar nature of their ecological niches excludes competition and, consequently, parasites would be the only animals that are spared the struggle for existence.

INDEX

Italic numbers refer to text illustrations

215

Haptophrya, 12
  gigantea, 7 B
Harpyrhynchus, location on host, 73
Hectopsylla psittaci, hosts of, 90, 157
Heligmosomoides polygyra, reaction of host to, 177
Hemibdella soleae, mode of attachment to host, 42·
Hemilaelaps, hosts of, 76
Hemioniscus balani, hosts of, 71
Hemiparonia, 152, 141
Hemistema ambigua, hosts of, 22
Henneguyia mictospora, 19
  oviperda, 19
  psorospermica, 19
Hepatotaenia, 141
Hepatoxylon, 141
Hermit crab and sea anemone, 4
Heterakis, life cycle of, 100
Heterobothrium, 134 J
Heterodera, 95
  marioni, cultures of, 206
  radicicola, hosts of, 163
  schachti, 122 C
Heterotylenchus aberrans, life cycle of, 124, 98
Hexabothrium, hosts of, 124
Hippobosca, 85
Histriobdella, 38
Hoploplana inquilina, 34
Hoplopsyllus glacialis, hosts of, 157
Horsehair worms; see Gordiacea
Host, as biotope, 12, 155
  intermediate, definition of, 12
  paratenic, definition of, 12
  specificity, a problem of ecology, 155
    definition of, 155
Hyalospira, 15
Hydrachnids, protelian parasitism of, 76
Hylecthrus, ecology of, 89
Hymenolepis, 141, 168
  cytology of species, 139
  anatina, intermediate hosts of, 169
  diminuta, intermediate hosts of, 169
  erinacei, life cycle of, 148
  gracilis, intermediate hosts of, 169
  microstoma, location in gall bladder of host, 177
  nana fraterna, artificial immunity to, 177
    larval development of, 158, 169
    life cycle of, 148
Hymenoptera, host specificity in larval, 161
  respiration in parasitic larvae of, 83
Hymenopteran larvae, parasitic, 86
Hypoderma bovis, life cycle of, 81
  lineatum, life cycle of, 82
Hypotrichina marsilensis, 34
  tergestina, 34
Hyria tibialis, attachment of larva to host, 106 B

Ichneumonid flies, olfactory conditioning of, 93
Ichthyotaenia macrocephala, hosts of, 171
Ichthyotomus sanguinarius, anatomy of, 40–43, 36
  host specificity of, 38
Ichthyoxenos, location on host, 66
Idiogenes horridus, 170

Illiosentis cetratus, hosts of, 130 B-C, 167
  undulatus, hosts of, 167
Insects, parasitic, 78
Intestinal parasites, effects upon host, 176
  immunity reactions to, 176
Ione thoracica, larval distribution of, 71
  life cycle of, 81, 83
Irona, 66
Ischnocera, 159
Ischnopsyllines, specificity of, 156
Isopods, host specificity of parasitic, 158
Itch-mites, specificity of, 158
Ixodes, 101, 73
  ricinus, choice of hosts, 75
  vespertilionis, hosts of, 78

Jardugia, 141

Kiricephalus, hosts of, 109
  coarctatus, resistance of eggs, 107
Knemidocoptes, 76
Kuhnia, hosts of, 124

Laelaps muris, hosts of, 16
Laminiosioptes cysticola, 89
Lampsilis anodontoides, 22
  luteola, 22
Lampretes, 20
Lankesterella, life cycle of, 18
Lecanicephalum, 167
Leeches as temporary parasites, 41
Leiperia, 106, 109
  gracilis, 126 B
Leishmania, growth factors for, 185
Lepidophthirius, adaptation of, 93
  macrorhinus, 121
Lepidopterans, parasitic, 90
Lepidotrema, hosts of, 124
Leptophallus nigrovenosus, 146, 149
Leptorhynchoides thecatus, re-encapsulation of larvae, 115
Lernaea, mode of attachment of copepodid to host, 52
  branchialis, 60, 61
Lernaeascus, location on host, 47
Lernaeenicus encrassicola, 59 B
  sprattae, 59 A, 52
Lernaeids, lesions caused by, 52
  life cycle of, 47
  location on host, 51
  mode of attachment to host, 47
Lernaeocera, mode of attachment, 52
  respiration of, 58
Lernaeodiscus ingolfi on Munida, 63
Lernaeopoda, 53
  scyllicola, 63, 53
Lernaeopodids, grappling organs of, 47
  life cycle of, 47, 53
Leucochloridium, life cycle of, 129
  paradoxum, 148
Lice, biting, ecology of, 159
  sucking, ecology of, 160
Ligula, 141
  intestinalis, culture of larva, 206

221

Spiroxys contorta, life cycle of, 101
Sporoza, blood-inhabiting species, origin of, 18
   life cycles in, *11*, *12*, *13*, 16
Staphylocystis, *155* G, 145
Staurosoma caulleryi, sexual dimorphism in, *57*, 51
Stenopteryx, 85
Stichorchis, miracidium of, 127
Stilesia hepatica, location in host of, 177
Stilifer celebensis, *23*, 24
   linckiae, *24*, 24
   sibogae, hermaphroditism in, 24
   sp., *25*, 24
Stratiodrilus, distribution of, 38
Strebilids, hosts of, 86
Strebilomastix strix, food of, 187
Strepsiptera, adaptations to parasitism of, 87
Strigea vaginata, 170
Strigeids, host distribution of, 165
   larval metamorphosis of, 131
Strigomonas, growth factors for, 185
   culicidarum culicis, synthesis of hematin in, 185
Strongyloides stercoralis, life cycle of, 98
Strongylus edentatus, lipase in gut of, 197
   equinus, lipase in gut of, 197
Strophitus, 20
   edentulus, 22
Stylochus inimicus, 34
Stylopids, life cycle of, *115*, 88
Stylops, ecology of, 89
Subulura allodapa, 170
   suctoria, 170
Sylon, parthenogenesis in, 63
   hippolytes, hosts of, 63
Symbiosis, definition of, 6
Synagoga, location upon host, 65
Syngamus, life cycle of, 101
   paratenic hosts, effects of, 104

Tachina larvarum, 82
Tachinids, entomobius larvae of, 82
Tachygonetria vivipara, life cycle of, 101
Taenia crassiceps, budding of larvae, 145
    location of adult in host, 176
   hydatigena, carbohydrate metabolism of, 194
   multiceps, location of, 176
   pisiformis, artificial immunity to larvae of, 178
    larval hosts of, 169
    location of adult in host, 176
   polyacantha, location of adult in host, 176
   taeniaeformis, artificial immunity to larvae of, 178
    larval hosts of, 169
    structure of larva, 146
   tenuicollis, larval hosts of, 169
   solium, larval hosts of, 169
Taeniacanthines, life cycle of, 48
Tanaorhamphus, hosts of, 167
Tapeworms, an aid to host taxonomy, 170
   antienzymes in, 195
   bacteriostatic effects of, 178
   host specificity of, 148, 167
   immunity to larval, 177, 178
   life history of, 146

   metabolism of adult, 193
   necessary growth factors for, 207
   paratenic hosts in, 146
   phylogenetic specificity in, 168
   reduplication of sexual organs in, 139, 141, *152*
   serological affinities among, 195
   specificity of intermediate hosts in, 190
   suggested origin of parasitism in, 150
Tatria, hosts of, 168
Taufikia, hosts of, 168
Telorchis robustus, hemoglobin in, 200
Temnocephalans, 3
Tetrabothrium, hosts of, 168
Tetrameres, 93
   fissispina, *122* D
Tetraphyllids, scolex structure of, 141
Tetrapodili, isolation of, 73
Tetrarhynchids, scolex of, 141
Tetrarhynchobothrium, *153* F
Tetrathyridium, *155* K, *157*
Thaumatocotyle, *134* I
Theromyzon, hosts of, 41
Thompsonia, parthenogenesis in, 63
   regeneration of, 63
Thyca cristallina, sexual dimorphism in, *23*
   entoconcha, 18
   stellasteris, 17
Thyonicola, *34*, *35*, *36*, 27
   mortenseni, *32* A
Thysanosoma, 168
Tomite, *10*, 15
Tomont, *10*, 15
Toxocara canis, larval migration of, 104
Trematode larvae, ecological segregation of, 133
Trematodes, digenetic, host relations of, 133
    host specificity of, 166
   monogenetic, host specificity of, 158
Trachelosaccus hymenodorae, larval development of, 64
Triaenophorus, 141
   hosts of adult, 167
   hosts of larvae, 169
Triangulus munidae, life history of, 61
Trichinella, artificial immunity to, 177
   culture of larvae, 206
   spiralis, life cycle of, 100, 102
Trichocyllibia comata, 95
Trichomonad flagellates, effects of high protein diet of host upon, 175
Trichomonads, cultures *in vitro*, 188
Trichonympha, ingestion of wood by, *6*
Trichostrongylus, life cycle of, 99
Trichuroidea, life cycle of, 100
Triganodistomum mutabile, cercariae of, 131
Triplotaenia, hosts of, 168
Tristoma, *134* F
Tritestis, *134* E
Triunguloid larvae, phoresis of, 2
Trochopus, *134* D
Trophont, *10*, 15
Trombicula autumnalis, 76
Trypanosoma equiperdum, glucose metabolism of, 186
   evansi, physiology of, 186